Study Guide for

Pharmacology
A Nursing Process Approach

Fourth Edition

Joyce LeFever Kee, MS, RN
Associate Professor Emerita
College of Health and Nursing Sciences
Department of Nursing
University of Delaware
Newark, Delaware

Evelyn R. Hayes, PhD, RN, CS-FNP
Professor
College of Health and Nursing Sciences
Department of Nursing
University of Delaware
Newark, Delaware

Saunders
An Imprint of Elsevier

SAUNDERS

An Imprint of Elsevier

The Curtis Center
Independence Square West
Philadelphia, Pennsylvania 19106-3399

NOTICE

Pharmacology is an ever-changing field. Standard safety precautions must be followed, but as new research and clinical experience broaden our knowledge, changes in treatment and drug therapy become necessary or appropriate. The editors of this work have carefully checked the generic and trade drug names and verified drug dosages to ensure that the dosage information in this work is accurate and in accord with the standards accepted at the time of publication. Readers are advised, however, to check the product information currently provided by the manufacturer of each drug to be administered to be certain that changes have not been made in the recommended dose or in the contraindications for administration. This is of particular importance in regard to new or infrequently used drugs. It is the responsibility of the treating physician/health care provider, relying on experience and knowledge of the patient, to determine dosages and the best treatment for the patient. The editors cannot be responsible for misuse or misapplication of the material in this work.

THE PUBLISHER

Study Guide for Kee and Hayes
Pharmacology: A Nursing Process Approach (4th ed.)

ISBN 0-7216-9346-6
part number 9996009378

Printed in the United States of America.

Last digit is the print number: 9   8   7   6   5

Preface

This comprehensive *Study Guide* is designed to provide the learner with clinically based situation practice problems and questions. This book accompanies the text *Pharmacology: A Nursing Process Approach* (4th edition) and may also be used independent of the text. Chapters have a user-friendly format beginning with an outline and objectives.

Opportunities abound for the enhancement of critical thinking and decision-making abilities. More than 1800 study questions and answers are presented on nursing responsibilities in therapeutic pharmacology. For example, Chapter 3 details the principles of drug administration. Chapter 4 is composed of six sections, each devoted to a specific area of medications and calculations. Multiple practice opportunities are provided in the areas of measurement, methods of drug calculations, calculation of oral and injectable dosages including for pediatrics, and calculation of intravenous fluids. Each of the 55 chapters has questions in a variety of formats including multiple choice, matching, word searches, crossword puzzles, and completion.

There are more than 160 drug calculation problems and questions; many relating to actual client care situations and enhanced with actual drug labels. The learner is also expected to recognize safe dosage parameters for the situation. The combination of the instructional material in the text and the multiplicity of a variety of practice prob-

lems in this Study Guide preclude the need for an additional drug dosage calculation book.

The nursing process is used throughout the client situation-based questions and critical thinking exercises. Chapters have questions that relate to assessment data including laboratory data and side effects, planning and implementing care, client/family teaching, cultural and nutritional considerations, and the effectiveness of the drug therapy regimen.

Answers to clinical situations are presented in the Answer Key. In addition to the answers to the drug dosage calculation problems, the thought process and actual solving of the problem is outlined in many instances.

Additional resources are found in the appendices including: (A) basic math review and (B) prototype drug chart format for your use.

The Study Guide is part of a comprehensive pharmacology package including text and Instructor's Electronic Resource. The IER is a CD-ROM containing the Instructor's Manual, Test Manual, and Lecture View. This comprehensive package and each of its components was designed to promote critical thinking and learning. We are excited about this edition of the Study Guide because it offers the learner a variety of modalities for mastering the content.

Acknowledgments

We extend most sincere appreciation to the many professionals who facilitated the development of this *Study Guide To Accompany Pharmacology: A Nursing Process Approach, (4th edition)*. We especially thank the following for their assistance with questions for the respective chapters: Larry Purnell and Helene De Hann, Chapter 6; Judith Herrman, Chapter 9; Patricia Lincoln, Chapter 33; Lynette Wacchholz, Chapter 34; Anne E. Lara, Chapter 36; Jane Purnell Taylor and Linda Goodwin, Chapters 49, 50, 51, and 52; Nancy C. Sharts-Hopko and Kathleen Jones, Chapters 53 and 54; and Linda Laskowski-Jones, Chapter 55. Also, our sincere thanks to the reviewers selected from a variety of programs across the nation.

We are most grateful to pharmaceutic companies for permission to use their drug labels in the drug dosage calculation problems. Pharmaceutic companies that extended their courtesy to this book include: Abbott Laboratories, American Regent Laboratories, Inc., Astrazeneca Pharmaceuticals, Bayer Corporation, Bristol-Myers Squibb Co., DuPont-Merck Pharmaceutical Co., Eli Lilly and Co., Elkins-Sinn Inc., Glaxo-Wellcome Inc., Lederle Pharmaceuticals Inc., Marion Merrell Dow Inc., McNeilab Inc., Merck and Co. Inc., Pfizer Labs, SmithKline Beecham Pharmaceuticals, Warner-Lambert Co., and Wyeth-Ayerst Laboratories.

We are indebted to the students and clients we have had the privilege of knowing during our many years of professional nursing practice. From you we have learned many important aspects about the role of therapeutic pharmacology in nursing practice.

To the staff at W.B. Saunders, especially Robin Carter, Executive Editor, Nursing Books; Gina Hopf, Developmental Editor; and Lee Henderson, Managing Editor, we thank you for your reviews and suggestions.

We offer our appreciation and love to my husband, Edward D. Kee and to my parents Margaret K. and Justin F. Hayes for their ongoing love and support.

Joyce LeFever Kee

Evelyn R. Hayes

Contents

1 Drug Action: Pharmaceutic, Pharmacokinetic, and Pharmacodynamic Phases

Study Questions

Crossword puzzle: Use the definition to determine the pharmacologic term.

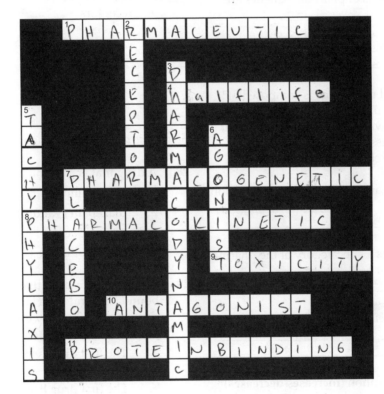

Across

1. Dissolution of the drug
4. One-half of the drug concentration to be eliminated
7. Effect of drug action because of hereditary influence
8. Four processes of drug movement to achieve drug action
9. Toxic effect as a result of drug dose or therapy
10. Drug that blocks a response without a chemical structure
11. Drug bound to protein

Down

2. Located on a cell membrane to enhance drug action
3. Effect of drug action on cells
5. Drug tolerance to a repeated administration of a drug
6. Drug that produces a response
7. Psychologic benefit from a compound

Complete the following questions.

12. Which drug form is most rapidly absorbed from the gastrointestinal (GI) tract? (**tablet/ enteric-coated pill/suspension**) (Circle correct answer)

13. Enteric-coated tablets or pills are absorbed from the (**stomach/intestine**) (Circle correct answer)

    Why? *bc they're absorbed best in an alkaline environment*

14. Usually, food (**enhances/interferes with**) dissolution and absorption. (Circle correct answer)

15. The four processes of pharmacokinetics are *absorption , elimination , distribution , and metabolism* .

16. Gastrointestinal membrane is composed of lipid and protein. Drugs that are (**lipid-soluble/water-soluble**) and (**ionized/ nonionized**) pass rapidly through the GI membrane. (Circle the correct answers)

17. Factors other than food that affect drug action are *pain , stress , and hunger* .

18. Bioavailability is a subcategory of the pharmacokinetic category *absorption* .

    Define *bioavailability*: *% that reaches systemic circulation*

19. Rapid oral absorption (**increases/decreases**) the bioavailability of the drug. (Circle correct answer)

20. Drug excretion in the urine is a daily process. What might occur if a client is taking a therapeutic drug dose and has renal dysfunction? *Could lead to toxicity if its accumulated*

21. What are the four main influences on drug therapy? *clinical factors , route , pharmacokinetics , and pharmacodynamics* .

Match the following terms with their descriptions.

E 22. protein-bound drug

D 23. unbound drug

B 24. hepatic first pass

A 25. dissolution

F 26. passive absorption

C 27. nonselective receptors

a. breakdown of a drug into smaller particles

b. proceeds directly from intestine to the liver

c. drugs that affect various receptors

d. free active drug causing a pharma- cologic response

e. causes inactive drug action/ response

f. drug absorbed by diffusion

g. drug requiring a carrier for absorp- tion

Select the appropriate response.

28. A drug that is NOT highly protein-bound is:
    a. amoxicillin.
    b. diazepam (Valium).
    c. valproic acid.
    d. chlorpromazine (Thorazine).

29. E.T. is taking a drug that is highly protein- bound. Several days later, E.T. takes a second drug that is 90% protein-bound. What hap- pens to the first drug?
    a. The first drug remains highly protein-bound.
    b. The first drug becomes increasingly inactive.
    c. More of the first drug is released from the protein and becomes more pharma- cologically active.
    d. The first drug is excreted in the urine.

30. The major site of drug metabolism is the:
    a. kidney.
    b. liver.
    c. lung.
    d. skin.

31. The route for drug absorption that has the greatest bioavailability is:
    a. oral.
    b. intramuscular.
    c. subcutaneous.
    d. intravenous.

32. The serum half-life of a drug is the time required:
    a. for half of a drug dose to be absorbed.
    b. after absorption for half of the drug to be eliminated.
    c. for a drug to be totally effective.
    d. for half the drug dose to be completely distributed.

33. T.C. has liver and kidney disease. He is given a medication with a serum half-life of 30 hours. You expect the duration of action of this medication to:
    a. increase.
    b. decrease.
    c. remain unchanged.
    d. dissipate.

34. Drugs with a half-life of 24 to 30 hours would probably be administered on a dose schedule of:
    a. three times a day.
    b. twice a day.
    c. once a day.
    d. every other day.

35. For elimination through the kidneys to be possible, a drug must:
    a. be lipid-soluble.
    b. be water-soluble.
    c. be protein-bound.
    d. have a long half-life.

36. Creatinine clearance test is a determinant of renal function. In the elderly and those with renal dysfunction, the creatinine clearance is usually:
    a. substantially increased.
    b. slightly increased.
    c. decreased.
    d. in normal range.

37. Mrs. T. has a renal disorder. Her creatinine clearance is 40 ml/min. Her drug dose should be:
    a. increased.
    b. decreased.
    c. the same for one week.
    d. discontinued.

38. The biological activity of a drug is determined by the:
    a. fit of the drug at the receptor site.
    b. misfit of the drug at the receptor site.
    c. inability of the drug to bind to a specific receptor.
    d. ability of the drug to be rapidly excreted.

39. Drugs that prevent or inhibit a response are known as:
    a. antagonists.
    b. agonists.
    c. depressants.
    d. antiseptics.

40. A receptor located in different parts of the body may initiate a variety of responses depending upon its anatomical site. The receptor is:
    a. nonselective.
    b. drug-enzyme interaction.
    c. primary response.
    d. nonspecific.

41. Which receptor does epinephrine NOT act upon?
    a. alpha
    b. beta$_1$
    c. beta$_2$
    d. cholinergic

42. Knowledge of drug potency does NOT enable us to predict whether a potent drug is more or less toxic. The valid indicator that measures the margin of safety of the drug is its:
    a. therapeutic range.
    b. therapeutic index.
    c. duration of action.
    d. biological half-life.

43. Drugs with narrow therapeutic ranges, such as digoxin (0.5-2 µg/ml), require plasma/serum drug level monitoring _____ to avoid drug toxicity.
    a. yearly
    b. daily
    (c.) at periodic intervals
    d. weekly

44. After drug administration, the highest plasma/serum concentration of the drug at a specific time is called:
    (a) peak level.
    b. trough level.
    c. half-life.
    d. minimum effective concentration (MEC).

45. Prior to the administration of a medication, the nurse should check a drug reference book or the drug pamphlet to obtain the following pertinent data EXCEPT for:
    a. protein-binding effect.
    b. half-life.
    c. therapeutic range.
    (d.) maximum efficacy.

46. Physiologic effects not related to the desired effect(s) that can be predictable or associated with the use of a drug are called:
    a. severe adverse reactions.
    (b) side effects.
    c. synergistic effects.
    d. toxic effects.

47. Adverse effects:
    a. are desirable.
    (b.) are undesirable.
    c. may be desirable.
    d. are mild.

48. When immediate drug response is desired, a large initial dose is given to rapidly achieve an MEC in the plasma. This is called the:
    a. peak level.
    b. trough level.
    (c) loading dose.
    d. therapeutic range.

49. A time-response curve evaluates three parameters of drug action, which does NOT include:
    (a) therapeutic range.
    b. onset of action.
    c. peak action.
    d. duration of action.

50. Nursing interventions concerning drug therapy include the following EXCEPT:
    a. assessing for side effects of drugs, especially those that are nonselective.
    b. checking drug reference books for dosage ranges, side effects, protein-binding percentage, and half-life.
    (c) teaching the client to wait a week after the occurrence of signs and symptoms to see if they disappear.
    d. checking the client's serum therapeutic range of drugs that are more toxic or have a narrow therapeutic range.

Critical Thinking Exercises

J.R., an elderly client, has been taking digoxin 0.25 mg daily and warfarin (Coumadin) 5 mg daily for several months. J.R. noticed that large purple spots (purpura) developed on her hands, arms, and ankles. She tells the nurse that she has never had these types of "spots" before.

1. What is purpura?
   bleeding under your skin

2. Can purpura occur because of protein-binding percentage and half-life of the drug, drug dosages, and/or drug interaction? Explain.

   - can occur b/c of protein binding w/ highly protein bound drugs bleeding can occur w/ warfarin release

   - An ↑ of half life can contribute to a drug accumulation

3. What are the nursing responsibilities related to J.R.'s clinical problem?

   - to inform his healthcare provider and ask for specific lab test

4. What is an appropriate response by the nurse to J.R.'s concerns?

   - tell him his drugs & doses may be changed after they view test results.

5. J.R.'s serum digoxin level is 2.5 μg/ml. Her urine output has decreased. Is J.R.'s serum digoxin level within normal therapeutic range? Explain the possible cause of her serum digoxin level.

   - NO

   - digoxin could have been replaced from the site

6. What effects might occur as a result of J.R.'s urine output and drug therapy?

   urine output and drug therapy may cause drug accumulation or drug toxicity (b/c of the ↓ in urine output)

7. What are the recommended nursing interventions related to her serum digoxin level and urine output?

   check vitals
   monitor urine output
   run appropriate test

2 Nursing Process and Client Teaching

Study Questions

Define the following:

1. Assessment

2. Planning

3. Implementation/intervention

4. Evaluation

Match the step of the nursing process in Column II with the phrases in Column I.

	Column I		Column II
A 5.	nursing diagnosis	a.	assessment
A 6.	current health history	b.	planning
B 7.	goal setting	c.	implementation/ intervention
A 8.	client's environment	d.	evaluation
U 9.	action to accomplish goals		
A 10.	drug allergies or reactions		
D 11.	referral		
C 12.	client/significant other education		
C 13.	use of teaching drug cards		
A 14.	laboratory test results		
D 15.	effectiveness of health teaching and drug therapy		

Complete the following:

16. Client symptoms and degree of compliance with the regimen are examples of (**objective/ subjective**) data. (Circle correct answer)

17. Laboratory tests and physical assessment data are examples of (**objective/subjective**) data. (Circle correct answer)

18. List two possible nursing diagnoses commonly associated with drug therapy:

    a. Knowledge deficit

    b. altered thought process

19. List four essential qualities of an effective goal:

    a. Client centered

    b. realistic

    c. dont give false hope/expectations

    d. approachable

20. Write two goals incorporating the essential qualities:

    a.

    b.

21. List the four suggested topics for client teaching related to pharmacotherapeutics:

    a. Skill

    b. General

    c. diet

    d. side effects

22. Teaching plans that stimulate multiple senses and require active participation by the client and significant others enhance learning. List four teaching tips to be considered in each teaching plan:

    a. give written instructions

    b. give time for questions.

    c. use graphs + charts

    d. review community resources

23. List four factors commonly resulting in noncompliance with drug therapy:

    a. forgetfulness

    b. depression

    c. lack of interest

    d. (any) barriers.

24. Identify at least two questions to ask the client or significant others that will elicit unique information to help the nurse to enhance adherence to the drug therapy regimen:

    a. Why do you take the certain meds.

    b. what should you do when you forget to take one?

25. The client benefit of the nursing diagnosis is quality health care plan

Match the following examples with the letter of the phase of the nursing process.

	Example		Phase of Nursing Process
B	26. risk for injury	a.	assessment
A	27. obtain weight to be used for future comparison	b.	potential nursing diagnosis
C	28. the client will receive adequate nutritional support through enteral feedings	c.	planning
		d.	nursing intervention
C	29. client will be free from hyperactivity	e.	evaluation
D	30. instruct client to avoid caffeine-containing foods		
E	31. evaluate effectiveness of drug therapy		
B	32. sleep pattern disturbance		
D	33. advise client to report adverse reactions such as nausea to health care provider. Drug choice or dosage may need modification		
E	34. evaluate periodically the client's and family's management of biologic response modifier (BRM)-related side effects		
B	35. anxiety		
D	36. instruct client not to discontinue medication abruptly		

3 Principles of Drug Administration

Study Questions

Define the following:

1. Absorption *the taking in / incorporating something*

2. Cumulative effect *state at which rapid admin of a drug may produce effects that are more pronounced than those produced by the 1st dose*

3. Distribution *apportionment, diffusion*

4. Informed consent *permission*

5. Metabolism *energy yielded for vital processes*

6. Toxicity *the quality/state/relative degree of being toxic/poisonous*

Complete the following:

7. List the "five plus five rights" of drug administration and nursing implications for each:

Rights	Nursing Implications
a. right patient	• verify client by checking the identification bracelet
b. right dose	• distinguish b/w 2 clients w/ same last name
c. right drug	• check med order is complete, legible
d. right time	• know reason client is receiving med
e. right route	• admin drugs at specified times
f. right assessment	• assess clients ability to swallow before the admin of oral meds.
g. right evaluation	
h. right documentation	• check drug label 3x before giving
i. right to refuse	• check allergy status to drug
j. right education	

8.   Identify six factors modifying drug response and specific nursing interventions for each:

Factors	**Nursing Implications**
pg 28 a. AGE – METABOLISM	– see chart/documents for age
b. ROUTE (absorption)	make sure its the correct route
c. BODY WEIGHT (metabolism)	check accurate body weight, etc
d. TOXICITY	– first adverse symptoms that occur at a particular dose. – check allergies
e. PHARMACOGENETICS (EMOTIONAL STATE – PK)	– talk w/ client + check emotional state – review past records
f. Type of administration	– make sure they have proper administration

9.   The order to "give multivitamins ii caps po qd" is an example of ___Standing___ category of drug order.

10.   J.T. has an order to receive Demerol 100 mg, IM, STAT. This is an example of a ___STAT___ drug order.

11.   The remaining two categories of drug orders are ___one time___ and ___PRN___.

12.   When you calculate the dosage for A.B.'s cardiac medication, the drug dose is large. The best initial action for you to take is ___recheck your calculations___.

13.   Two advantages of the unit dose system include ___saves time___ and ___no calc. are required___.

14.   Drugs with a (short/long) half-life are administered more than once a day to maintain the ___plasma___ level of the drug. (Circle correct answer)

15.   The nurse is required to chart the client's response to the following groups of medications: ___analgesics___, ___narcotics___, ___antiemetics___, ___sedatives___, and ___unexpected rxns.___.

16.   The preferred way to correct a charting error is to ___draw a single line through___ and ___initial___.

Situation: You are preparing to give R.T. his medications. He is alert, oriented, and sitting up in bed. The following five questions relate to this situation.

17.   You read in the chart that R.T. is allergic to one of his prescribed medications. Your first nursing action is ___notify charge nurse and document it.– but dont give it___

18.   In the process of administering the medication, you would check the drug label at which times? ___when you 1st find drug___, ___when you handle container___, and ___when its returned___.

19. One of R.T.'s medications is in a liquid form. You pour the medication with container at _eye_ level. You read the meniscus at what point? _pt of curve_ .

20. The meniscus is _curved line formed by liquids in cont._ .

21. The client is not wearing an identification band. What should be your first nursing action? ~~xxxxxxxxxxxxxxxxxxx~~ _have a band put on it._

22. After you have administered the medications, when and what do you document? _immediatly after - med/dose/time/route, etc_ .

23. In the following table, the routes for parenteral administration of drugs are identified. For each route of administration, provide the following: a) common needle size, b) angle of insertion, and c) common site(s).

Route	Needle Size	Angle of Insertion	Sites
ID	26-27 G	10-15°	where inflammed
SQ	23, 25-27 G	45-90°	abdomen, upper hips, upper back, lat upper arms
IM	18-23 G	90°	deltoid, vastus lateralis, lat upper thighs
IV	20-21 G		basilic vein, cephalic vein, radial vein, median cubital vein

Complete the following (word search) questions 24–31. Circle your responses.

S	I	L	A	R	E	T	A	L	S	U	T	S	A	V
O	M	D	V	Z	T	W	G	G	K	N	E	Y	I	E
B	U	D	L	E	A	M	F	L	O	H	S	C	P	N
J	I	R	D	O	N	O	T	U	D	X	Q	M	U	T
D	O	R	S	O	G	L	U	T	E	A	L	G	H	R
E	F	B	D	I	O	T	L	E	D	W	A	N	B	O
S	B	E	I	M	C	R	L	A	F	Z	I	Y	K	G
D	C	O	P	A	J	T	I	L	Q	O	T	R	N	L
R	E	F	U	S	A	L	R	E	A	S	O	N	A	U
D	E	N	E	P	O	E	M	I	T	E	T	A	D	T
S	L	A	I	T	I	N	I	F	Y	M	W	H	J	E
B	N	T	U	O	X	R	N	T	R	L	D	A	P	A
T	D	E	M	N	T	R	W	I	G	Q	M	H	U	L

24. The injection site that is well-defined by bony anatomical landmarks is _Ventrogluteal_ .

25. The preferred site for intramuscular injections for infants and children is _vastus lateralis_ .

26. The site that is easily accessible but not suitable for repeated or injections over 2 ml is _deltoid_ .

27. The preferred site for the Z-track technique is _gluteal_ .

28. The site (not visible to the client) that has the danger of injury if incorrect technique is used is _dorsogluteal_ .

29. Universal precautions require that you (**do**/**do not**) recap needles. (Circle correct answer)

30. Before storing unused stable solutions from open vials in the refrigerator, the nurse should write the following information on the label: _date/time opened_ and _initials_ .

31. When a client refuses to take a medication, the nurse must record _why they refused_ .

Match the letter from Column II with the correct response in Column I.

Column I	Column II

___A___ 32. drugs poured by others

       (a) do not administer

       (b) do administer

___A___ 33. client states that drug is different than usual

___B___ 34. offer ice to numb tastebuds for distasteful drugs

___A___ 35. drugs transferred from one container to another

___B___ 36. record fluids taken with medications on the intake and output sheet

___A___ 37. medications left with visitors

Complete the following:

38. Medications via the ___oral___ route are contraindicated for clients who are vomiting or are comatose.

39. The two types of capsules that should not be crushed or chewed are ___time release___ and ___enteric coated___.

40. Administer oral medications on ___an empty stomach___ if food interferes with absorption of the medication.

41. Administer irritating drugs with food to (**decrease**/increase) gastric secretions. (Circle correct answer)

42. When applying medication topically or transdermally, the nurse/applier should avoid skin contact with the medication. What can the nurse/applier use? ___use gloves or applicator___.

43. When administering a medication by nasogastric tube, it is essential first to check the ___placement of the tube___.

44. Explain the health teaching related to the correct use of the metered dose inhaler (MDI). ___Box 3-1 pg 34___

45. If a glucocorticoid inhalant is ordered with a bronchodilator, you need to wait ___5___ minutes after administering the bronchodilator before administering glucocorticoid.

46. When administering ear drops, the client should be sitting with the head tilted toward the (**affected**/**unaffected**) side. (Circle correct answer)

47. In an adult, pull (up/**down**) and back on the auricle before instilling ear drops. (Circle correct answer)

48. Ear drops (**should**/**should not**) be instilled right after removal from the refrigerator. (Circle correct answer)

49. Explain the purpose of self-medication administration: ___help client manage meds___

50. Identify at least two specific nursing interventions when administering drugs to pediatric clients: ___be creative___ and ___anticipate dev needs___.

4 Medication and Calculations

Introduction

The medication and calculation chapter in this Study Guide is subdivided into six sections: (4A) Systems of Measurements; (4B) Methods for Calculation; (4C) Calculations of Oral Dosages; (4D) Calculations of Injectable Dosages; (4E) Calculations of Intravenous Fluids; and (4F) Pediatric Drug Calculations. Before reading and working the drug calculation problems, the student/nurse may find it helpful to review Appendix A: Basic Math Review, located in the Study Guide. The student should review and memorize the abbreviations that are presented in the inside back cover of the text.

Numerous drug labels appear in the drug calculation problems. The purpose is to familiarize the student/nurse with reading drug labels and calculating drug dosages from the information provided on the drug labels.

Drug calculation practice problems in each of the six sections provide an opportunity for the student/nurse to gain skill and competence in collecting and organizing the required data. Practice problems have examples of the administration of medications via a variety of routes including both oral and parenteral (subcutaneous, intramuscular, and intravenous).

It is recommended that the student/nurse first think though the practice problem and estimate an answer. The student/nurse should select one of the three methods (basic formula, ratio and proportion, or dimensional analysis) for drug calculations that are presented in the pharmacology textbook. After completing the required calculations, the student/nurse can compare the estimate with the calculated answer. In the event of a discrepancy, the student/nurse should review both the thought process used in answering the problem and the actual mathematical calculation. It may be necessary to review the related section in Chapter 4 of the text. Practice problems provide reinforcement for the student/nurse to gain expertise in the process of actually calculating drug dosages.

SECTION 4A—SYSTEMS OF MEASUREMENTS

Metric, Apothecary, and Household Systems

Complete the following:

1. The system of international units of measurement is __metric__. The units of these measurements are: weights __gram__; volume __liter__; and length __meter__.

2. In the metric system, to convert larger units to smaller units, move the decimal point to the (**right**/ **left**) for each unit changed. (Circle correct answer)

3. In the metric system, to convert smaller units to larger units, move the decimal point to the (**right**/ **left**) for each unit changed. (Circle correct answer)

4. With the Apothecary system, the unit of weight is __gram__, and units of volume are __fluid ounce__, __minim__, and __fluid dram__.
   quart · pint

5. When are household measurements used? __in home settings/environments__

6. Household measurements include __cup__, __glass__, and __spoonful__.

Give the abbreviations for the following units:

7. __g__ gram

8. __ml__ milligram

9. __L__ liter

10. __ml__ milliliter

11. __kg__ kilogram

12. __mcg__ microgram

13. __ng__ nanogram

14. __m__ meter

15. __g__ grain

16. __fl oz__ fluid ounce

17. __fl dr__ fluid dram

18. __qt__ quart

19. __pt__ pint

20. __m__ minim

21. __c__ cup

22. __T__ tablespoon

23. __t__ teaspoon

24. __gtt__ drops

25. The most frequently used conversions within the metric system are:
   a. 1 g = __1000__ mg
   b. 1 l = __1000__ ml
   c. 1 mg = __1000__ μg (mcg)

Complete the unit equivalent for the following measurements:

26.   3 grams = __3000__ milligrams

27.   1 ½ liter = __1500__ milliliters

$$\frac{1.5\,L}{1} \times \frac{1000\,mL}{1\,L} = 1500\,mL$$

28.   0.1 gram = __100__ milligrams

29.   2500 milliliters = __2.5__ liter

30.   250 milliliters = __.25__ liter

$$\frac{250\,ml}{1} \times \frac{1\,L}{1000\,mL} = .25$$

31.   500 milligrams = __.5__ gram

32.   2 quarts = __4__ pints

$$\frac{2g}{1} \times \frac{2\,pints}{1g} =$$

33.   2 pints = __32__ fluid ounce

34.   1.5 quarts = __48__ fluid ounce

35.   32 fluid ounce = __2__ pints

36.   2 fluid ounce = __16__ fluid dram

37.   Complete the chart on household measurements:

1 medium-sized glass	=	__8__ ounces
1 coffee cup	=	__6__ ounces
1 ounce	=	__2__ tablespoons
1 tablespoon	=	__3__ teaspoons
1 drop	=	__1__ minim

Conversion Among the Metric, Apothecary, and Household Systems

38.   When converting a unit of measurement from one system to another, convert to the unit on the drug container.

Example:

Order: V-Cillin K 0.5 g, po, q8h.

Available:

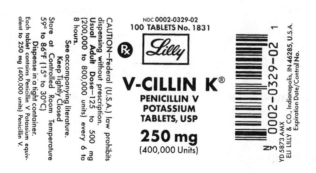

Convert __grams__ to __milligrams__.

Convert the following units of measurement to metric, Apothecary, and household equivalences. Refer to Table 4A–4 in text as needed.

39.   1 g = __600__ mg, or __15__ gr

40.   __.5__ g = 500 mg, or __7.5__ gr

41.   0.1 g = __100__ mg, or __1.5__ gr

42.   1 gr = __60__ mg

43.   0.4 mg = __1/150__ gr

44.   __1__ l = 1000 ml, or __1__ qt

45.   240 ml = __8__ fl oz, or __1__ glass

46.   30 ml = __1__ oz, or __2__ T, or __6__ t

47.   5 ml = __1__ t

48.   1 ml = __15__ m, or __15__ gtt

49.   3 T = __1.5__ oz, or __9__ t

50.   5 oz = __150__ ml, or __10__ T

SECTION 4B—METHODS FOR CALCULATION

Complete the following:

1.   Before calculating drug dosages, all units of measurement must be converted to one system. Convert to the system used on the __drug label__.

Give the following metric and Apothecary equivalents. Refer to Tables 4A–4 or 4B–1 as needed.

2.   1000 mg = __1__ g

3.   1 g = __15__ gr

4.   30 mg = __.5__ gr

5.   0.25 g = __250__ mg

6.   300 (325) mg = __5__ gr

7.   0.3 mg = __1/200__ gr

8.   2 ½ ounces = __75__ ml, or __5__ T

9.   15 ml = __.5__ ounce, or __1__ T, or __3__ t

10.   4 T = __12__ t

11.   30 gtt = __2__ ml

12.   10 ml = __2__ t

Interpretation of Drug Label

Give information concerning the following drug label:

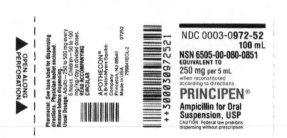

13.   Brand name _Pricipen_

14.   Generic name _ampicillin_

15.   Dosage _250 mg / 5 ml_

16.   Drug form _oral suspension_

Methods for Drug Calculation

Use the basic formula, ratio and proportion, or dimensional analysis method to calculate the following drug problems:

17.   Order: codeine gr 1, q4–6h, PRN.
      Available:

a.   The drug is in grains and the unit on the bottle is in milligrams. Conversion to the same unit is necessary to work the problem. Conversion is to (**grains/milligrams**). (Circle correct answer) Refer to Table 4A–4 in text as needed. gr 1 = 60 mg

Basic Formula

b. $\dfrac{D}{H} \times V = \dfrac{\cancel{60}\,mg}{\cancel{60}} \times 1\,tab =$
      $\qquad\qquad \dfrac{1}{1\,tablet}$

Ratio and Proportion

$$H \quad : \quad V \quad :: \quad D \quad : \quad X$$
$$60\,mg \; : \; 1\,tab \; :: \; 60\,mg \; : \; X\,tab$$
$$60\,X = 60$$
$$X = \dfrac{60}{60} = 1\,tablet$$

Dimensional Analysis

$$V = \dfrac{V\,(vehicle)}{H\,(on\,hand)} \times \dfrac{C\,(H)}{C\,(D)} \times \dfrac{D\,(desired)}{1} =$$

(drug label)   (conversion factor,   (desired order)
                   see textbook)

$$tab = \dfrac{1\,tab}{60\,mg} \times \dfrac{1000\,mg}{15\,gr} \times \dfrac{1\,gr}{1} = \dfrac{1000}{900} = 1.1\,or\,1\,tab$$

Note: 1.1 tablet should be rounded off to 1 tablet.

18. Order: Norvir (ritonavir) 0.2 g, po, bid.

    Available:

NDC 0074-9492-54
84 Capsules

NORVIR™
RITONAVIR CAPSULES
100 mg

Caution: Federal (U.S.A.) law prohibits dispensing without prescription.

ⓐ   TM-Trademark

Do not accept if seal over bottle opening is broken or missing.

Dispense in a USP tight, light-resistant container.

Each capsule contains: 100 mg ritonavir.

See enclosure for prescribing information.

©Abbott
Abbott Laboratories
North Chicago,
IL 60064, U.S.A.

$$\frac{1\ tab}{100mg} \times \frac{1000mg}{1g} \times .2g = 2\ caps.$$

a. Is conversion needed? Explain. yes

b. $\dfrac{D}{H} \times V =$ H : V :: D : X $100 x = 20 g$
                       100mg 1 cap 200mg x caps   x = 2 caps Norvir

    $\dfrac{200mg}{100mg} \times 1\ capsule = 2\ capsules\ of\ Norvir$

19. Order: Benadryl (diphenhydramine) 25 mg, po, q6h, PRN.

    Available: Benadryl 12.5 mg/5 ml

    a. Is conversion needed? Explain.

        No   units from drug order + drug label are same.

    b. How many ml would you give? Calculate the drug problem using the method you selected.

        $\dfrac{D}{H} \times V = \dfrac{25\ mg}{12.5\ mg} \times 5\ ml = 10\ ml\ Benadryl$

        H : V :: D : V
        25 mg : 5 ml :: 5mg : ml   ⟹   12.5 x = 125
                                          x = 10 ml Benadryl

20. Order: Biaxin (clarithromycin) 0.25 g, po, bid.

    Available:

Store granules at 15° to 30°C (59° to 86°F).
CONSTITUTING INSTRUCTIONS:
VOLUME OF WATER: 55 mL.
Measure the required volume of water using a graduated cylinder. Add half the volume of water to the bottle and shake vigorously. Add the remainder of water to the bottle and shake.
Contains 2.5 g clarithromycin. When mixed as directed, each teaspoonful (5 mL) contains:
Clarithromycin..................125 mg in a fruit punch-flavored, aqueous vehicle.
DOSAGE MAY BE ADMINISTERED WITHOUT REGARD TO MEALS.
Usual dose: Children: 15 mg/kg/day divided in 2 equal doses. See enclosure for adult dose and full prescribing information.
Abbott Laboratories
North Chicago, IL 60064, U.S.A.

NDC 0074-3163-13
100 mL (when mixed)

BIAXIN®
GRANULES
clarithromycin for oral suspension
125 mg per 5 mL
when reconstituted
Flavor change adopted Sept. 1995.

Caution: Federal (U.S.A.) law prohibits dispensing without prescription.

order

a. Is conversion needed? Explain.

    yes   need to convert g to mg

    $\dfrac{250mg}{125mg} \times 5ml$

b. How many ml would you give?

    $\dfrac{250\ mg}{125\ mg} \times 5\ ml = 10\ ml\ of\ Biaxin$ $\dfrac{1\ tab}{125mg} \times 5ml$

21. Order: hydroxyzine (Vistaril) 100 mg, IM, q6h.

Available:

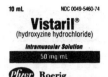 

a. Is conversion needed? Explain.

No units are same

b. How many ml would you give?

$$\frac{100 \text{ mg}}{50 \text{ mg}} \times 1 \text{ ml} = 2 \text{ ml of Vistaril}$$

22. Order: cefazolin (Kefzol) 500 mg, IM, q8h.

Available: (NOTE—Redi-vial container has diluent in a separate compartment of the vial. Push plug to release diluent for reconstitution.)

a. Is conversion needed? Explain.

Yes   mg => g (b/c drug label is in g)

b. How many ml would you give?

$$\frac{.5 g}{1 g} \times 3 ml = 1.5 ml \text{ of Kafzol}$$

Dimensional Analysis

23. Order: Precose (acarbose) 50 mg, po, tid.

Available:

a. How many tablet(s) would you give?

$$tab = \frac{1 \text{ tab}}{25 \text{ mg}} \times \frac{50^{2} \text{ mg}}{1} = 2 \text{ tables}$$

b. Which drug label(s) would you select? Explain.

select the 25 mg drug label

24. Order: Losartan potassium (Cozaar) 0.1 g, daily.
    Available:

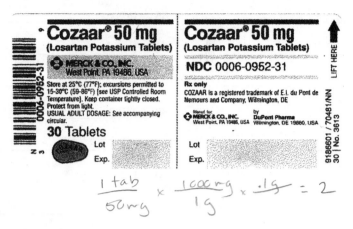

$$\frac{1\ tab}{50mg} \times \frac{1000mg}{1g} \times .1g = 2$$

How many tablet(s) should the client receive per day?

$$\frac{1\ tab}{1\ 50mg} \times \frac{1000mg}{1g}^{20} \times \frac{.1g}{1} = 2\ tabs$$

Abbreviations (refer to last right-hand page in the text as needed):

Define the following abbreviations.

25. cc ___cubic centimeter___

26. g ___gram___

27. gtt ___drops___

28. l, L ___liter___

29. μg ___microgram___

30. mEq ___milliequivalent___

31. ml ___milliliter___

32. mg ___milligram___

33. kg ___kilogram___

34. fl oz ___fluid ounce___

35. s̄s̄ ___one half___

36. T ___Tablespoon___

37. t _teaspoon_

38. supp _suppository_

39. > _greater than_

40. < _less than_

41. T.O. _telephone #_

42. A.D. _right ear_

43. A.S. _left ear_

44. A.U. _both ears_

45. O.D. _right eye_

46. O.S. _left eye_

47. O.U. _both eyes_

48. IM _intramuscular_

49. IV _intravenous_

50. KVO _keep vein open_

51. SL _sublingual_

52. SC _subcutaneous_

53. P.O., po _by mouth_

54. AC, ac _before meals_

55. PC, pc _after meals_

56. c̄ _w/_

57. s̄ _w/o at_

58. NPO _nothing by mouth_

59. PRN _whenever necessary_

60. hs _hr of sleep_

61. qd _every day_

62. q8h _every 8 hrs_

63. bid _2x / day_

64. tid _3x / day_

65. What is the difference between qid and q6h? _~4x/day_
    q6 - every 6 hrs

66. What is the difference between cc and ml?
    for liquids use ml
    but they are interchangeable

SECTION 4C—CALCULATIONS OF ORAL DOSAGES

The drug calculation problems include oral dosages for adults.

1. Order: benztropine (Cogentin) 1 mg, po, daily.
   Available:

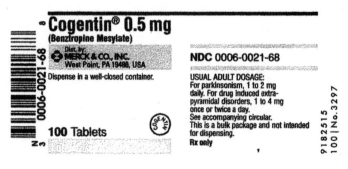

   How many tablet(s) would you give?

   $$\frac{D}{H} \times V = \frac{1\ mg}{.5\ mg} \times 1\ tab = 2\ tabs.$$

   $$.5x = 1$$
   $$x = 2$$

   $$\frac{1\ tab}{.5\ mg} \times 1\ mg = 2$$

2.   Order: codeine sulfate 60 mg, po, q6h, PRN.

Available: Tablets are available at your institute in two forms (see drug labels). Which container would you use? Why?

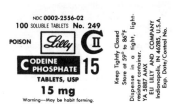

How many tablet(s) would you give?

2 tabs of the 30 mg tablets. $\frac{1 \, tab}{30mg} \times \overset{2}{6\cancel{0}mg} = 2 \, tabs.$

give fewer pills when possible

3.   Order: propranolol (Inderal) 15 mg, po, q6h.

Available: propranolol 10 mg and 20 mg tablets.

Which tablet strength would you use? How many tablet(s) would you give?

1½ tabs. propranolol 10 mg

It would be difficult to obtain 3/4 of a tab.   1½ tabs

4.   Order: penicillin V potassium 250 mg, po, q6h.

Available: (NOTE—The generic name of the drug may be given instead of the brand name. Check the label for both names.)   ½ tabs   V-cillin K 500 mg.

 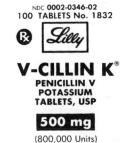 

$\frac{1 \, tab}{500mg} \times 250 \, mg = \frac{1}{2} \, tab$

How many tablet(s) would you give?

$\frac{250 \, mg}{\underset{2}{500 \, mg}} \times 1 \, tab = \frac{1}{2} \, tab$

$\frac{1 \, tab}{500mg} \times \frac{250}{mg} = \frac{1}{2} \, tab$

$500x = 250$

$x = \frac{1}{2} \, tab.$

5.   Order: cimetidine (Tagamet) 600 mg, po, hs.

Available: ~~cimetidine~~ cimetidine 200 mg

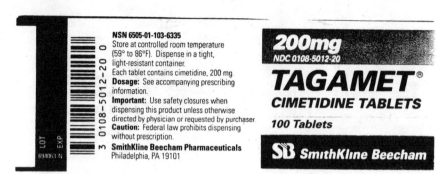

How many tablet(s) would you give?

$$\frac{1 \ tab}{200 \ mg} \times 600 \ mg = 3$$

3 tabs.

6.   Order: verapamil 60 mg, po, qid.

Available: verapamil 120 mg   or   verapamil 80 mg

Which strength of verapamil would you select?

120 mg

Tablets are scored. How many tablet(s) would you give?

½ tab

$$\frac{1 \ tab}{120 \ mg} \times 60 \ mg = \frac{1}{2} \ tab.$$

7. Order: Artane SR 10 mg, po, qd.

    Available: *Artane 5 mg + 5 mg tabl.*

    sequel

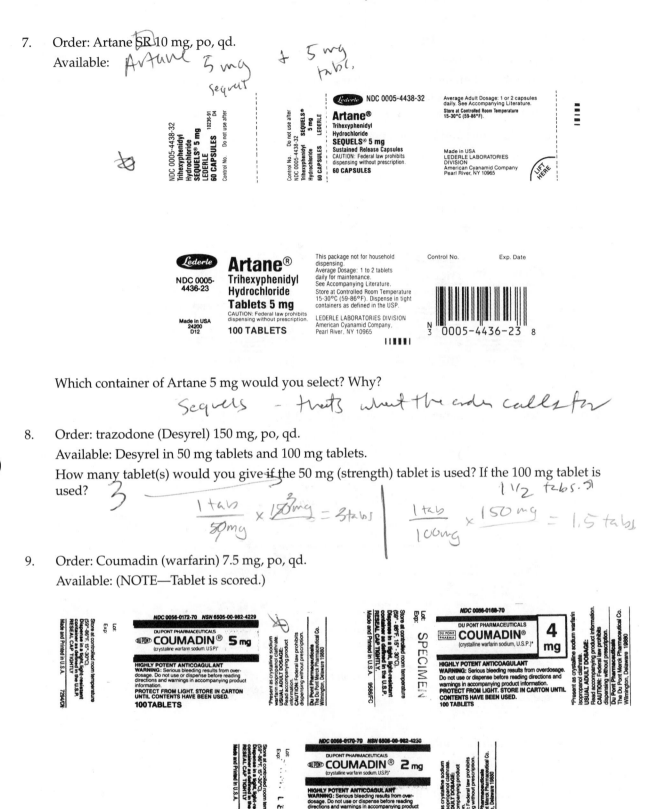

    Which container of Artane 5 mg would you select? Why?

    Sequels – that's what the order calls for

8. Order: trazodone (Desyrel) 150 mg, po, qd.

    Available: Desyrel in 50 mg tablets and 100 mg tablets.

    How many tablet(s) would you give if the 50 mg (strength) tablet is used? If the 100 mg tablet is used? *3*

    $$\frac{1\ tab}{50\ mg} \times 150\ mg = 3\ tabs \qquad \frac{1\ tab}{100\ mg} \times 150\ mg = 1.5\ tabs$$

    1 ½ tabs.

9. Order: Coumadin (warfarin) 7.5 mg, po, qd.

    Available: (NOTE—Tablet is scored.)

    Which container of Coumadin would you select? How many tablet(s) would you give?

    5 mg   *1½*

10. Order: lithium carbonate, 300 mg, po, tid.

Client's serum lithium level is 1.8 mEq/L (normal value is 0.5–1.5 mEq/L). *not up in norm*

Available: lithium carbonate in 150 and 300 mg capsules, and 300 mg tablets. Because the serum lithium level is 1.8 mEq/L, would you:

a.   give 150 mg (half the dose)?

b.   give 300 mg tablet and not capsule?

c.   advise the client not to take the dose for a week?

d.   withhold the drug and contact the health care provider?

11. Order: nitroglycerin gr ½₀₀, po, SL, STAT.

Available:

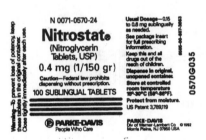
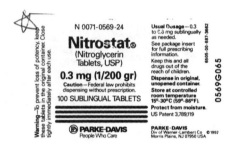

Which nitroglycerin container would you select, the 0.4 mg or the 0.3 mg? Why?

*.3 mg = (gr 1/200)
order*

12. Order: Coreg (carvedilol) 25 mg, po, bid.

Available:

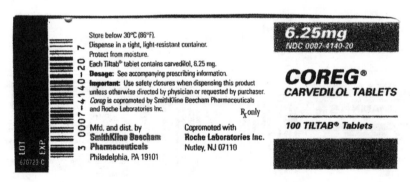

a.   How many tablets would you give per dose?

4

b.   How many tablets should the client receive in 24 hours?

8

13. Order: azithromycin (Zithromax) 400 mg, qd first day, then 200 mg, qd next 4 days.

Available:

FOR ORAL USE ONLY.
Store dry powder below 86°F (30°C).
PROTECT FROM FREEZING.
DOSAGE AND USE
See accompanying prescribing information.
MIXING DIRECTIONS:
Tap bottle to loosen powder.
Add 12 mL of water to the bottle.
After mixing, store suspension at
41° to 86°F (5° to 30°C).
Oversized bottle provides extra space
for shaking.
After mixing, use within 10 days. Discard
after full dosing is completed.
SHAKE WELL BEFORE USING.
Contains 900 mg azithromycin.

NDC 0069-3130-19
22.5 mL (when mixed)
Zithromax®
(azithromycin for
oral suspension)
CHERRY FLAVORED
200 mg* per 5 mL
Pfizer **Pfizer Labs**
Division of Pfizer Inc, NY, NY 10017

6417
MADE IN USA
Rx only
05-5014-32-2

FOR ORAL USE ONLY.
Store dry powder below 86°F (30°C).
PROTECT FROM FREEZING.
DOSAGE AND USE
See accompanying prescribing information.
MIXING DIRECTIONS:
Tap bottle to loosen powder.
Add 9 mL of water to the bottle.
After mixing, store suspension at
41° to 86°F (5° to 30°C).
Oversized bottle provides extra space
for shaking.
After mixing, use within 10 days. Discard
after full dosing is completed.
SHAKE WELL BEFORE USING.
Contains 600 mg azithromycin.

NDC 0069-3120-19
15 mL (when mixed)
Zithromax®
(azithromycin for
oral suspension)
CHERRY FLAVORED
200 mg* per 5 mL
Pfizer **Pfizer Labs**
Division of Pfizer Inc, NY, NY 10017

6416
MADE IN USA
Rx only
05-5013-32-1

Which bottle would you select? Why?

2   22.5 mg/bottle not sufficient for 5 days.

How many ml would you give the first day and how many ml per day for the next 4 days?

10 ml   1st day.
5 ml   rest of days.

14. Order: Artane (trihexyphenidyl) Elixir 1 mg, po, bid.

Available: Artane 2 mg/5 ml.

Lederle   NDC 0005-
4440-65

Artane®
Trihexyphenidyl
Hydrochloride
Elixir
This package not for
household dispensing.
EACH TEASPOONFUL (5 mL)
CONTAINS:
Trihexyphenidyl HCl 2 mg
Alcohol 5%
Preservatives:
Methylparaben 0.08%
Propylparaben 0.02%
AVERAGE DOSAGE:
3 to 5 teaspoonfuls (15-25 mL)
daily for maintenance.
See Accompanying Literature.
CAUTION: Federal law prohibits
dispensing without prescription.
Store at Controlled Room
Temperature 15-30°C (59-86°F).
DO NOT FREEZE
Dispense in tight containers
as defined in the USP.
Control No.   Exp. Date

22619 D5
LEDERLE LABORATORIES DIVISION
American Cyanamid Company
Pearl River, NY 10965 Made in U.S.A.

1 Pint (473 mL)

How many ml would you give?   2½ ml

15.   Order: doxycycline (Vibra-Tabs), 0.2 g, po first day, then 0.1 g, po qd x 6 days.

Available:

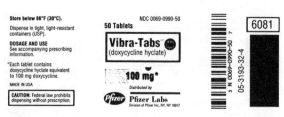

How many tablets should the client receive the first day, then how many tablets per day for 6 days?

$$\frac{.2\,g}{1} \times \frac{1\,tab}{.1\,g} = 2\,tabs/day \;\; 1^{st}\,day$$

$$days\; 2-7 = 1\,tab/day$$

16.   Order: digoxin 0.25 mg, po, qd.

Available: Lanoxin (digoxin) 0.125 mg tablets. The drug comes in 0.25 mg tablets, but that strength tablet is not available.

How many tablet(s) would you give? If the client questions the tablets, what should your response be?

$$\frac{.25\,mg}{.125\,mg} = 2\,tabs$$

17.   Order: Augmentin, 400 mg, po, q6h.

Available:

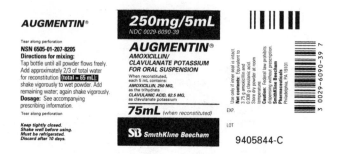

How many ml would you give? $\dfrac{400\,mg}{250\,mg} \times 5 = 8\,ml$

18.   Order: cefadroxil (Duricef) 1 g, po, qd.

Available:

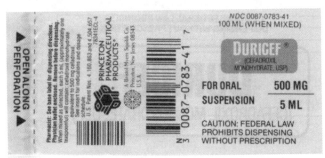

How many ml would you give? $\dfrac{1\,g}{.5\,g} \times 5 = 1\,g = 1000\,mg$

19. Order: prazosin (Minipress) 10 mg, po, qd.

    Available: prazosin 1 mg, 2 mg, and 5 mg tablets.

    Which tablet would you select and how much would you give?

    $$\frac{10mg}{5mg} = 2 \text{ tabs of } 5mg \text{ tabs.}$$

20. Order: carbidopa-levodopa (Sinemet), 12.5–125 mg, po bid.

    Available: Sinemet 25–100 mg, (25–250 mg) and 10–100 mg tablets.

    Which tablet would you select and how much would you give? $\frac{1}{2}$ tab.

Dimensional Analysis

21. Order: Vioxx (rofecoxib) 20 mg, po, per day.

    Available:

    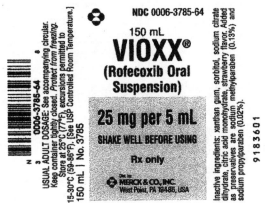

    How many ml should the client receive per day?

    $$\frac{20mg}{25mg} \times 5ml = 4ml$$

22. Order: ampicillin (Principen) 0.5 g, po, q6h.

    Available:

    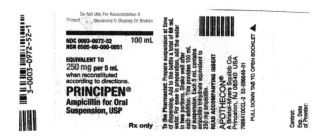

    How many ml should the client receive per dose?

    $$\frac{.5g}{.25g} \times 5ml = 10ml/dose$$

    STOP

SECTION 4D—CALCULATIONS OF INJECTABLE DOSAGES

Complete the following:

1. Methods for administering medications by parenteral routes include _____, _____, and _____.

2. Insulin and heparin may be administered by the routes of _____ and _____.

3. Vials are glass containers with (**self-sealing rubber top/tapered glass neck**). Vials are usually (**discarded/reusable if properly stored**). (Circle correct answers)

4. Before drug reconstitution, the nurse should check the drug circular and/or drug label for instructions. After a drug has been reconstituted and additional dose(s) are available, the nurse should write on the drug label _____, _____, and _____.

5. Tuberculin syringes are usually used for _____ and _____. A tuberculin syringe (**is/is not**) used for insulin administration. (Circle correct answer)

6. Insulin syringes are calibrated in (**units/ml**). (Circle correct answer)

7. After use of a prefilled cartridge and Tubex injector, which of the following should be discarded?
    a.   cartridge
    b.   Tubex injector
    c.   cartridge and Tubex injector
    d.   neither cartridge nor Tubex injector

8. The nurse is preparing an IM injection for an adult. The needle gauge and length should be:
    a.   20, 21 gauge; ½, ⅝ inch in length.
    b.   23, 25 gauge; ½, ⅝ inch in length.
    c.   19, 20, 21 gauge; 1, 1 ½, 2 inches in length.
    d.   25, 26 gauge; 1, 1 ½ inches in length.

9. The two parts of a syringe that must remain sterile are:
    a.   outside of syringe and plunger.
    b.   tip of the syringe and plunger.
    c.   both the tip and outside of the syringe.
    d.   tip and outside of syringe and plunger.

10. Subcutaneous injections can be administered in which of the following degree angle(s)?
    a.   10, 15° angles
    b.   45, 60, and 90° angles
    c.   45° angle only
    d.   90° angle only

11. You calculate the drug dosage to be 0.25 ml. What type of syringe should you select?
    a.   3 ml syringe
    b.   insulin syringe
    c.   tuberculin syringe
    d.   10 ml syringe

12. To mix 4 ml of sterile saline solution in a vial containing a powdered drug, which size syringe should you select?
    a.   tuberculin syringe
    b.   insulin syringe
    c.   3 ml syringe
    d.   5 ml syringe

Determine how many ml to give:

13. Order: heparin 3,000 U, SC, q6h.

    Available: Which heparin would you select?

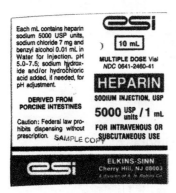 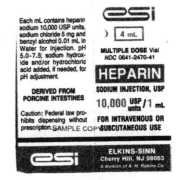

    How many ml would you give?

14. Order: codeine gr ss, q4–6h, SC, PRN.

    Available: Prefilled drug cartridge contains 60 mg/1 ml.

    How many ml would you give?

15. Order: Morphine SO₄ gr ⅙, SC, STAT.

    Available:

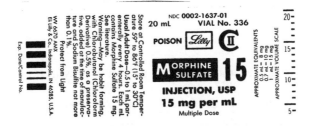

    How many ml would you give?

16.   Order: Humulin L (Lente) insulin 36 U, SC, qAM.

Available:

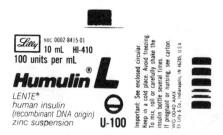

Indicate on the insulin syringe the amount of insulin to be withdrawn.

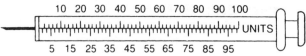

17.   Order: Regular insulin 8 U and NPH 44 U, SC, qAM.

Available: (NOTE—These insulins can be mixed together in the same insulin syringe.)

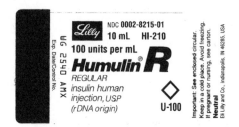   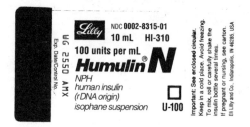

Indicate on the insulin syringe the amount of each insulin to be withdrawn. Which insulin should be drawn up first?

18.   Order: digoxin 0.25 mg, IM, STAT. (NOTE—Usually digoxin is administered intravenously; however, in this problem, IM is indicated.)

Available:

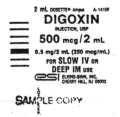

How many ml would you give?

19. Order: vitamin B$_{12}$ (cyanocobalamin) 400 mcg, IM, qd x 5 days.
     Available:

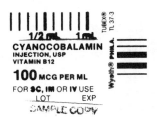   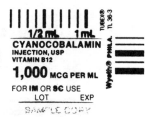

     Which prefilled cartridge would you select?

     How many ml would you give?

20. Order: clindamycin 300 mg, IM, q6h.
     Available:

     How many ml would you give?

21. Order: meperidine (Demerol) 60 mg, IM, and atropine 0.5 mg, IM, preoperatively.
     Available: (NOTE—These drugs are compatible and can be mixed in the same syringe.)

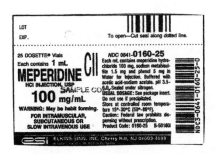   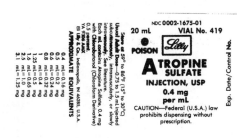

     How many ml of meperidine would you **discard**?

     How many ml of meperidine and how many ml of atropine would you give?

22.   Order: naloxone (Narcan) 0.8 mg, IM, for narcotic-induced respiratory depression. Repeat in 3 minutes if needed.

Available:

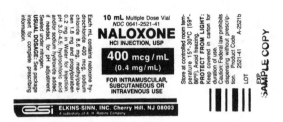

How many ml would you give?

23.   Order: hydroxyzine (Vistaril) 35 mg, IM, preoperatively.

Available:

How many ml would you give?

24.   Order: oxacillin sodium 500 mg, IM, q6h.

Available: Drug in powdered form. (NOTE—Convert to the unit system on the bottle.)

How many ml would you give?

25.   Order: oxacillin 300 mg, IM, q6h.

Available:

You are to add _____ ml of sterile water to yield _____ ml of drug solution.

How many ml would you give?

26. Order: nafcillin (Nafcil) 250 mg, IM, q4h.

Available:

You are to add _____ ml of diluent to yield _____ ml of drug solution.
How many ml would you give?

27. Order: trimethobenzamide (Tigan) 100 mg, IM, STAT.

Available: trimethobenzamide (Tigan) ampul, 200 mg/2 ml.

How many ml would you give?

28. Order: chlorpromazine (Thorazine) 20 mg, deep IM, tid.

Available:

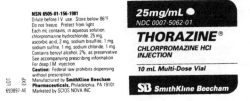

How many ml would you give?

29. Order ticarcillin (Ticar) 400 mg, IM, q6h.

Available:

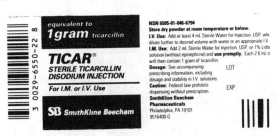

You are to add _____ ml of diluent to yield _____ ml of drug solution.
How many ml would you give?

30. Order: cefonicid (Monocid) 750 mg, IM, qd.
    Available:

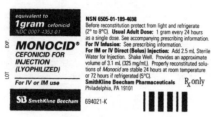

a. How many gram(s) is 750 mg?

b. How many ml of diluent should be injected into the vial? (See drug label.)

c. How many ml of cefonacid should the client receive per day?

Dimensional Analysis

31. Order: cefotetan sodium (Cefotan) 750 mg, IM, q12h.
    Available: (Note: Mix 2 ml of diluent; drug solution will equal 2.4 ml.)

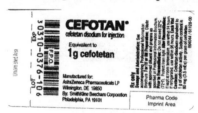

a. How many ml would you give per dose?

b. Can the remainder of the solution be used later? Explain.

32. Order: Unasyn (ampicillin sodium/sulbactam sodium) 1 g, IM, q6h.
    Available: (Note: Mix 2.2 ml of diluent; drug solution will equal 2.6 ml.)

How many ml would you give per dose?

SECTION 4E—CALCULATIONS OF INTRAVENOUS FLUIDS

Complete the following:

1. The health care provider orders the type and amount of intravenous (IV) solutions per 24 hours, and the nurse calculates the IV flow rate according to _____, _____, and, _____.

2. Macrodrip infusion sets deliver _____ gtt/ml; microdrip infusion sets deliver _____ gtt/ml.

3. If the infusion rate is *less* than 100 ml/hr, the preferred IV set is (**macrodrip/microdrip**). (Circle correct answer)

4. KVO means _____. The preferred size of IV bag for KVO is (**1000 ml/500 ml/250 ml**). (Circle correct answer)

5. When should drugs such as potassium chloride (KCl) and multiple vitamin solutions be injected into the IV bag or bottle? _____

Give the abbreviations for the following solutions:

6. 5% dextrose in water _____.

7. Normal saline solution or 0.9% sodium chloride (NaCl) _____.

8. 5% dextrose in ½ normal saline solution (0.45% NaCl) _____.

9. 5% dextrose in lactated Ringer's _____.

Complete the following:

10. Intermittent intravenous administration is prescribed when a drug is administered in a (**small/large**) volume of IV fluid over a (**long/short**) period of time. (Circle correct answers)

11. The Buretrol is a (**calibrated cylinder with tubing/small IV bag of solution with short tubing**). (Circle correct answer) It is used in administering _____.

12. The controller/pump infusion regulator that delivers ml/hr is a (**volumetric/nonvolumetric**) IV regulator. (Circle correct answer)

13. Patient controlled analgesic (PCA) is a method used to administer drug intravenously. The purpose/objective is to provide a _____.

Continuous Intravenous Administration

Select step method I, II, or III from the text to calculate the continuous IV flow rate. Memorize the step method.

14. Order: 1 liter or 1000 ml of D_5W to infuse over 6 hours.
     Available: Macrodrip set: 10 gtt/ml.
     a. The IV flow rate should be regulated as _____ gtt/min.

15. Order: 1000 ml $D_5/\frac{1}{2}$ NS with multiple vitamins and KCl 10 mEq to infuse over 8 hours.
    Available: Macrodrip set: 15 gtt/ml.

    KCl (potassium chloride) 20 mEq/10 ml ampule.

    Multiple vitamin (MVI) vial.

    a. When should KCl and MVI be injected into the IV bag?

    b. Calculate the IV flow rate for gtt/min. _____

16. Order: 1 liter of 0.9% NaCl (normal saline solution) to infuse over 12 hours.
    Available: Macrodrip set: 10 gtt/ml

    Microdrip set: 60 gtt/ml

    a Which IV set would you use? _____

    b. Calculate the IV flow rate for gtt/min according to the IV set selected. _____

17. Order: 2 ½ liters of IV fluids to infuse over 24 hours. This includes 1 liter of D_5W; 1 liter of $D_5/\frac{1}{2}$ NS; 500 ml of 5% D/LR.
    Available: The 3 above solutions.

    a. One liter is equal to _____ ml.

    b. Total number of ml of IV solutions to infuse in 24 hours is _____ ml.

    c. Approximate amount of IV solution to administer per hour is _____ ml.

    d. Which type of IV set would you select?

    e. Calculate the IV flow rate according to the IV set you selected. _____ gtt/min.

18. A liter of IV fluid was started at 7 AM and was to run for 8 hours. The IV set delivers 10 gtt/ml. At 12 PM only 500 ml were infused.

    a. How much IV fluid is left? _____

    b. Recalculate the flow rate for the remaining IV fluids. Keep in mind that if the client has a cardiovascular problem, rapid IV flow rate may not be desired.

Intermittent Intravenous Administration

(NOTE—Only add the volume of drug solution ≥ 5 ml to IV fluid to determine final drip rate.)

19. Order: cimetidine (Tagamet) 200 mg, IV, q6h.
    Available:

    Set and solution: Buretrol (calibrated cylinder set) with drop factor 60 gtt/ml; 500 ml of NSS. Instruction: Dilute cimetidine 200 mg in 50 ml of NSS and infuse in 20 minutes.

    Drug calculation:

    IV flow calculation (determine gtt/minute):

20. Order: cefamandole (Mandol) 500 mg, IV, q6h.

Available:

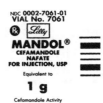

How many ml of diluent would you add?

Drug solution equals: _____.

Set and solution: Calibrated cylinder with drop factor, 60 gtt/ml; 500 ml of D_5W.

Instruction: Dilute cefamandole 500 mg reconstituted solution in 50 ml of D_5W and infuse in 30 minutes.

Drug calculation (convert to the unit on the drug label):

IV flow calculation (determine gtt/minute):

21. Order: nafcillin (Nafcil) 1000 mg, IV, q6h.

Available:

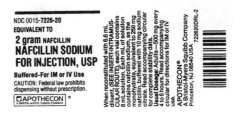

How many ml of diluent would you add?

Drug solution equals: _____

Set and solution: Secondary set with drop factor 15 gtt/ml; 100 ml of D_5W.

Instruction: Dilute nafcillin 1000 mg in 100 ml of D_5W and infuse in 40 minutes.

Drug calculation (convert to the unit on the drug label):

IV flow calculation (determine gtt/minute):

22.   Order: kanamycin (Kantrex) 250 mg, IV, q6h.

Available:

Set and solution: Secondary set with drop factor 15 gtt/ml; 100 ml of D_5W.

Instruction: Dilute kanamycin 250 mg in 100 ml of D_5W and infuse in 45 minutes.

Drug calculation (convert to the unit on the drug label):

IV flow calculation (determine gtt/minute):

23.   Order: ticarcillin (Ticar) 750 mg, IV, q4h.

Available:

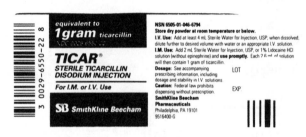

How many ml of diluent would you add?

Drug solution equals: _____

Set and solution: Buretrol set with drop factor 60 gtt/ml; 500 ml of D_5W.

Instruction: Dilute ticarcillin 750 mg solution in 75 ml of D_5W and infuse in 30 minutes.

Drug calculation (convert to the unit on the drug label):

IV flow calculation (determine gtt/minute):

Volumetric IV Regulator

24. Order: Septra: trimethoprim 80 mg and sulfamethoxazole 400 mg, IV, q12h.

    Available: Septra: trimethoprim 160 mg and sulfamethoxazole 800 mg/10 ml.

    How many ml would equal the drug order? _____

    Set and solution: Volumetric pump regulator and 125 ml of D_5W.

    Instruction: Dilute Septra 80/400 mg in 125 ml of D_5W and infuse in 90 minutes.

    Drug calculation:

    Volumetric pump regulator (How many ml/hr?):

25. Order: doxycycline (Vibramycin) 75 mg, IV, q12h.

    Available:

    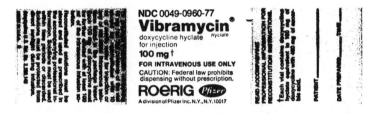

    How many ml would equal the Vibramycin 75 mg? _____

    Set and solution: Volumetric pump regulator; 100 ml of D_5W.

    Instruction: Dilute Vibramycin 75 mg solution in 100 ml of D_5W and infuse in 1 hour (60 minutes).

    Drug calculation:

    Volumetric pump regulator (How many ml/hr?):

26.   Order: amikacin sulfate 400 mg, IV, q12h.

Adult weight: 64 kg

Adult drug dosage: 7.5 mg/kg/q12h

Available:

How many ml would equal amikacin 400 mg? _____

Set and solution: Volumetric pump regulator; 125 ml of D_5W.

Instruction: Dilute amikacin 400 mg in 125 ml of D_5W and infuse in 1 hour.

Drug calculation:

Volumetric pump regulator (How many ml/hr?):

27.   Order: minocycline 75 mg, IV, q12h.

Available: Add 10 ml of diluent

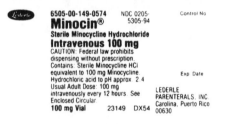

How many ml would equal minocycline 75 mg? _____

Set and solution: Volumetric pump regulator; 500 ml of D_5W.

Instruction: Dilute minocycline 75 mg in 500 ml of D_5W and infuse in 2 hours.

Drug calculation:

Volumetric pump regulator (How many ml/hr?):

28. Order: cefepime HCl (Maxipime) 500 mg, IV, q12h.

Available:

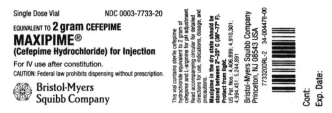

Set and solution: Calibrated cylinder set with drop factor.

Instruction: 60 gtt/ml; 100 ml of D_5W.

a.   How many ml of drug solution should the client receive?

The drug label does not indicate the amount of diluent to use. This may be found in the pamphlet insert. Usually if you inject 2.6 ml of diluent, the amount of drug solution may be 3.0 ml. If you inject 3.4 or 3.5 ml of diluent, the amount of drug solution should be 4.0 ml.

b.   Dilute cefepime 500 mg in 50 ml of D_5W and infuse in 30 minutes.

Dimensional Analysis

29. Order: Unasyn (ampicillin sodium/sulbactam sodium) 1.5 g, IV, q6h.

Available: (Note: Mix 3 g in 10 ml of diluent.)

Set and solution: Buretrol or like set with drop factor of 60 gtt/ml; 500 ml of D_5W.

Instruction: Dilute Unasyn 1.5 g solution in 100 ml of D_5W and infuse in 30 min.

Drug calculation:

IV flow calculation—determine gtt/min:

30. Order: Mefoxin (cefoxitin) 500 mg, IV, q6h.

Available: (Note: Mix 1 g in 10 ml of diluent.)

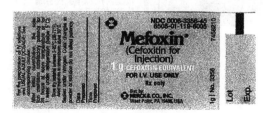

Set and solution: Volumetric pump regulator; 100 ml of D_5W.

Instruction: Dilute Mefoxin 500 mg in 100 ml of D_5W and infuse in 45 min.

Drug calculation:

Volumetric pump regulator—how many ml/hr?

SECTION 4F—PEDIATRIC DRUG CALCULATIONS

A: Orals

1. Order: penicillin V Potassium (V-Cillin K) 200,000 units, po, q6h.

    Child weighs 46 pounds or 21 kg.

    Child's drug dosage: 25,000–90,000 U/kg/day in 3–6 divided doses.

    Available: (NOTE—The dosage per 5 ml is in mg and units.)

    Is the prescribed dose safe? How many ml should the child receive for each dose?

2. Order: cefuroxime axetil (Ceftin), 200 mg, po, q12h.

    Child's age: 8 years; weight: 75 pounds

    Child's drug dosage: (3 mo–12 years) 10–15 mg/kg/d.

    Available:

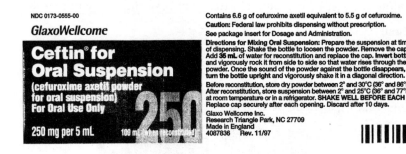

    a.   Is the prescribed dose safe?

    b.   How many ml should the child receive per dose?

3. Order: amoxicillin 75 mg, po, q6h.

    Child weighs 5 kg.

    Child's drug dosage: 50 mg/kg/day in divided doses.

    Available:

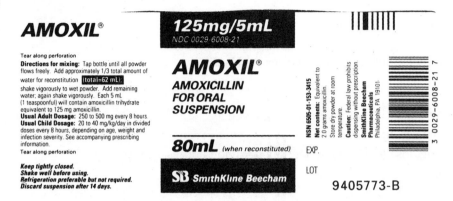

    Is the prescribed dose safe?

    According to the drug order, how many ml should the child receive per day (24 hours)?

4. Order: acetaminophen 250 mg, po, PRN.

    Available: 160 mg/5 ml.

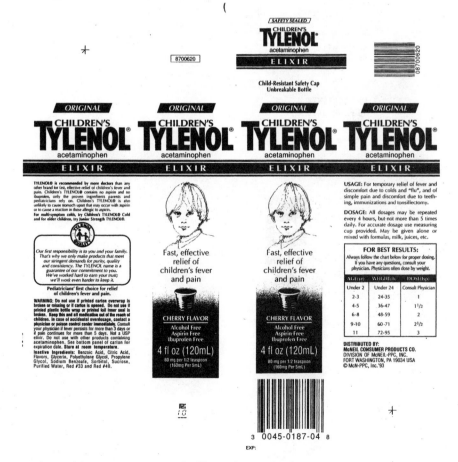

    How many ml would you give? Round off numbers when necessary.

5.   Order: cloxacillin 100 mg, po, q6h.

Child weighs 8 kg.

Child's drug dosage: 50–100 mg/kg/day in four divided doses.

Is the prescribed dose safe?

How many ml should the child receive per dose?

6.   Order: erythromycin suspension 160 mg, po, q6h.

Child weighs 25 kg.

Child's drug dosage: 30–50 mg/kg/day in divided doses, q6h.

Available:

NDC 0005-
3706-65

Lederle

NDC 0005-
3706-65

**ERYTHROMYCIN
ETHYLSUCCINATE
ORAL
SUSPENSION, USP**

200 mg/5 ml

CAUTION: Federal law
prohibits dispensing
without prescription.
This package not for
household dispensing.
USUAL DOSAGE:
For complete directions
for use, see accompany-
ing circular.
**SHAKE WELL
BEFORE USING**

14291
NA4

**NET CONTENTS
16 Fl. Oz. (473 ml)**

**ERYTHROMYCIN
ETHYLSUCCINATE
ORAL SUSPENSION, USP**

200 mg/5 ml

Each 5 ml (one teaspoonful) contains:
Erythromycin Ethylsuccinate
equivalent to Erythromycin....200 mg.
STORAGE: Store in refrigerator to
preserve taste until dispensed.
Refrigeration by patient is not required
if used within 14 days.
Protect from light. Dispense in
amber bottles.

Control No.   Exp. Date

Manufactured for
LEDERLE LABORATORIES DIVISION
American Cyanamid Company, Pearl River, N.Y. 10965
by BARRE-NATIONAL INC.
Baltimore, Maryland 21207

Is the prescribed dosage within dose parameters?

Explain.

Basic Formula and Dimensional Analysis

7.   Order: cefaclor (Ceclor) 75 mg, po, q8h.

Child weighs 22 pounds.

Child's drug dosage: 20–40 mg/kg/day in three divided doses.

Available: Ceclor suspension 125 mg/5 ml and 250 mg/5 ml.

Which Ceclor suspension bottle would you use?

How many ml per dose should be given?

8.   Order: Augmentin 150 mg, po, q8h.

Child weighs 26 pounds.

Child's drug dosage: 40 mg/kg/day in three divided doses.

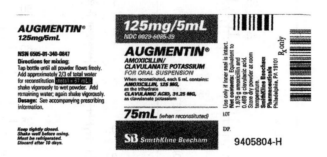

How many kg does the child weigh?

Is the prescribed dosage within dose parameters?

How many ml of Augmentin should the child receive per dose?

9.   Order: cyclophosphamide (Cytoxan).

Child's height is 48 inches; weight is 60 pounds.

Child's body surface area (BSA) is _____ m^2. Determine BSA by plotting the child's height and weight on the nomogram (p. 46).

Child's drug dosage: 60–250 mg/m^2.

What is the safe dosage range?

10.   Order: phenytoin (Dilantin)

Child's weight is 50 pounds; height is unknown.

Child's BSA is _____ m^2. Use the center graph of the nomogram (p. 46) since the height is unknown.

Child's drug dosage: 250 mg/m^2 in two divided doses.

Available: Dilantin 30 mg/5 ml.

How many ml should be given per dose? Round off numbers.

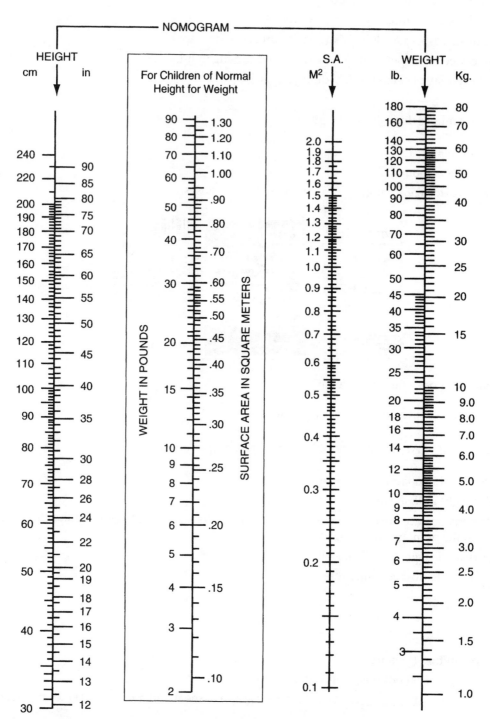

West Nomogram for Infants and Children

Directions: (1) Find height. (2) Find weight. (3) Draw a straight line connecting the height and weight. Where the line intersects on the SA column is the body surface area (m²). (Modified from data of E. Boyd and C. D. West, in Behrman, R. E. and Vaughan, V. C. (1992). *Nelson Textbook of Pediatrics,* 14th ed. Philadelphia, W. B. Saunders.)

B: Injectables

11. Order: ampicillin (Polycillin-N) 100 mg, IM, q6h.

    Child's weight: 26 pounds. (Convert pounds to kilograms [kg].)

    Child's drug dosage: 25–50 mg/kg/day.

    Available:

    Is the drug dose safe?

    How many ml per dose should the child receive?

12. Order: pentobarbital (Nembutal) 25 mg, IM, preoperatively.

    Child's weight: 40 pounds. (Convert pounds to kilograms.)

    Child's drug dosage: 3–5 mg/kg

    Available: Nembutal 50 mg/ml

    Is the drug dose safe?

    How many ml per dose should the child receive?

13. Order: kanamycin (Kantrex) 50 mg, IM, q12h.

    Child's weight: 10 kg.

    Child's drug dosage: 15 mg/kg/day in 2 divided doses.

    Available:

    Is the drug dose safe?

    How many ml per dose should the child receive?

14.   Order: amikacin sulfate (Amikin) 50 mg, IM, q12h.

Child's weight: 9 kg.

Child's drug dosage: 5 mg/kg/q8h OR 7.5 mg/kg/q12h.

Available:

Is the drug dose safe?

How many ml per dose should the child receive?

15.   Order: cefazolin (Kefzol) sodium 125 mg, IM, q6h.

Child's weight: 48 pounds.

Child's drug dosage: 25–50 mg/kg/day in 3–4 divided doses.

Available:

You are to add _____ ml of diluent to yield _____ ml of drug solution.
Is the drug dose safe?

How many ml per dose should the child receive?

Basic Formula and Dimensional Analysis

16.   Order: tobramycin (Nebcin) 25 mg, IM, q8h.

Child's weight: 22 kg

Child's drug dosage: 3–5 mg/kg/d in 3 divided doses.

Available:

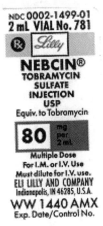

(80 mg/2 ml)

Is the drug dose safe?

How many ml per dose should the child receive?

5 The Drug Approval Process (U.S. and Canadian), Resources, and Ethical Considerations

Study Questions

Define the following:

1. Controlled substance *drugs given to ppl for appropriate reasons/doses*

2. Malfeasance *giving corr+ drug but wrong route + client dies.*

3. Misfeasance *negligence – wrong drug or dose*

4. Nonfeasance *omission – not giving the drug.*

Complete the following:

5. The resource that provides a basis for standards in drug strength and composition throughout the world is *the International Pharmacopeia*

6. The current authoritative source for drug standards is the *US Pharmacopia or Natnl Formulary*.

7. The primary purpose of federal legislation related to drug standards is *to assure safety.*

8. The *Food, Drug, and Cometic Act of 1938* Act empowered the Federal Drug Administration (FDA) to monitor and control the manufacture and marketing of drugs.

9. In 1952, the *Durham – Humphrey.* Amendment of the 1938 Act identified those drugs that required a prescription and those that required a new prescription for refill.

10. The Kefauver-Harris Amendment of the 1938 Act resulted from the use of thalidomide. The purpose of this amendment was *tighten controls on drug safety.*

11. Each state has laws which are part of the *Nurse Practice Acts* regarding drug administration by nurses.

12. List four provisions of the Comprehensive Drug Abuse Prevention and Control Act of 1970:
    a. *provision of drug education and research*

    b. *strengthen enforcement authority.*

    c. *estab treatment + rehab centers*

    d. *designate categories for controlled subst according to abuse liability.*

13. Controlled substances are described in schedules/categories. What is the number of schedules identified? *five*

14. Schedules II through V drugs (**have**/do not have) accepted medical use. (Circle correct answer)

15. Schedule I drugs have (less/**more**) potential for abuse than Schedule III drugs. (Circle correct answer)

16. LSD and heroin are Schedule *I* drugs.

17. Codeine in cough medicine is a Schedule *V* drug.

18. All controlled substances must be stored in a *locked location*.

19. In Canada the manufacture, distribution, and sale of drugs (except narcotics) are controlled by the _Canadian Food & Drug Act_, amended in 1953. The manufacture, distribution, and sale of narcotics are controlled by the 1961 _Narcotics Control Act_.

20. The regulations for narcotics by the United States and Canada are (**similar**/**dissimilar**). (Circle correct answer)

21. Drugs sold in Canada are assigned to one of ___3___ Schedules.

22. Drugs in Canada's Schedule G have moderate potential for abuse and require a prescription for new and refills. These drugs are similar to Schedule _III_ drugs in the United States.

23. In Canada, over-the-counter (OTC) preparations are administered by the _Pharmacy Acts_ of the respective provinces.

Match the letter from Column II with the applicable description in Column I.

Column I		Column II
_C_ 24. trade name	a.	chemical name
_C_ 25. owned by manufacturer	b.	generic name
	c.	brand name
_A_ 26. drug's chemical structure		
_B_ 27. official; nonproprietary		
_C_ 28. registered trademark		

Complete the following:

29. List two advantages associated with the use of generic drugs:

    a. _Cheaper_

    b. _Same active ingredients._

30. List two disadvantages associated with the use of generic drugs:

    a. _variation in action / response_

    b. _no extensive testing_

31. According to the FDA, a drug in pregnancy category A is considered (**to present**/**not to present**) a risk to the fetus? (Circle correct answer)

32. Drugs proven to be a risk to the human fetus are included in category(ies) _D and X_.

33. When a health care provider gives the wrong drug to the client and the client is harmed, the offense is termed _Negligence_.

34. A drug resource published annually and updated monthly is the _American Hosp. Formulary_. The _Physician's Desk Reference_ is published annually and its sources of information are the drug companies.

35. About 90% of poisonings occur in children under the age of _3_ years in the _home_ setting.

36. List at least two common drugs that children take and that may be toxic in large doses.

    a. _iron_

    b. _Choc. covered laxatives_

37. Regulations were changed to decrease time for approval of drugs for treating AIDS and cancer by passage of the _Drug Regulation_ Act of 1992.

38. Both the American Nurses Association (ANA) and the Canadian Nurses Association (CAN) have a _code of ethics_ which are standards for ethical practice in nursing. Identify at least six of these standards:

    a. respect

    b. commitment to patient & their family.

    c. client advocate.

    d. preserve integrity.

    e. collaborate w/ other health professionals.

    f. articulate nursing values.

39. The nurse's primary responsibility is to the _client_ _____.

6   Transcultural Considerations

Study Questions

Define the following:

1. Ethnocultural

2. Biocultural ecology

3. Racial

4. Temporality

Complete the following:

5. The two largest ethnocultural groups in the United States are _____ and _____.

6. The largest Native American Indian tribe in the United States is the _____.

7. The ethnic group whose religious beliefs obligate its members to care for themselves first before seeking care from a health care professional is _____.

8. Balancing the Yin and Yang qualities of foods are important to _____.

9. Obesity is prevalent and is seen as positive for which ethnic groups? _____

10. Tay-Sachs disease is a common genetic disease among which ethnic group? _____

11. Most drug testing in the United States has which ethnic group for research participants? _____

12. Timeliness for appointments is important for which ethnocultural groups? _____

13. The laws of _____ dictate which foods are permissible for traditional Jews.

14. English is the language used by Amish people when communicating with physicians and nurses; the language used at home is called _____.

Select the most appropriate response.

15. Factors that affect clients' physiological responses to medications include all of the following EXCEPT:
    a. genetics.
    b. diet.
    c. age.
    d. values.

16. Factors that affect clients' compliance with medication prescriptions include all of the following EXCEPT:
    a. beliefs.
    b. living conditions.
    c. cultural values.
    d. heredity.

17. Primary characteristics of culture include:
    a. generation.
    b. religion.
    c. marital status.
    d. urban versus rural status.

18. Secondary characteristics of culture include:
    a. age.
    b. length of time away from the country of orgin.
    c. nationality.
    d. race.

19. African-Americans:
    a. are less responsive to beta blockers than are European-Americans.
    b. are more responsive to beta blockers than are European-Americans.
    c. experience fewer toxic side effects with psychotrophic medications than do European-Americans.
    d. experience fewer toxic side effects with antidepressant medications than do European-Americans.

20. The diet of most Native Americans:
    a. is high in fruits and vegetables.
    b. is low in fat and carbohydrates.
    c. includes corn as a staple.
    d. includes rice as a staple.

21. The Amish population has:
    a. low rates of hemophilia B.
    b. low rates of twinning.
    c. high rates of hemophilia B.
    d. low rates of maple syrup urine disease.

22. Many Asian/Pacific Islanders have lactose intolerance. Symptoms of lactose intolerance include:
    a. constipation.
    b. palpitations.
    c. elevated enzymes.
    d. bloating.

23. José Gonzalez, age 45, has developed lactose intolerance. Dietary counseling to meet calcium requirements include encouraging him to eat:
    a. leafy green vegetables.
    b. chicken.
    c. flour tortillas.
    d. gelatin.

24. Factors that influence a client's compliance with medication prescriptions include:
    a. race.
    b. genetics.
    c. heredity.
    d. culture.

25. Communications, one of the domains of culture, includes:
    a. maintenance of eye contact.
    b. use of traditional healthcare providers.
    c. use of complementary/alternative medicine.
    d. primary occupation.

26. Lisa, age 22, is from the Caribbean. She is 6 months pregnant. At her mother's request, she eats red clay to provide minerals for the fetus, a practice she intends to continue. You would:
    a. insist that she stop the practice immediately.
    b. determine the amount of clay she eats daily.
    c. ask her to substitute corn starch for the clay.
    d. double her daily iron supplement.

27. Pablo de Omedo is newly diagnosed with diabetes and is taking an oral hypoglycemic. His *curandero* has recommended that he drink sabila tea three times a day to improve his nutrition. As his home health nurse, you would:
    a. encourage him to drink it four times a day.
    b. discourage the practice; sabila tea potentiates oral hypoglycemics.
    c. discourage the practice; sabila tea decreases the effects of oral hypoglycemics.
    d. encourage him to drink the tea, but be sure to continue taking his oral hypoglycemic medication.

Critical Thinking Exercises

A Chinese couple, Foua and Nao Liu, bring their 6-year-old daughter, Lia Liu, to the Emergency Department. The child had a pulmonary infection and was last seen in the Emergency Department two days ago. At that time, Lia was prescribed erythromycin 150 mg. She does not seem to be improving. The parents bring the bottle of liquid erythromycin with them in a plastic bag. Included in the bag is a porcelain Chinese soup-spoon, which is about the size of a tablespoon. The instructions on the bottle read: Take 1 teaspoon every 6 hrs. for ten days. The bottle is almost half-empty. When the nurse begins to examine Lia, she notices 6 quarter-size round ecchymotic areas on her back. The following conversation ensues:

Nurse: (Looking at first the mother and then the father). What made these marks?

Parents: Both parents have puzzled looks on their faces and do not look at the nurse.

Nurse: (Pointing at the bruises). These marks, what caused them?

Foua: Father and I do them.

Nurse: You and your husband hit the child? With what did you hit the child?

Nao: (With a puzzled frown on his face). No hit Lia. Help her.

Nurse: What did you hit Lia with?

Foua: We help the breathing.

Nurse: (Indignantly). I don't know about this. I must get the doctor to look at this.

The nurse left the room to get someone else to look at the ecchymotic areas. When she returned, the parents were gone.

1. Why did the parents leave the Emergency Department?

2. What do you think made the round ecchymotic areas on Lia's back? Is this practice harmful?

3. Why did the parents not maintain eye contact with the nurse?

4. The parents were giving Lia a tablespoon of erythromycin each time instead of a teaspoon. What is the normal dosage of erythromycin for a six-year-old child?

5. How much more erythromycin was the child receiving than prescribed?

6. Is this a potentially dangerous dose?

7. How might this over-dosage have been prevented?

9. If you had needed an interpreter, who would be the "ideal interpreter"?

8. Why do the parents only speak in the present tense?

10. If you needed an interpreter and one was not available, how might you have communicated with the parents?

7 Drug Interactions, Over-the-Counter Drugs, and Drug Abuse

Study Questions

Define the following:

1. Addiction

2. Drug abuse

3. Drug incompatibility

4. Drug interaction

5. Withdrawal

Match the following terms with the letter of the definition.

	Terms		**Definitions**
____ 6.	drug interaction	a.	undesirable drug effect
____ 7.	drug incompatibility	b.	changes that occur in the absorption, distribution, metabolism, or excretion of one or more drugs
____ 8.	adverse drug reaction		
____ 9.	pharmacokinetic interaction	c.	altered effect of a drug as a result of interaction with other drugs
____ 10.	pharmacodynamic interaction	d.	reaction that occurs *in vitro*
		e.	interaction that results in additive, synergistic, or antagonistic drug effects

Match the following agents with the letter of the action.

	Agents		**Action**
____ 11.	laxatives	a.	decrease drug absorption
____ 12.	aspirin		
____ 13.	antacids	b.	increase drug absorption
____ 14.	food		
____ 15.	narcotics	c.	block drug absorption
		d.	change urine pH to alkaline
		e.	change urine pH to acidic
		f.	increase or decrease absorption
		g.	increase drug excretion

Select the appropriate response:

16. Which of the following drug groups is primarily absorbed by the small intestine?

    a. barbiturates

    b. salicylates

    c. anticonvulsants

    d. theophylline

17. Your client is receiving two analgesics for pain relief. Two drugs with similar action are administered to achieve which of the following effects?

    a. additive

    b. synergistic

    c. agonistic

    d. antagonistic

18. Your client had surgery yesterday. He is taking two drugs at the same time: a narcotic and an antihistamine. This is an example of which of the following drug effects?

    a. additive

    b. synergistic

    c. agonistic

    d. antagonistic

19. When two drugs that have opposite effects are administered (e.g., stimulant and blocker), the drug effects are canceled. This is an example of which of the following effects?

    a. additive

    b. synergistic

    c. agonistic

    d. antagonistic

20. A major drug-food interaction occurs between monoamine oxidase (MAO) inhibitors and foods rich in which of the following?

    a. caffeine

    b. fiber

    c. tyramine

    d. acetylcholine

21. Your client is taking digoxin and a diuretic. You need to be aware of digitalis toxicity and which of the following serum levels?

    a. potassium

    b. sodium

    c. calcium

    d. chloride

22. Which of the following is NOT a sign of digitalis toxicity?

    a. nausea

    b. vomiting

    c. bradycardia

    d. tachycardia

Complete the following:

23. Drug distribution to tissues is influenced by its binding to _____ protein.

24. Increased drug metabolism (**increases/ decreases**) drug elimination and (**increases/ decreases**) concentration of the drug. (Circle correct answers)

25. Most drugs are excreted in the _____.

26. Most drug-induced photosensitive reactions can be avoided by the following two actions: _____ and _____.

27. Theophylline has been ordered for your client who smokes cigarettes. Since tobacco is an _____, the theophylline dose may need to be (**decreased/increased**). (Circle correct answer)

28. Regulations for the use of narcotics are set forth in the _____ Act of 1970.

29. Addiction is a serious physical and behavioral problem. It is characterized by the following three behaviors: a)_____ drug use, b) drug _____, and c) drug _____.

30. Two physical effects commonly occurring when an addicted person abruptly discontinues taking the drug are _____ and _____.

31. Intense desire for a drug when it is not available is _____. The person (**does/does not**) experience physical or withdrawal effects. (Circle correct answer)

32. Risk factors for abuse of drugs by nurses include _____, _____, and _____.

33. When a drug problem is suspected, the nurse should encourage the individual to seek _____.

34. Peer assistance programs usually include one or more of the following services: _____, _____, and _____.

35. The addicted person and significant others often experience frustration and "trying times." Encourage significant others to be _____ of the client.

36. The _____ Amendment approved drugs safe for consumption that may be sold as OTC drugs.

37. The _____ Amendment required proof of efficacy and safety of the drug.

38. Based on review by the FDA, the OTC drugs are assigned to one of _____ categories.

39. The major ingredient in many OTC weight control products is _____ and is contraindicated for clients with _____ disease, hypertension, _____, and thyroid disease.

40. Alcohol and tobacco (**may/may not**) alter the action and absorption of medications. (Circle correct answer)

41. The client should consult with a health care provider (**before/during/after**) use of OTC preparations. (Circle correct answer)

42. OTC category I drugs are judged to be _____ and _____.

43. Drugs not included in nonprescription products because they are unsafe or ineffective are category _____ drugs.

44. Aspirin (**is/is not**) recommended for children with flu-like symptoms. (Circle correct answer)

45. Aspirin (**increases/decreases**) effects of oral anticoagulants. (Circle correct answer)

46. Clients with impaired renal function (**should/ should not**) avoid aspirin, acetaminophen, and ibuprofen.

47. Good sources for information about OTC drugs are _____ and _____.

48. E.J., four years old, is complaining of a sore throat, a cough productive of green sputum, and bilateral knee pain. Her mother is about to administer several OTC preparations. Four concerns about OTC drugs in this situation include:

a.

b.

c.

d.

8 Herbal Therapy with Nursing Implications

Study Questions

Match the description with the letter of the reference:

Description

____ 1. "Reasonable certainty" reported on specific herbal remedy

____ 2. St. John's wort was its first monograph

____ 3. International cooperative to develop botanical monograph

____ 4. The authoritative source for therapeutic substances

____ 5. Supports study of alternative therapies

____ 6. Supportive of 1976 resolution for health care for world's population by 2000

____ 7. Plant-based remedies

____ 8. Translating Commission E monographs into English

____ 9. Two primary types of herbal monographs

____ 10. Clarified marketing regulations for herbal remedies

Reference

a. *United States Pharmacopeia*

b. World Health Organization

c. European Scientific Cooperative of Phytomedicines

d. *American Herbal Pharmacopeia*

e. Phytomedicine

f. German Commission E

g. American Botanical Council

h. Office of Alternative Medicine

i. Dietary Supplement Health and Education Act of 1994

j. Therapeutic and qualitative

Complete the following (word search). Clues are provided in questions 11–16. Circle your responses.

```
O  M  D  V  Z  T  W  A  E  T
F  R  E  S  H  H  E  R  B  C
J  I  R  D  O  S  L  I  O  A
D  S  B  I  D  Y  C  U  T  R
E  J  B  D  I  R  T  L  E  T
D  I  N  C  T  U  R  E  A  X
D  A  O  P  A  P  T  R  E  E
R  P  F  U  S  A  L  R  R  A
D  E  N  Y  P  S  E  U  I  W
S  X  A  K  T  I  L  I  F  Y
```

11. Adding a sweetener to an herb and cooking it results in a _____.

12. Soaking dried or fresh herbs in boiling water makes a _____.

13. _____ are derived from soaking fresh or dried herbs in a solvent.

14. _____ have more reliable dosing by isolating certain components.

15. Soaking dried herbs in oil and heating for a long time results in an _____.

16. Enzyme activity may cause _____ _____ to decay in a few days.

Multiple choice:

17. An herb commonly used for external treatment of insect bites and minor burns is:
    a. feverfew.
    b. yarrow.
    c. aloe vera.
    d. licorice.

18. A popular tea for relief of digestive and gastrointestinal distress is:
    a. chamomile.
    b. licorice.
    c. St. John's wort.
    d. Kava kava.

19. Which herb is popularly known as "herbal valium"?
    a. saw palmetto
    b. valerian
    c. echinacea
    d. St. John's wort

20. Frequently mixed with fillers, a popular all-purpose woman's tonic herb is:
    a. kava kava.
    b. dong quai.
    c. ginseng.
    d. elderberry.

21. An herb frequently used for relief of migraine headache is:
    a. garlic.
    b. feverfew.
    c. peppermint oil.
    d. yarrow.

22. Worldwide, the most commonly prescribed herbal remedy is:
    a. gingko biloba.
    b. echinacea.
    c. ginger.
    d. licorice.

23. Extract of which herb may prevent damage to liver cells?
    a. peppermint
    b. psyllium
    c. milk thistle
    d. ginkgo biloba

24. An herb that is a natural estrogen promoter and that may lower the seizure threshold if taken with anticonvulsants is:
    a. ginger.
    b. psyllium.
    c. feverfew.
    d. evening primrose.

25. The herb of endurance is:
    a. echinacea.
    b. ginger.
    c. garlic.
    d. ginseng.

26. "Drug holiday" is recommended with
    a. St. John's wort.
    b. echinacea.
    c. ginkgo biloba.
    d. valerian.

27. An herb of CNS sedation without loss of mental acuity or memory and no risk of tolerance used to treat anxiety and insomnia is:
    a. licorice.
    b. kava kava.
    c. peppermint.
    d. milk thistle.

Match the herb with the letter of its description.

Herb

_____ 28. ginkgo biloba
_____ 29. peppermint oil
_____ 30. yarrow
_____ 31. saw palmetto
_____ 32. kava kava
_____ 33. goldenseal
_____ 34. psyllium
_____ 35. echinacea
_____ 36. ginger
_____ 37. St. John's wort

Description

a. provides muscle relaxation
b. widely used as laxative and with Crohn's disease
c. immune enhancer
d. may be helpful in Raynaud's and Alzheimer's diseases
e. relief from stiffness and pain of osteo- and rheumatoid arthritis
f. tonic, astrigent, and to relieve congestion of common cold
g. may be effective treatment for tension headache
h. stops wound bleeding
i. "herbal Prozac"
j. "plant catheter"

38. Identify at least five guidelines for the responsible use of herbs:

a.

b.

c.

d.

e.

Critical Thinking Exercises

J.C., a 24-year-old male teacher, visits his health care provider for a pre-employment physical examination. During the nursing history, J.C. tells you that he has several questions about the use of herbs. His questions/statements are:

a. "How do I know what to take . . . there are so many varieties, almost as many as cough meds." What advice would be appropriate for you to give J.C.?

b. "My friend tells me that if I take echinacea, St. John's wort, and valerian every day, that I will live longer." What cautions (with rationale) would you give J.C. about this combination?

c. "Oh yes, and what about the use of ma huang for weight loss and energy booster?" What would be an appropriate response?

9 Pediatric Pharmacology

Study Questions

Define the following:

1. Developmental age

2. Chronological age

Complete the following:

3. Identify two reasons that pediatric drugs are less researched than those used in the adult population:

   a.

   b.

4. Name the four components of pharmacokinetics:

   a.

   b.

   c.

   d.

5. You are administering a medication to a 2-week-old infant. You note that the medication is acidic. How will the client's age impact the absorption of this medication?

6. A 2-year-old child is to receive a water-soluble medication. In order to reach therapeutic levels and based on your knowledge of medication distribution, how may the dosage need to be changed for this client?

7. Infants have _____ protein sites than adults, so lower dosages are needed.

8. Infants' blood-brain barrier allows medication into nervous system tissue more easily than in adults. This increases the likelihood for _____ in young infants.

9. Topical drugs are absorbed more _____ in children than adults.

10. Children have higher metabolic rates than adults. How does this fact affect the medication for pain in children?

11. How can being an adolescent potentially affect the excretion of a medication in a teenaged child?

12. Define *pharmacokinetics*. How will these factors affect a child who is receiving insulin therapy?

13. Describe two methods of calculating pediatric medication dosages:

    a.

    b.

14. Describe three ways to involve parents/significant other family members in the administration of medications to pediatric clients.

    a.

    b.

    c.

15. Describe one cognitive element that needs to be considered when administering medications to children in each of the following age groups:

    a.   Infant

    b.   Toddler

    c.   Preschool

    d.   School age

    e.   Adolescent

16. Describe the procedure for applying EMLA to a 6-year-old child:

17. Discuss why a plastic bandage is so important to the preschool child following an injection:

18. List five elements of medication administration that are key in teaching families to give medications to their children:

    a.

    b.

    c.

    d.

    e.

Critical Thinking Exercises

You are a nurse on a busy pediatric unit. You need to provide medications for five clients. These five clients include a 10-month-old receiving oral elixir antibiotics for an ear infection, a 10-year-old receiving subcutaneous insulin for diabetes mellitus, a 4-year-old receiving EMLA topically in preparation for insertion of an IV, a 2-year-old receiving eye drops for an infection, and a 16-year-old receiving intramuscular pain medication on a one-time basis. Answer the following questions about these clients:

a.   What are the ways to most successfully administer the oral medications to the 10-month-old client?

b.   What special considerations exist for the child receiving EMLA?

c.   Describe the procedure for administering the intramuscular and subcutaneous injections to those two children.

d.   In what ways do the pharmacokinetics and pharmacodynamics differ with each route?

e.   In what ways do the pharmacokinetics and pharmacodynamics differ with each age group?

10 Geriatric Pharmacology

Study Questions

Define the following:

1. Biotransformation

2. Compliance

3. Noncompliance

4. Polypharmacy

Physiologic changes in the adult influencing the therapeutic drug regimen include: (Circle correct answers)

5. pH of gastric secretions (**increases/decreases**).

6. Cardiac output and blood flow (**increases/decreases**).

7. Hepatic enzyme function (**increases/decreases**).

8. Glomerular filtration rate (**increases/decreases**).

9. When the efficiency of hepatic and renal systems is decreased, the half-life of the drug is (**increased/decreased**).

Complete the following:

10. An indicator of the glomerular filtration rate is _____. The normal value for an adult is _____ ml/min.

11. Drug dosages are adjusted according to the older adults' _____, _____, and _____.

12. The first benzodiazepine hypnotic introduced in 1970 that has three metabolites and is not recommended for clients over age 65 is _____.

13. Choice antihypertension agents due to their low incidence of electrolyte imbalance and central nervous system side effects are _____ and _____.

14. Digoxin (Lanoxin), a cardiac glycoside, has a long half-life. In the older adult, >80 years old, digoxin accumulation might cause _____.

    Explain why:

15. The drug dose of antidepressants is usually _____ to _____% of the dose for a middle-aged adult.

Select the appropriate response:

16. Physiologic changes of aging that can affect drug activity include all of the following EXCEPT:

    a. increased fat-to-water ratio.
    b. decreased liver enzyme production.
    c. loss of nephrons.
    d. increased gastrointestinal blood flow.

17. When administering drugs to the elderly, the nurse must have the following information EXCEPT:
    a. whether the drug is highly protein-bound.
    b. half-life of the drug.
    c. availability of drug.
    d. serum levels of drugs with narrow therapeutic ranges.

18. Factors contributing to adverse reactions in the elderly include:
    a. loss of protein-binding sites.
    b. decline in hepatic first-pass metabolism.
    c. prolonged half-life of the drug.
    d. all of the above.

19. Which drug would have fewer adverse and toxic effects?
    a. fat soluble, half-life of 50 hours
    b. fat soluble, 90% protein-bound
    c. half-life of 4 hours, 50% protein-bound
    d. half-life of 30 hours, 90% protein-bound

20. Which of the following organs are especially significant in drug therapy of the elderly and should be monitored?
    a. kidney and pancreas
    b. kidney and liver
    c. liver and pancreas
    d. kidney and lungs

21. Adverse reactions and drug interactions occur frequently in the elderly due to all of the following EXCEPT:
    a. consumption of numerous drugs due to chronic multiple illnesses.
    b. self-medication with OTC preparations.
    c. drugs ordered by several health care providers.
    d. increased incidence of allergic responses.

22. E.B. reports dizziness every morning when he gets out of bed. E.B. is probably experiencing:
    a. bradycardia.
    b. orthostatic hypotension.
    c. intermittent claudication.
    d. hyperventilation.

23. The nurse should recommend that E.B.:
    a. take his pulse before getting out of bed.
    b. take deep breaths.
    c. move a chair close to the bed.
    d. change position slowly.

Situation: Following hospitalization, A.E. receives a home visit from the nurse. A.E. asks questions concerning her medications.

24. A.E. asked if she should continued to take the medications she took prior to hospitalziation. What may be the most appropriate response?
    a. "Yes, you should continue to take the drugs that you took before going to the hospital."
    b. "You should take one-half the dosage of each drug that you took prior to hospitalization."
    c. "You should take only the drugs that have been prescribed on discharge and not drugs that you took prior to hospitalization unless otherwise indicated."
    d. "You should continue to take those drugs that have been helpful to you."

25. A.E. says that before hospitalization, she was taking digoxin 0.125 mg per day. The new prescription is digoxin 0.25 mg per day. What should she do? Your response would be for AE to take:
    a. digoxin 0.125 mg per day.
    b. digoxin 0.25 mg per day.
    c. digoxin 0.125 mg in the morning and 0.25 mg in the evening.
    d. both digoxins at least one hour apart.

26. A.E. says she has problems opening the bottle tops of the drugs. An appropriate response is to:
    a. ask the pharmacist to place the drugs in non-child–proof bottle caps.
    b. tell A.E. to put her medications in glass cups and place them in the cabinet.
    c. put the drugs in individual envelopes.
    d. ask a family member to help her daily with the medications.

27. A.E. says that she is to take the newly pre-
     scribed drugs at different times. She has vision
     problems. What would your suggestion be so
     that she would comply with her medication
     regimen?

     a.   Line up the bottles of medications on a
           table and instruct her to take them in that
           order.

     b.   Obtain a daily (preferably) or weekly pill
           container from the drug store and fill the
           container the day or week before with
           the drugs.

     c.   Ask a neighbor to give her her daily
           medications.

     d.   Tell her to write down drugs that she has
           taken that day.

28. List four reasons commonly given by the
     elderly for noncompliance with drug therapy
     and a specific nursing intervention for each.

                     Reason   **Nursing Interventions**

a.

b.

c.

d.

Critical Thinking Exercises

M.Z., a basically healthy octagenarian, visits her health care provider for her annual "check-up." During the health history, she complains of "trouble falling asleep and staying asleep and having to get up to the bathroom several times each night."

1. What laboratory tests would be helpful to determine if M.Z. was having kidney problems, especially because of her frequent nocturia?

2. How might M.Z.'s sleep deprivation be corrected?

She thinks her current meds are HydroDIURIL and Halcion. "I try to remember to take my meds, and sometimes I take an extra one, just in case I missed a dose."

3. What information, if any, needs to be reported to the health care provider?

4. What are M.Z.'s health teaching needs?

11 Medication Administration in Community Settings

Study Questions

Complete the following (word search). Clues are given in questions 1–7. Circle your responses.

```
T  F  M  L  E  I  B  G  H  M  X  Y  I  B  P  N  L  D  E  T  S  A
B  W  U  O  G  Z  H  K  L  Y  C  D  V  R  T  L  E  N  L  E  C  Q
S  T  C  E  F  F  E  E  D  I  S  L  T  A  C  L  S  F  L  G  T  O
V  A  R  U  I  M  T  S  D  L  A  E  G  J  E  L  B  F  L  I  P  M
H  E  T  B  V  P  X  I  K  N  R  G  R  B  T  S  A  F  E  T  Y  R
F  M  I  K  B  S  A  U  O  Y  T  A  A  C  X  D  E  M  J  L  K  D
I  G  C  J  G  F  U  I  M  H  J  L  L  R  M  O  Y  P  L  I  B  A
R  E  O  B  E  X  S  C  S  U  T  B  H  I  D  I  E  T  O  N  E  B
J  H  I  B  N  S  C  E  Y  A  M  K  N  P  E  A  V  J  H  Q  O  D
Y  T  P  M  E  E  T  O  B  J  E  I  D  F  O  L  K  M  O  L  A  S
A  S  D  F  R  E  T  N  U  M  S  W  I  M  V  D  I  U  Q  E  R  Y
N  Y  O  E  A  T  M  J  K  T  Y  R  O  T  A  L  U  G  E  R  U  H
B  R  P  W  L  I  Y  R  E  A  F  G  N  H  T  E  L  L  I  A  C  U
P  E  Y  B  V  R  I  A  K  L  J  C  H  I  L  D  S  A  F  E  M  N
A  G  O  C  U  L  T  U  R  A  L  B  H  T  E  S  S  C  P  O  L  Q
L  K  K  R  E  I  E  P  E  R  S  O  N  A  L  B  E  L  I  E  F  S
R  E  J  N  O  R  I  G  I  N  A  L  I  T  B  O  P  E  M  Y  E  V
T  Q  I  N  P  R  T  R  A  D  I  T  I  O  N  A  L  V  U  A  S  F
```

1. Medication administration in any community setting must be consistent with _____, _____, and _____ requirements.

2. Communication and tracking are required to _____ untoward responses and medication error.

3. The five areas of suggested client teaching are: _____, _____, _____, _____, and _____.

4. In all aspects of medication administration, client _____ is of primary concern.

5. Two necessary qualities related to the storage of medications are: _____, _____ containers; with _____ caps, as necessary.

6. As part of the cultural assessment, the nurse initially assesses the client's _____.

7. Nurses may demonstrate respect for cultural diversity by including _____ and _____ practices into the health care plan.

Multiple choice:

8. Commonly used OTC preparations that may not be compatible with prescription medications include:

    a. cough and cold preparations.

    b. diet aids.

    c. fat-soluble vitamins.

    d. all of the above.

9. Clients allergic to medications are advised to do which of the following?

    a. wear medic-alert identification

    b. take extra vitamin C

    c. avoid use of penicillin

    d. have annual CBC

10. Areas of diet teaching include advice about:

    a. drug-food interactions.

    b. alcohol use.

    c. foods to avoid.

    d. all of the above.

11. Administration of medication is ultimately regulated by which of the following?

    a. guidelines of the agency

    b. state's Nurse Practice Act

    c. ANA guidelines

    d. state nurses association

12. A nurse at the work site may be responsible for identifying self-care centers for specific conditions. Which of the following conditions are best suited for this level of service?

    a. abdominal pain and low-grade fever

    b. common cold and chest pain

    c. common cold and minor cuts

    d. headache and numbness in arm

Complete the following:

13. A complete medication includes the following: _____, _____, _____, _____, and _____.

14. Labeling of the medication must be by the _____ or the _____.

15. In the event of a medication error, the nurse's role is to report it to the _____ and participate in a plan to prevent future occurrences.

16. When a narcotic order is discontinued in the home setting, the health care provider is notified of any _____ narcotics.

17. The home health aides may only have involvement that the client _____; this involvement may only be of assistance.

18. In the school setting, the policy for medication administration should promote _____ programs of students with chronic conditions.

19. Two factors contributing to the need for health services and medication administration in the work site are _____ and _____.

20. Health care providers permitted to give medications in the home include _____ _____.

Critical Thinking Exercise

Chris is an 8-year-old carefree second grader who was just started on an inhaler PRN for exercise-induced asthma. As the school nurse, what information would you discuss with Chris and his family about the requirements of the medication order and labeling of the medication that will be kept at school?

12 The Role of the Nurse in Drug Research

Study Questions

Define the following:

1. Informed consent

2. Control group

3. Experimental group

4. Placebo

Complete the following:

5. A basic ethical principle states that individuals should be treated as _____.

6. Duty not to harm others is referred to as _____.

7. Objective allocation of social benefits and burdens is included in the principle of _____.

8. Analysis of possible consequences based on inherent risk and anticipated benefits describes the _____ to _____ ratio.

9. Only (**1 in 10,000/1 in 1,000**) of potential drugs is used in clinical situations based on the findings of the research and development process. (Circle correct answer)

10. Experimentation usually done in a test tube is known as _____.

11. Experimentation done on living organisms is known as _____ testing.

12. Identification of the safe therapeutic dose and drug-related abnormal changes in animal organs are the objectives of

_____

_____.

13. In Phase _____ of human experimentation, a multidisciplinary team assures that data will answer the clinical questions.

14. Phase IV trials address _____ use of the drug.

Match the letter from Column II to the applicable description in Column I.

Column I		**Column II**
____ 15. descriptive design	a.	comparison of effectiveness of two antibiotics using two groups: clients receiving antibiotic A and clients receiving antibiotic B
____ 16. quasi-experimental design		
____ 17. intervening variables		
____ 18. probability sampling	b.	subjects randomly selected from the population
____ 19. crossover design	c.	subject is its own control
____ 20. matched pair design	d.	a chart review of hospitalized clients who received ritodrine at Evergreen Hospital in 1992
____ 21. double and triple design		
____ 22. independent variable	e.	preferred for drug research
____ 23. control group	f.	subjects matched on intervening variables and randomly assigned to experimental or control group
____ 24. experimental group		
____ 25. dependent variable		
	g.	may include disease and state of severity, age, and weight
	h.	participant receives treatment
	i.	the drug itself
	j.	provides a baseline to measure the effects
	k.	subjects' clinical reactions

Select the appropriate response:

26. Informed consent includes all of the following EXCEPT:
    a. avoidance of fraud in health care.
    b. promotion of rational decision making among clients.
    c. assurance of health-care outcomes.
    d. promotion of self-determination.

27. The experimental study design requires all of the following EXCEPT:
    a. researcher controls treatment.
    b. alternate treatment methods.
    c. control groups.
    d. random assignment.

28. All of the following are components of assessment EXCEPT:
    a. recruitment of subjects.
    b. assurance that the subject gives informed consent.
    c. communication of concerns to the health care provider.
    d. thorough knowledge of all criteria for subjects.

Complete the following:

29. Describe two roles of the nurse in clinical drug trials: _____ and _____.

30. Identify at least three new drugs and the purpose of each.
    a.

    b.

    c.

31. Identify at least three medications that have been FDA-approved for expanded indications.
    a.

    b.

    c.

13 Vitamin and Mineral Replacement

Study Questions

Define the following:

1. Fat-soluble vitamins

2. Megavitamin

3. Minerals

4. Water-soluble vitamins

Select the appropriate response:

5. Vitamins are organic chemicals that are necessary for which of the following?
   a. tissue healing
   b. tissue growth
   c. metabolic functions
   d. all of the above

6. Vitamin intake should be increased in the presence of which of the following conditions?
   a. alcoholism
   b. breastfeeding
   c. fad diets
   d. all of the above

7. Inappropriate indications for vitamin therapy include which of the following?
   a. feeling tired
   b. debilitating illness
   c. improvement of overall health
   d. a and c only

8. The USDA's Food Guide Pyramid recommends that fat be limited to what percentage of caloric intake?
   a. 10%
   b. 20%
   c. 30%
   d. 40%

Match the letter of fat- or water-soluble vitamins in Column II with the appropriate word or phrase in Column I:

Column I	Column II
____ 9. vitamin A	a. fat-soluble vitamins
____ 10. vitamin B complex	
____ 11. vitamin C	b. water-soluble vitamins
____ 12. vitamin D	
____ 13. vitamin E	
____ 14. vitamin K	
____ 15. toxic in excessive amounts	
____ 16. metabolized slowly	
____ 17. minimal protein binding	
____ 18. readily excreted in urine	
____ 19. slowly excreted in urine	

Match the letter of the common food sources with the appropriate vitamin.

Vitamin		Food Sources
_____ 20. vitamin A	a.	fermented cheese, egg yolk, milk
_____ 21. vitamin B$_{12}$		
	b.	wheat germ, egg yolk, liver
_____ 22. vitamin C		
_____ 23. vitamin D	c.	fish, liver, egg yolk
_____ 24. vitamin E	d.	green and yellow vegetables
	e.	tomatoes, pepper, citrus fruits
	f.	whole grains and cereals
	g.	milk and cream

Complete the following:

25. Regulation of calcium and phosphorus metabolism and calcium absorption from the intestine is a major role of vitamin _____.

26. Synthesis of prothrombin and other clotting factors is a role of vitamin _____.

27. Protection of red blood cells from hemolysis is a role of vitamin _____.

28. The acid required for body growth; without _____ acid there is disruption in cellular division.

29. The mineral essential for regeneration of hemoglobin is _____.

30. Sixty percent of iron is found in what red blood cell component? _____

31. Foods rich in iron include _____, _____, and _____.

32. Antacids and vitamin C (**slow/hasten**) iron absorption. (Circle correct answer)

33. Iron toxicity is a serious cause of poisoning in children and may be fatal by causing _____ due to an ulcerogenic effect.

34. The client is advised to drink liquid iron preparations through a straw because it may _____ _____ _____.

Select the appropriate response:

Situation: J.P., 15 years old, has a skin disorder that is diagnosed as acne. J.P. is taking large doses of vitamin A. The next four questions refer to this situation.

35. Vitamin A is essential for maintaining the following body tissues EXCEPT:
    a. skin.
    b. hair.
    c. ovaries.
    d. eyes.

36. Vitamin A is stored in the liver, kidneys, and fat. It is excreted:
    a. rapidly from the body.
    b. slowly from the body.
    c. only in the bile and feces.
    d. several hours after ingestion.

37. Massive doses of vitamin A may be toxic; therefore, client teaching for J.P. should include all of the following EXCEPT:
    a. encouraging J.P. to contact the health care provider concerning drug dosing.
    b. informing J.P. that high doses of vitamin A could cause toxicity (hypervitaminosis A).
    c. teaching J.P. not to exceed the recommended dietary allowance without health care provider approval.
    d. instructing J.P. that massive doses of vitamin A are needed for months to alleviate acne.

38. Signs and symptoms of vitamin A toxicity include all of the following EXCEPT:

    a. euphoria.

    b. headaches.

    c. drowsiness.

    d. vomiting and diarrhea.

39. Which vitamin would be considered less toxic than vitamin A?

    a. vitamin K

    b. vitamin D

    c. vitamin E

    d. vitamin C

40. List two nursing interventions related to the administration of vitamins:

    _____ and

    _____.

41. Which of the following statements is/are true about zinc?

    a. found in lamb, eggs, and leafy vegetables

    b. to be taken 2 hours after antibiotic

    c. adult RDA is 12–19 mg

    d. all of the above

42. Chromium is thought to be helpful in control of:

    a. non-insulin dependent diabetes

    b. common cold

    c. Raynaud's phenomenon

    d. Alzheimer's disease

43. Which of the following statements is/are true about copper?

    a. deficiency corrected by iron supplements

    b. deficiency associated with Wilson's disease

    c. found in shellfish, legumes, and cocoa

    d. all of the above

44. List three health teaching suggestions for a client taking or contemplating taking an over-the-counter (OTC) iron preparation.

    a.

    b.

    c.

Critical Thinking Exercises

P.J., a 48-year-old attorney, is an avid weight lifter and takes multiple vitamin and mineral supplements. He indicates that he tries to eat one full meal a day and "catches bites" as time permits.

a. What dietary suggestions do you have for P.J.?

b. What vitamins and minerals would you recommend for P.J.? Suggest doses of each with rationale.

14 Fluid and Electrolyte Replacement

Study Questions

Define the following:

1. Hypercalcemia

2. Hyperkalemia

3. Hypernatremia

4. Hypocalcemia

5. Hypokalemia

6. Hyponatremia

7. Osmolality

8. Tonicity

Complete the following:

9. Normal serum osmolality is _____.

10. Explain how serum osmolality can be calculated.

11. If the serum osmolality is 285 mOsm/kg, the body fluid is (**hypo-osmolar/iso-osmolar/ hyperosmolar**). (Circle correct answer)

12. The type of intravenous solution based on osmolality of 540 mOsm is considered to be a(n) _____ solution.

13. Four groups of intravenous solutions used for fluid replacement are
    _____,
    _____,
    _____, and
    _____.

14. Potassium, sodium, calcium, and magnesium are electrolytes that are necessary for the transmission and conduction of _____ and the contraction of _____.

15. Potassium is primarily found in the (**cells/ tissues**). (Circle correct answer)

16. The majority of potassium is excreted by the _____.

17. When potassium is administered orally, it should be taken with at least _____ of water or juice.

18. The solutions for intravenous fluid replacement for a serum sodium deficit of 125 mEq/L is _____, and for a serum sodium deficit of 115 mEq/L is _____.

19. Vitamin D is needed for calcium absorption from the _____.

20. Calcium is in both the _____ and _____ fluid compartment in approximately equal proportions.

21. If the serum protein/albumin levels are decreased, there will be (**more/less**) circulating calcium (free calcium). (Circle correct answer)

22. Thiazide diuretics such as hydrochlorothiazide (HydroDIURIL) (**increase/decrease**) the serum calcium level. (Circle correct answer)

23. If there is a calcium deficit, tetany symptoms could be present. Symptoms of tetany include _____, _____, and _____.

24. Two groups of drugs that contain magnesium are _____ and _____.

Give the normal serum level ranges for the following electrolytes:

29. Potassium

   _____

30. Sodium

   _____

31. Calcium

   _____

32. Magnesium

   _____

Match the terms in Column II with the descriptions in Column I.

Column I		Column II
____ 25. similar to plasma concentration	a.	osmolality
	b.	osmolarity
____ 26. based on milliosmols per kilogram of water	c.	iso-osmolar
	d.	hypo-osmolar
	e.	hyperosmolar
____ 27. fluids contain fewer particles and more water		
____ 28. fluids have a higher solute/ particle concentration		

Match the electrolyte in Column II with the related drug in Column I.

Column I		Column II
____ 33. normal saline	a.	potassium
____ 34. Kaon chloride	b.	sodium
____ 35. Maalox	c.	calcium
____ 36. Epsom salt	d.	magnesium
____ 37. CaCl		
____ 38. Slow K		

Give the rationale for the nursing interventions
related to potassium drug administration.

Nursing Interventions		**Rationale**

39. Give oral potassium with a sufficient amount of water or juice (6–8 ounces) or at mealtime.

39.

40. Dilute IV potassium chloride in the IV bag several times to promote thorough mixing of potassium in the IV solution.

40.

41. Check the IV site for infiltration, especially when potassium chloride is in the IV fluids.

41.

42. Monitor the amount of urine output, hourly and at 24 hours.

42.

43. Monitor the serum potassium level.

43.

44. Monitor the ECG.

44.

45. Instruct the client who is taking potassium-wasting diuretics or a cortisone preparation to eat foods rich in potassium or take a potassium supplement as needed.

45.

46. Instruct the client to report signs and symptoms of hypokalemia or hyperkalemia, which are:

46.

47. Assess for signs and symptoms of digitalis toxicity when the client is taking digoxin and a potassium-wasting diuretic and/or cortisone.

47.

Select the appropriate response:

Situation: B.Z. is receiving two liters of intravenous (IV) fluids: 1000 ml (1 liter) of D_5W and 1000 ml of $D_5/0.45\%$ NaCl ($D_5/$ ½ NS). The next six questions relate to this situation.

48. These IV solutions are classified as:
  a. colloids.
  b. crystalloids.
  c. lipids.
  d. blood products.

49. One liter (1000 ml) of 5% dextrose in ½ normal saline solution ($D_5/0.45\%$ NaCl) is what type of IV fluid?
  a. isotonic
  b. hypotonic
  c. hypertonic
  d. iso-hypotonic

50. If D_5W is used continuously over several days, the IV solution becomes:
  a. hypotonic.
  b. hypertonic.
  c. isotonic.
  d. iso-hypertonic.

51. What is B.Z.'s serum osmolality according to the following current laboratory values: serum sodium 140 mEq/L; BUN 15 mg/dl; blood glucose 110 mg/dl?
    a. 280 mOsm
    b. 285 mOsm
    c. 291 mOsm
    d. 296 mOsm

52. B.Z.'s serum osmolality is:
    a. iso-osmolar.
    b. hypo-osmolar.
    c. hyperosmolar.
    d. iso-hyperosmolar.

53. Lactated Ringer's IV solution has similar composition to:
    a. white blood cells.
    b. plasma.
    c. body tissue.
    d. skin.

Situation: E.R., 43 years old, is taking Slow K. She is taking hydrochlorothiazide 50 mg daily to control her hypertension. The next five questions relate to this situation.

54. E.R.'s serum potassium level was 3.2 mEq/L. Her serum potassium level was:
    a. increased.
    b. decreased.
    c. normal.
    d. extremely low.

55. The Slow K should be given:
    a. when the client's stomach is empty.
    b. at bedtime.
    c. with eight ounces of water.
    d. two hours before meals.

56. E.R. complains of nausea, vomiting, and abdominal distention. These are probably related to:
    a. hyponatremia.
    b. hypernatremia.
    c. hyperkalemia.
    d. hypokalemia.

57. You advise E.R. to eat foods rich in potassium. Which of the following foods are NOT rich in potassium?
    a. dry fruits
    b. bananas, prunes
    c. broccoli, peanut butter
    d. egg, whole-grain breads

58. E.R. asks why she has to take potassium. The best response would include all of the following EXCEPT:
    a. "Your diuretic causes not only water and sodium to be excreted but also potassium."
    b. "Your serum potassium level is low, and Slow K helps to prevent a potassium deficit."
    c. "Your health care provider should discontinue the potassium supplement after a week."
    d. "The potassium supplement should maintain a normal potassium level in your body while you are taking the diuretic (potassium-wasting diuretic)."

Situation: P.H., 65 years old, is hospitalized with hyperkalemia. P.H.'s urine output has been markedly decreased. The next four questions relate to this situation.

59. Which of the following serum potassium levels would indicate hyperkalemia?
    a. 5.9 mEq/L
    b. 4.6 mEq/L
    c. 3.8 mEq/L
    d. 2.9 mEq/L

60. Which of the following is NOT a cause of hyperkalemia?
    a. renal insufficiency
    b. administration of IV solutions with large doses of potassium chloride in each solution
    c. potassium-wasting diuretics
    d. poor urine output for days

61. P.H.'s serum potassium level is 6.1 mEq/L. The nurse should observe for signs and symptoms of hyperkalemia which include all of the following EXCEPT:

    a. abdominal cramps.

    b. muscular weakness.

    c. tachycardia and later bradycardia.

    d. oliguria.

62. Which of the following is NOT used to treat hyperkalemia?

    a. glucagon

    b. IV sodium bicarbonate, calcium gluconate

    c. insulin and glucose

    d. Kayexalate and sorbitol

Situation: I.Q., 68 years old, has a calcium deficit. Her serum calcium level is 3.6 mEq/L. The next three questions refer to this situation.

63. I.Q.'s serum calcium level is:

    a. slightly low

    b. severely low

    c. low average

    d. normal

64. The health care provider orders calcium chloride in 5% dextrose and 0.45% sodium chloride (D_5/½ NS). What effect may saline solution have on calcium chloride?

    a. It may increase the effects of calcium.

    b. It has little or no effect on the calcium additive.

    c. Calcium additives should always be added to IV solutions containing sodium chloride.

    d. Sodium encourages calcium loss; calcium should not be mixed with a saline solution.

65. The best response by the nurse to this IV order is to:

    a. explain to the client that she should not accept this intravenous fluid.

    b. suggest to the health care provider to change the IV order to 5% dextrose in water (D_5W) and explain why.

    c. do nothing, because this solution would not have any effect on the calcium chloride additive.

    d. report the health care provider to the chiefs of nursing and medicine.

Critical Thinking Exercises

A.F. is taken to the emergency room after an automobile accident. He is losing large amounts of blood. Vital signs (VS) are BP 100/60; P 112; R 32.

1. What are the advantages of the use of crystalloids versus colloids when there is an acute blood loss?

2. What are the advantages of the use of whole blood versus packed red blood cells (RBCs)?

3. Explain the significance of A.F.'s VS.

A.F. is admitted to the hospital after receiving two liters of crystalloids and two units of whole blood. After receiving the IV fluids, his VS are BP 122/65; P 92; R 28. His urine output is 400 ml in eight hours.

4. Urine output can be increased by using intravenous fluids except in the case of renal disease. Explain.

5. Why did A.F.'s VS improve?

During the next 23 hours, A.F. receives three liters of D_5W with 20 mEq of potassium chloride in two of the liters. His serum potassium level is 3.3 mEq/L.

6. What type of IV solution is missing with this 24-hour IV fluid order? Explain.

7. What is the difference in the fluid osmolalities of the following crystalloids: D_5W, $D_5/0.45\%$ NaCl, and lactated Ringer's solution?

8. What may occur if all of the IV solutions are hypertonic?

9. What is the purpose of the potassium chloride (KCl)? What effect does the potassium order have on A.F.'s serum potassium level?

10. What should the nursing assessment for A.F. include related to his IV therapy?

15 Nutritional Support

Study Questions

Define the following:

1. TPN

2. Valsalva maneuver

3. Intermittent enteral feedings

4. Nutritional support

5. Label the routes for enteral feedings:

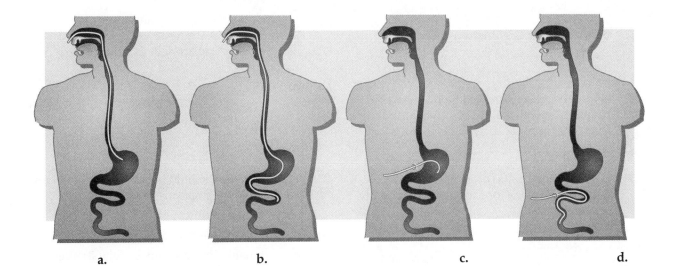

a.

b.

c.

d.

a. _____

b. _____

c. _____

d. _____

Complete the following:

6. The two routes for administering nutritional support are _____ and
    _____.

7. Nutritional support aids an ill client by _____ and
    _____.

8. The three routes for enteral feedings are
    _____,
    _____, and
    _____.

9. The three nutritional components of enteral solutions are _____,
    _____, and
    _____.

10. A cyclic method of continuous enteral feedings is _____.

11. Major problems that may occur following enteral feeding are _____,
    _____, and _____.

12. Another name for total parenteral nutrition (TPN) is
    _____.

13. Indications for TPN therapy include
    _____, _____,
    or _____.

14. Hyperglycemia (increased blood sugar) is a complication related to TPN. A contributing factor that may cause hyperglycemia is
    _____.

15. Hypoglycemia could occur to a client receiving TPN. Reasons for occurrence of hypoglycemia include _____,
    _____, or
    _____.

Select the appropriate response:

16. A type of solution used for nutritional support is:
    a. 5% dextrose in water (D_5W).
    b. 0.9% sodium chloride (normal saline).
    c. lactated Ringer's.
    d. Ensure.

17. Ensure and Sustacal are examples of:
    a. blenderized solutions.
    b. polymeric, lactose-free solutions.
    c. polymeric, milk-based solutions.
    d. elemental or monomeric solutions.

18. An enteral feeding administered over 30–60 minutes by drip or pump infusion is known as a(n) _____ enteral feeding.
    a. bolus
    b. intermittent
    c. gravity
    d. continuous

19. Blended enteral solutions include all of the following EXCEPT:
    a. Osmolite.
    b. Compleat B (Sandoz).
    c. baby food with water added.
    d. foods blenderized into liquid consistency.

20. TPN is administered:
    a. orally.
    b. via a peripheral vein.
    c. via a central venous line.
    d. via a subcutaneous line.

21. The percent of dextrose in TPN is approximately:
    a. 5%.
    b. 10%.
    c. 25%.
    d. 50%.

22. Enteral feeding should be used before TPN for all the following reasons EXCEPT:
    a. it is less costly.
    b. it poses less risk of infection.
    c. it maintains gastrointestinal (GI) integrity.
    d. there is less risk of aspiration.

23. All of the following are complications associated with use of TPN EXCEPT:
    a. pneumothorax.
    b. aspiration.
    c. air embolism.
    d. infection.

24. Continuous feedings into the small intestine are commonly infused at which of the following rates/hour?

    a. 25–50 ml

    b. 50–125 ml

    c. 100–175 ml

    d. 150–200 ml

25. Diarrhea associated with enteral feedings may be managed by which of the following?

    a. changing the enteral solution

    b. decreasing rate of infusion

    c. diluting the solution

    d. all of the above

Critical Thinking Exercises

T.A. is unable to swallow fluids. She received IV parenteral fluids for one week. A nasogastric tube was inserted for intermittent enteral feedings. The family asked how long T.A. would receive "tube feeding."

1. What are some of the advantages and disadvantages of each of the four methods used to administer enteral feedings?

2. Cite possible reasons that T.A.'s intravenous therapy was discontinued.

3. How often should T.A. receive enteral feedings? Explain.

4. How would you respond to the family's question about the length of time T.A. will be receiving enteral feedings?

5. How can aspiration be prevented?

T.A. developed diarrhea after receiving Ensure Plus for 36 hours. The order for Ensure Plus was changed to 300 ml of a 70% solution of Ensure Plus every six hours.

6. How can diarrhea be managed?

7. What amount of the Ensure Plus and water mixture is needed to produce a 70% enteral solution? (See Chapter 4–C in text if necessary.)

16 Central Nervous System Stimulants

Study Questions

Define the following:

1. Attention deficit hyperactivity disorder

2. Narcolepsy

3. Dependence

4. Tolerance

5. Hyperkinesis

Complete the following:

6. The drug group that acts on the brain stem and medulla to stimulate respiration is _____.

7. Long-term use of amphetamines can produce _____ dependence.

8. Narcolepsy is characterized by falling asleep during (**early morning/normal waking/ evening**) hours. (Circle correct answer)

9. Amphetamine-like stimulants are frequently prescribed for children with _____.

10. Amphetamines (**are/are not**) recommended for use as appetite suppressants. (Circle correct answer)

11. The action of amphetamine-like drugs is enhanced by drugs such as _____, and is decreased by _____ and _____.

12. Diamphetamine (Benzedrine) may cause CNS (**depression/stimulation**) and cardiac _____. (Circle correct answer)

13. Caffeine and theophylline belong to the _____ group.

14. Caffeine is used to treat newborns with _____ or _____.

15. More than _____ mg of caffeine affects the CNS and heart.

16. CNS stimulants (**do/do not**) pass into the breast milk. (Circle correct answer)

Select the appropriate response:

Situation: E.B. is 16 years old and is receiving methylphenidate (Ritalin) for treatment of attention deficit hyperactivity disorder (ADHD). The next four questions refer to this situation.

17. ADD has also been referred to as which of the following?
   a. minimal brain dysfunction
   b. hyperkinesis
   c. hyperkinetic syndrome
   d. all of the above

18. You would tell E.B. that common side effects include all of the following EXCEPT:
    a. euphoria and alertness.
    b. hypertension.
    c. irritability.
    d. orthostatic hypotension.

19. The half-life of Ritalin requires dosing:
    a. daily.
    b. 1–3 times per day.
    c. every 3 hours.
    d. every 12 hours.

20. E.B. develops CNS toxicity. The treatment now includes:
    a. decreasing urine pH.
    b. increasing urine pH.
    c. decreasing fluids.
    d. increasing fluids.

21. The best time to administer amphetamines is:
    a. at bedtime.
    b. 1–2 hours before sleep.
    c. with meals.
    d. 6–8 hours before sleep.

22. Long-term use of amphetamines can result in:
    a. diarrhea.
    b. cardiac dysrhythmias.
    c. urinary retention.
    d. rash.

23. J.W. is 11 years old and is taking anorexiants. Your health teaching should include:
    a. that children under 12 should not take anorexiants.
    b. the need to monitor dose.
    c. that the drug should be taken at regular mealtimes.
    d. that the drug should be taken with limited fluid.

24. Which of the following anorexiants has a high potential for abuse?
    a. phentermine (Adipix)
    b. phenylpropanolamine (Dexatrim)
    c. phenmetrazine (Preludin)
    d. mazindol (Sanorex)

25. Which of the following statements is/are true of Ritalin?
    a. may increase hypertensive crisis with monoaminenanhydrase inhibitors
    b. may increase effects of oral anticoagulants
    c. may alter effects of insulin
    d. all of the above

26. If CNS toxicity from amphetamines is suspected, which of the following aids in the excretion of the drug?
    a. increasing urine pH
    b. decreasing urine pH
    c. increasing fluids
    d. use of diuretics

27. CNS stimulants are contraindicated for clients with:
    a. heart disease and renal disease.
    b. heart disease and liver disease.
    c. heart disease and hyperthyroidism.
    d. all of the above.

28. Modafinil (Provigil) is a new drug prescribed for treatment of:
    a. narcolepsy.
    b. ADHD.
    c. memory loss.
    d. weight loss.

29. List the four conditions for which CNS stimulants are medically approved:
    a.

    b.

    c.

    d.

30. List four nursing implications of administering CNS stimulants:
    a.

    b.

    c.

    d.

31. Describe at least four health teaching considerations for clients taking CNS stimulants:

    a.

    b.

    c.

    d.

Critical Thinking Exercises

You are the new school nurse at Countryside Elementary, which has 1000 students. You note that more than 100 students come to the nurse's office "around midday" to take their meds for ADHD. The majority of them take pemoline and the rest take methylphenidate.

1. What is the recommended time to take these medications in relation to food?

2. What are the nursing implications of this timing?

3. What might be some of the reasons for the majority of these students taking pemoline?

4. What assessments are important for these students?

5. What laboratory tests require monitoring?

6. There is an outbreak of respiratory illness at the school. What specific health teaching is appropriate for the children taking these drugs?

7. You start a support group for parents and teachers of these children. What are the most likely topics of concern for this group?

17 Central Nervous System Depressants: Sedative-Hypnotics and Anesthetics

Study Questions

Define the following:

1. Balanced anesthesia

2. Dependence

3. NREM sleep

4. REM sleep

5. Sedation

Complete the following:

6. The broad classification of central nervous system (CNS) depressants includes the following seven groups:

   _____,
   _____,
   _____,
   _____,
   _____,
   _____, and
   _____.

7. The two phases of sleep are _____ and _____.

8. The mildest form of CNS depression is _____.

9. There is a high incidence of sleep disorders; thus, _____ drugs are among the most frequently prescribed.

10. Identify at least four nonpharmalogic ways to promote sleep:

    a.

    b.

    c.

    d.

11. Anesthesia (**may/may not**) be achieved with high doses of sedative-hypnotics. (Circle correct answer)

12. Thiopental is used in general anesthesia as an _____ anesthetic.

13. General anesthesia depresses the _____ system, alleviates _____, and causes a loss of _____.

14. The first anesthetic developed was _____.

15. An operation is performed during the _____ stage of anesthesia. The other three stages include _____, _____, and _____.

16. Bupivacaine and tetracaine are drugs commonly used for _____ anesthesia.

17. A major potential adverse effect of spinal anesthesia is

_____.

18. The type of spinal anesthesia frequently used for clients in labor is a _____

_____.

19. Muscle relaxants (**are/are not**) part of balanced anesthesia. (Circle correct answer)

20. For the control of seizures, _____-acting barbiturates are frequently prescribed.

21. Drugs used to induce sleep in those who have difficulty getting to sleep are _____ -acting barbiturates.

22. A popular nonbenzodiazepine for the treatment of insomnia is

_____.

23. The drug of choice for the management of benzodiazepine overdose is

_____.

24. Local anesthetics are divided into two groups: _____ and _____.

Match the letter of the description with the common side effect of sedative-hypnotics.

Side Effect		Description
____ 25. hangover	a.	need to increase dosage to get desired effect
____ 26. REM rebound		
____ 27. dependence	b.	suppression of respiratory center in the medulla
____ 28. tolerance		
____ 29. respiratory depression	c.	skin rashes
	d.	residual drowsiness
____ 30. hypersensitivity	e.	results in withdrawal symptoms
	f.	vivid dreams and nightmares

31. E.D., a 25-year-old mother of four young children, reports that she takes 150 mg of phenobarbital (Nembutal) every night at bedtime. List four points you would include in E.D.'s health teaching plan related to this practice:

a.

b.

c.

d.

Situation: J.B., 48 years old, returns to the unit following surgery; she has had spinal anesthesia. The next four questions relate to this situation.

32. To decrease the possibility of a spinal headache, you suggest that J.B.:
   a. be in high-Fowler's position.
   b. be flat in bed.
   c. increase fluid intake.
   d. b and c.

33. The reason for the client's position after spinal anesthesia is to:
   a. decrease leakage of spinal fluid.
   b. increase leakage of spinal fluid.
   c. has no relation to leakage of spinal fluid.
   d. maintain body in good alignment.

34. Possible complications as a result of spinal anesthesia include all of the following EXCEPT:
   a. hypertension.
   b. headache.
   c. hypotension.
   d. respiratory distress.

35. On the night of postoperative day four, J.B. requests a sleeping pill. Which of the following barbiturates may be used when the person has difficulty falling asleep and the nonpharmacologic measures have not been effective?

    a.   secobarbital

    b.   amobarbital

    c.   butabarbital

    d.   aprobarbital

36. Balanced anesthesia is comprised of all of the following EXCEPT:

    a.   hypnotic the night before.

    b.   narcotic analgesic and anticholinergic about one hour preoperatively.

    c.   long-acting barbiturate.

    d.   inhaled gas.

37. The advantage(s) of balanced anesthesia include(s):

    a.   slow induction of anesthesia.

    b.   reduction of drugs to maintain desired state of anesthesia.

    c.   maximum adverse effects postoperatively.

    d.   all of the above.

38. Lidocaine is frequently used for:

    a.   spinal anesthesia.

    b.   local anesthesia.

    c.   intravenous anesthesia.

    d.   general anesthesia.

39. Local anesthesia is indicated for all the following EXCEPT:

    a.   dental procedures.

    b.   suturing a skin laceration.

    c.   long-duration surgery at a localized area.

    d.   diagnostic procedures.

40. The primary ingredients of over-the-counter (OTC) sleep medications are:

    a.   barbiturates.

    b.   benzodiazepines.

    c.   tranquilizers.

    d.   antihistamines.

41. Which of the following drugs is considered safer than the barbiturates in the elderly?

    a.   estazolam (ProSom)

    b.   temazepam (Restoril)

    c.   triazolam (Halcion)

    d.   all of the above

Critical Thinking Exercises

B.Z. visits the clinic complaining of "trouble sleeping." He states, "I'm afraid to take anything because I may sleep through the alarm clock set for work."

1. Identify three factors that would be part of your nursing assessment of B.Z.

2. The health care provider has ordered a hypnotic, Nembutal. List two characteristics of an ideal hypnotic.

3. In addition, hypnotic therapy should be short-term to prevent _____ and _____.

4. Was Nembutal a drug of choice for this client? Give your rationale.

5. What is the onset and duration of action of this drug?

6. What would you include in your health teaching for this client?

18 Nonnarcotic and Narcotic Analgesics

Study Questions

Define the following:

1. Abstinence syndrome

2. Mixed narcotic agonist-antagonist

3. Narcotic agonist

4. Narcotic antagonist

It is important to identify the type of pain a client is experiencing and to know what group of drugs is most effective in providing relief.

Match the type of pain with the letter of the appropriate drug group.

Type of pain		Drug group
_____ 5. moderate acute pain	a.	nonnarcotic and comfort measures
_____ 6. chronic pain	b.	NSAIDs
_____ 7. deep pain	c.	combination of narcotic and nonnarcotic
_____ 8. mild superficial pain		
	d.	narcotic
_____ 9. somatic pain	e.	nonnarcotic
	f.	antipyretics
	g.	antihistamines

Complete the following:

10. Most _____ will lower an elevated body temperature.

11. NSAIDs from the _____ _____ group, such as ibuprofen, fenoprofen, and suprofen, have an analgesic effect.

12. Aspirin is not recommended for the treatment of a (**viral/bacterial**) infection. (Circle correct answer)

13. Aspirin and NSAIDs relieve pain by inhibiting the synthesis of

    _____.

14. These drugs should be taken with _____, at _____, or with a full _____ to reduce gastric irritation.

15. The most serious result of an overdose of acetaminophen (Tylenol) that extends beyond several days is

    _____.

16. Acetaminophen (**is/is not**) the drug of choice to treat an inflammatory process. (Circle correct answer)

17. Identify four areas of nursing intervention or areas for health teaching for clients taking nonnarcotic analgesics:

    a.

    b.

    c.

    d.

18. Narcotics act primarily on the _____ and nonnarcotic analgesics act on the _____ at the pain receptor sites.

19. In addition to suppressing pain impulses, narcotics also suppress _____ and _____.

20. In addition to pain relief, many narcotics have _____ and _____ effects.

21. Narcotics are contraindicated for use in clients with _____ and _____.

22. Identify two areas for client teaching related to analgesics/narcotics:

    a.

    b.

Select the appropriate response:

Situation: E.A., age 53, has just returned to the unit from the OR for the placement of a pin to stabilize her fractured hip. For the first 48 hours postoperatively, meperidine (Demerol) is ordered for pain control. The next five questions refer to this situation.

23. The usual adult dose of meperidine postoperatively is:
    a. 50 mg q3h.
    b. 50–100 mg q3–4h PRN.
    c. 25–100 mg q6h.
    d. 50–100 mg qd PRN.

24. During the time E.A. is taking meperidine, frequent monitoring of _____ is required.
    a. urine output
    b. temperature
    c. pulse
    d. blood pressure

25. You assess for toxic effects of the drug. Which of the following effects is an adverse reaction?
    a. tachycardia
    b. constipation
    c. urinary retention
    d. constricted pupils

26. Which nursing assessment would not be necessary when monitoring a client on meperidine?
    a. fluid intake
    b. bowel sounds
    c. urinary output
    d. vital signs

27. Your client teaching plans for E.A. would include:
    a. not to use alcohol and central nervous system (CNS) depressants while taking meperidine.
    b. to report side effects.
    c. prevention of constipation.
    d. all of the above.

28. For clients taking meperidine, drugs belonging to the _____ category are contraindicated.

29. Your client on meperidine reports blurred vision. You know this is a _____ and would report this finding to the _____.

30. List three side effects of narcotics with specific nursing interventions for each:

    Side Effects   **Nursing Interventions**

    a.

    b.

    c.

Select the appropriate response:

31. A severe side effect of narcotic analgesics/agonists is:
    a. sedation.
    b. respiratory depression.
    c. nausea and vomiting.
    d. constipation.

32. Based on your knowledge of analgesia, which factor is most relevant to the relief of chronic pain?
    a. administration of drugs at client's request
    b. use of injectable drugs
    c. narcotic analgesics
    d. use of drugs with long half-life

33. The narcotic antagonist used to treat an overdose of morphine-like substance is:
    a. pentazocine/Talwin.
    b. ibuprofen/Motrin.
    c. naloxone/Narcan.
    d. probenecid/Benemid.

34. Mixed narcotic agonist-antagonists were developed in hopes of decreasing _____.

35. Pentazocine, a narcotic agonist-antagonist, is classified as a Schedule _____ drug.

36. Withdrawal symptoms usually occur _____ hours after the last narcotic dose.
    a. 6–12
    b. 24–48
    c. 48–72
    d. 72–96

37. Methadone treatment programs can be effective in helping the narcotic-addicted person withdraw. Which of the following is the recommended maintenance dose of methadone?
    a. 100–150 mg/day
    b. 40–120 mg/day
    c. 10–35 mg/day
    d. 2–10 mg/day

38. The benefits of methadone over other narcotics is (are):
    a. less dependency.
    b. shorter half-life.
    c. daily dosing.
    d. a and c only.

39. Elder clients frequently require a reduction in narcotic dosage to avoid severe side effects. Reasons for this include which of the following?
    a. decreased excretion of drug
    b. decreased metabolism of drug
    c. polypharmacy
    d. all of the above

40. Which of the following drugs trends to be more toxic in elderly clients than middle-aged clients?
    a. Vicodin
    b. morphine
    c. Demerol
    d. all of the above

41. It may be difficult to assess pain in children. Pain management is more apt to be successful if the nurse includes which of the following?

    a.   uses age-appropriate communication skills

    b.   uses "ouch scale"

    c.   discusses child's response with parents

    d.   all of the above

42. Drug-food interactions with acetaminophen include which of the following?

    a.   increase effect with caffeine and diflunisal

    b.   increase effect with oral contraceptives

    c.   increase effect of alcohol

    d.   decrease effect of antibiotics

Critical Thinking Exercises

E.K., 55 years old, is brought to the ER complaining of severe chest pain of 30 minutes duration that began after a tense business meeting and was unrelieved by nitroglycerin. The nurse does a thorough assessment. The health care provider orders include morphine sulfate, 10 mg, for the severe pain.

Morphine sulfate is available as follows:

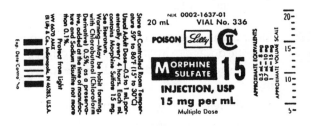

1. What quantity of the drug should be administered? What is the preferred route of administration?

2. Is the dose within the acceptable range?

3. What precautions must be observed when administering this medication?

Three hours later, E.K. is resting more comfortably in high-Fowler's position and complains, "I'm not able to pass my water." You also note that his blood pressure has dropped to 120/40. Laboratory test results are pending.

4. What is the most likely cause of urinary retention?

5. Are you concerned about his blood pressure? Give rationale.

6. What effects does morphine sulfate have on laboratory tests associated with acute myocardial infarction?

7. What would you include in your health teaching for E.K.?

19 Anticonvulsants

Define the following:

1. Idiopathic

2. Status epilepticus

3. Tonic-clonic (grand mal) seizures

4. Absence (petit mal) seizures

5. Hydantoins

Complete the following:

6. Epilepsy occurs in approximately _____ % of the population.

7. To diagnose epilepsy, results of an _____ is useful.

8. Fifty percent of all epilepsy is considered to be primary or _____.

9. The international classification of seizures describes the two categories of seizures as _____ and _____.

10. Anticonvulsant drugs suppress abnormal electrical impulses, thus _____ the seizure, but they (**do/do not**) eliminate the cause. (Circle correct answer)

11. Anticonvulsants (**are/are not**) used for all types of seizures. (Circle correct answer)

12. Identify at least three types of anticonvulsants used in the treatment of epilepsy: _____, _____, and _____.

13. The first anticonvulsant used to treat seizures was _____, discovered in 1938, and today the most commonly used drug for this condition.

14. The drug of choice for seizure disorders that have not responded to other anticonvulsant drug therapy is _____.

15. It is strongly recommended that the client check with the health care provider before taking _____ preparations.

16. Administration of phenytoin via the (**oral/ intramuscular/intravenous**) route is not recommended due to its erratic absorption rate. (Circle correct answer)

17. Which of the following is/are true about seizures and anticonvulsant use during pregnancy?
    a. Seizures increase 25% in epileptic women.
    b. Many anticonvulsants have teratogenic properties.
    c. Anticonvulsant use increases loss of folic acid.
    d. All of the above are true.

18. Which of the following statements is true about anticonvulsants?
    a. Phenytoin has been linked to cardiac defects.
    b. Valproic acid is associated with cleft palate.
    c. Anticonvulsants are vitamin K agonists.
    d. Trimethadione is recommended.

19. Vigabatrin is a relatively new anticonvulsant. Its qualities include which of the following?
    a. inhibits enzyme that destroys GABA
    b. adult dose is 1–4 g/d in divided doses
    c. used to treat complex partial seizures
    d. all of the above

Select the appropriate response:

Situation: J.A., 24 years old, has a seizure disorder and is going to start on phenytoin, the drug of choice to control her seizure activity. The next eleven questions relate to this situation.

20. J.A. will initially receive intravenous (IV) medication. Intravenously, phenytoin should be administered at a maximum rate of:
    a. 0.5 mg/minute.
    b. 5 mg/minute.
    c. 50 mg/minute.
    d. 500 mg/minute.

21. After several days of IV medication, J.A.'s medication is changed to the oral form. Oral doses of phenytoin are generally scheduled:
    a. once daily.
    b. 2–3 times daily.
    c. every 4 hours.
    d. every 12 hours.

22. When J.A. is started on the oral medication, the nurse should know that the dose will most likely be:
    a. low.
    b. high.
    c. changed daily.
    d. blood-level based.

23. J.A. asks how long she will be on these medications. The nurse's answer is based on the understanding that:
    a. the medications are taken for a lifetime.
    b. the medications are taken until the client is seizure-free.
    c. seizures are unpredictable, and therefore so is the drug regimen.
    d. seizure disorders are cured by medications.

24. For maintenance control of seizures in the adult, the usual dose of phenytoin is:
    a. 100 mg qd.
    b. 100 mg tid.
    c. 300 mg tid.
    d. 3 g qd.

25. Serum phenytoin levels should be monitored to determine if the blood serum level is within the therapeutic range, thus avoiding toxic levels. The therapeutic range of phenytoin is:
    a. $<5 \, \mu g/ml$.
    b. $10–20 \, \mu g/ml$.
    c. $20–40 \, \mu g/ml$.
    d. $40–50 \, \mu g/ml$.

26. You assess the client for side effects of the drug, which may include all of the following EXCEPT:
    a. nausea.
    b. vomiting.
    c. diarrhea.
    d. headache.

27. You are knowledgeable about drug interactions with phenytoin. Which of the following drugs are NOT known to alter the action of phenytoin?
    a. antacids and calcium preparations
    b. antineoplastics
    c. sulfonamides
    d. laxatives

28. In the event that J.A. experiences a seizure, you would document all of the following EXCEPT the:

    a.   type of movements.

    b.   time the movements started and ended.

    c.   ability to stop the movements.

    d.   progression of movement.

29. You observe that J.A. is receiving adequate nutrition. Phenytoin may cause all of the following EXCEPT:

    a.   anorexia.

    b.   nausea.

    c.   diaphoresis.

    d.   vomiting.

30. Your health teaching plan for J.A. would include all EXCEPT which of the following?

    a.   restrict fluids

    b.   urine may be a harmless pink color

    c.   alcoholic beverages are not recommended

    d.   drug may have a teratogenic effect on a fetus

31. List at least four additional items to be included in J.A.'s health teaching plan:

    a.

    b.

    c.

    d.

Situation: E.K. has been taking phenytoin for 20 years. He has not reported any seizure activity while on the maintenance dose. The next two questions relate to this situation.

32. You would assess the client for which common side effect of the drug?

    a.   gingival hyperplasia

    b.   polyuria

    c.   weight gain

    d.   irritability

33. Due to E.K.'s long-term use of phenytoin, which laboratory test results would be monitored?

    a.   potassium (K)

    b.   complete blood count (CBC)

    c.   platelets

    d.   blood sugar

34. Trimethadione and succinimides are effective drug therapy for:

    a.   grand mal seizures.

    b.   mixed seizures.

    c.   petit mal seizures.

    d.   status epilepticus.

35. Diazepam is the drug of choice for the treatment of:

    a.   grand mal seizures.

    b.   mixed seizures.

    c.   petit mal seizures.

    d.   status epilepticus.

36. Phenytoin is effective in the treatment of:

    a.   grand mal seizures.

    b.   mixed seizures.

    c.   petite mal seizures.

    d.   status epilepticus.

37. Zonisamide (Zonegran) is contraindicated if the client is allergic/sensitive to which of the following?

    a.   cephalosporins

    b.   sulfonamides

    c.   aminoglycosides

    d.   fluoroquinolones

38. List four nursing implications/interventions related to the administration of anticonvulsants:

    a.

    b.

    c.

    d.

39. Identify three purposes of community groups and associations for individuals taking anticonvulsants:

    a.

    b.

    c.

Critical Thinking Exercises

Many clients in your clinic have epilepsy. M.B. is a 44-year-old executive secretary who has been taking anticonvulsants for more than 25 years. Review of her records indicate she has missed several of her regularly scheduled appointments. You discuss this with her and her response is, "I know all about the disease and the drugs."

1. What is the main variable in determining the dosage of anticonvulsants? Provide your rationale.

2. On what basis is the drug dosage adjusted?

3. Describe the implications for the client when the serum level is below, within, and above the therapeutic range?

4. M.B. has been taking ethotoin, the newest hydantoin. What are the advantages of this drug?

5. Why are drug interactions common with hydantoins?

6. What is the serum therapeutic range for ethotoin?

8. What specific health teaching is appropriate for M.B.?

7. M.B.'s ethotoin serum level is 32 μg/ml. What nursing interventions are indicated?

20 Antipsychotics and Anxiolytics

Study Questions

Define the following:

1. Acute dystonia

2. Akathisia

3. Anxiolytics

4. Neuroleptic

5. Psychosis

6. Schizoprenia

7. Tardive dyskinesia

Select the appropriate response:

8. Antipsychotic drugs are useful in the management of:
   a. anxiety and neurosis.
   b. psychotic illnesses.
   c. depression and lifting of mood.
   d. psychosomatic disorders.

9. A full effective therapeutic response to antipsychotics usually takes:
   a. 24 hours.
   b. 3 days.
   c. 1 week.
   d. 3–6 weeks.

10. Client education for use of these drugs is important. The nursing actions for these individuals include advising client and significant others that:
    a. a therapeutic response to the medication is expected in a few days.
    b. the drug should be taken as prescribed and to consult the health care provider before discontinuing use.
    c. taking alcohol or barbiturates with the drug is acceptable.
    d. rapid change in position from supine to standing may cause vertigo.

11. Typical or traditional antipsychotics may cause extrapyramidal symptoms (EPS) or pseudoparkinsonism. Which of the following symptoms is NOT caused by EPS?
    a. stooped posture with masklike facies
    b. shuffling gait
    c. tremors at rest
    d. sucking and smacking movements of the lips

12. Clients taking high-potency typical antipsychotics may develop adverse extrapyramidal reactions, such as:
    a. paralysis of the extremities.
    b. akathisia.
    c. disorientation.
    d. talking excessively.

13. The most severe adverse extrapyramidal reaction is:
    a. acute dystonia.
    b. akathisia.
    c. tardive dyskinesia.
    d. pseudoparkinsonism.

14. Anticholinergic agents are used to decrease these extrapyramidal symptoms. Examples include:

    a. benztropine (Cogentin) and trihexyphenidyl (Artane).

    b. atropine and bethanechol (Urecholine).

    c. doxepin (Sinequan) and nortriptyline (Aventyl).

    d. diazepam (Valium) and alprazolam (Xanax).

Situation: D.S. has been vomiting for the last two days. The health care provider prescribed Compazine 5 mg, IM, STAT and q4h, PRN. The next four questions relate to this situation.

15. Prochlorperazine (Compazine) is classified as a(n):

    a. aliphatic phenothiazine.

    b. piperazine phenothiazine.

    c. piperidine phenothiazine.

    d. thioxanthene.

16. Compazine produces many effects but it does NOT cause:

    a. strong antiemetic effect.

    b. hypertension.

    c. low sedative effect.

    d. strong extrayramidal symptoms.

After three dosages of compazine, D.S.'s vomiting has subsided. Oral Compazine 5 mg, q4h, PRN was ordered.

17. D.S. asked how often should she take the Compazine tablet. The nurse's response would most likely be which of the following?

    a. "Take the oral Compazine if you become increasely nauseated; however, if you do take it, leave 4 hours between doses."

    b. "Compazine can be taken whenever necessary regardless of the time when it was last taken."

    c. "Do not take the oral Compazine until you have had several episodes of severe vomiting."

    d. "Take oral Compazine every 8 to 12 hours for 3 days."

18. Contraindications for taking Compazine include the following EXCEPT:

    a. severe liver disease.

    b. narrow-angle glaucoma.

    c. severe cardiovascular disease.

    d. neuromuscular pain.

19. Antipsychotic dosage for older adults should be:

    a. the same as an adult dose.

    b. 10% less than an adult dose.

    c. 25 to 50% less than an adult dose.

    d. avoided by clients who are >70 years old.

20. Haloperidol (Haldol) is frequently used as an antipsychotic. The nurse should know that it:

    a. has a sedative effect on agitated, combative persons.

    b. is the drug of choice for older clients with liver disease.

    c. will not cause extrapyramidal symptoms.

    d. can be used by clients with narrow-angle glaucoma.

21. Your client is taking Haldol 5 mg tid. The next day the client complains of nearly falling down when he gets out of bed. The client is most likely experiencing:

    a. anticholinergic reaction.

    b. tardive dyskinesia.

    c. orthostatic hypotension.

    d. tachycardia.

22. The category for atypical antispychotics is:

    a. phenothiazines.

    b. serotonin/dopamine antagonists.

    c. butyrophenones.

    d. thioxanthenes.

23. The atypical antipsychotics, marketed in the US since 1990, have a weak affinity for the D_2 receptors; thus, these agents cause:

    a. an increase in EPS.

    b. fewer EPS.

    c. absence of EPS.

    d. no effect on EPS.

24. Atypical antisychotics have a stronger affinity to:
    a. D_1 receptors.
    b. D_2 receptors; block serotinin receptors.
    c. D_3 receptors.
    d. D_4 receptors; block serotinin receptors.

Complete the following:

25. Antipsychotic drugs were developed to improve the _____ and _____ of clients with psychotic symptoms resulting from an imbalance in the neurotransmitter _____ .

26. Antipsychotic drugs are not used to treat _____ or _____ .

27. Antipsychotics belong to one of four classes: _____(largest), _____, _____, and _____ .

28. The atypical antipsychotics do not cause _____ side effects.

29. The most common side effect of all antipsychotics is _____ .

30. Dermatologic side effects include _____ and _____ .

31. Phenothiazines (**increase/decrease**) the seizure threshold; adjustment of anticonvulsants may be required. (Circle correct answer)

Match the following drugs with their drug classification.

	Drug		Drug Classification
____ 32.	Clozapine (Clozaril)	a.	phenothiazines
____ 33.	Chlorpromazine (Thorazine)	b.	non-phenothiazines
____ 34.	Fluphenazine (Prolixin)	c.	atypical antipsychotics
____ 35.	Droperidol (Inapsine)		
____ 36.	Haloperidol (Haldol)		
____ 37.	Risperidone (Risperdal)		

38. Serotonin antagonists, atypical antipsychotics, are effective for treating which type(s) of schizophrenia?
    a. positive symptoms
    b. negative symptoms
    c. both postive and negative symptoms
    d. anxiety

39. The largest group of anxiolytics is:
    a. antihistamines.
    b. azapirones.
    c. benzodiazepines.
    d. propanediol.

40. Dependency can occur when taking benzodiazepines over extended periods. Withdrawal symptoms can occur when benzodiazepines are abruptly stopped, such as:
    a. gastrointestinal discomfort.
    b. drowsiness.
    c. increased thirst.
    d. irritability and nervousness.

Situation: J.T. has anxiety over the recent terrorist attacks. The health care provider prescribed diazepam (Valium) 5 mg, bid. The next four questions relate to the situation.

41. Valium is classified as a(n):
    a. phenothiazine.
    b. benzodiazepine.
    c. antihistamine.
    d. serotonin antagonist.

42. J.T. asks what "bid" means. Your response would be which of the following?
    a. "Once a day."
    b. "Twice a day."
    c. "Three times a day."
    d. "Four times a day."

43. Diazepam was one of the first anxiolytic drugs; however, it may be prescribed for other clinical problems. For which of the following is it NOT prescribed?
    a. anxiety
    b. musculoskeletal spasms
    c. status epilepticus
    d. depression and delusions

44. J.T. should be told NOT to take Valium with:

    a. vitamins, because they increase the effects of Valium to toxic levels.

    b. antacids, because they increase serum Valium levels.

    c. alcohol, because it can cause CNS depression and respiratory distress.

    d. an antihypertensive agent, because J.T.'s blood pressure could be increased.

Complete the following:

45. Anxiolytics (**are/are not**) usually given for secondary anxiety. (Circle correct answer)

46. Long-term use of anxiolytics is not recommended because _____ may develop within a short time.

47. The action of anxiolytics resembles that of _____ _____, not antipsychotics.

48. Symptoms of a severe anxiety attack include _____, _____, _____, and _____

49. Nonpharmacologic measures to decrease anxiety include _____, _____, and _____.

50. The newest anxiolytic, _____, has fewer side effects than other drugs in this group; it is not clinically effective until 1–2 weeks after continuous use.

51. Hydroxyzine hydrochloride (Atarax, Vistaril) and diphenhydramine hydrochloride (Benadryl) can cause drowsiness and have a sedative effect. Though they are not anxiolytic drugs, they may be used for short-term relief of anxiety. These drugs are classified as _____.

52. List five side effects of benzodiazepines with specific nursing interventions for each:

Side Effects	Nursing Interventions
a.	
b.	
c.	
d.	
e.	

Critical Thinking Exercises

Clozapine (Clozaril) was the first atypical antipsychotic that has been effective in treating clients with severe schizophrenia. B.B. had been taking mesoridazine besylate (Serentil) which has been ineffective in treating his withdrawal behavior and lack of interest in himself and his surroundings. B.B. was prescribed clozapine (Clozaril) 50 mg per day for the initial doses. If tolerated, the dosage would increase to 100 mg, tid.

1. For treating B.B.'s symptoms, how does clozapine differ from mesoridazine?

2. What is the most severe side effect of clozapine? With long-term use, how should this be managed?

3.   Would B.B.'s daily doses of clozapine be within normal therapeutic range?

5.   What drug-drug interactions should be considered when taking clozapine?

4.   B.B. asked if it is OK to miss one of the daily doses which he may forget to take. What may your response be?

6.   What assessment and teaching strategies should be implemented for B.B.?

21 Antidepressants and Mood Stabilizers

Study Questions

Key terms: Identify the terms according to the definitions. Circle the term in the word search puzzle.

```
P  M  T  R  O  V  S  K  L  N  Q  M  B  C  E  I  B
J  A  N  T  I  D  E  P  R  E  S  S  A  N  T  S  W
P  O  X  R  J  T  W  Z  N  A  C  U  Y  K  H  F  L
K  I  W  I  Q  P  U  A  R  I  H  O  E  Y  I  R  W
Q  S  E  C  J  U  T  A  l  E  M  V  O  D  N  Z  S
R  X  C  Y  I  P  L  N  E  N  I  U  B  M  Z  A  I
T  W  R  C  I  O  J  P  X  T  Z  B  V  R  O  P  M
P  H  D  L  P  Y  M  N  C  R  S  B  I  E  W  F  H
R  O  U  I  I  N  M  A  N  I  C  A  P  C  Q  J  W
V  T  B  C  I  S  E  M  N  X  Z  P  O  T  A  W  E
F  R  P  S  S  R  I  S  I  W  T  J  O  B  M  I  A
```

1. Swing-type moods

2. Abbreviation for selective serotonin reuptake inhibitors

3. Abbreviation of monoamine oxidase inhibitors

4. A sense of euphoria

5. Groups of drugs to treat depression

6. A depression that has a sudden onset

7. Blocks the uptake of the norepinephrine and serotonin in the brain

Select the appropriate response:

8. The three groups of antidepressants are _____, _____, and _____.

9. The clinical response from tricyclic antidepressants (TCAs) is expected after _____ weeks of drug therapy.

10. TCAs are usually administered at _____ to minimize problems caused by the sedative action.

11. The drug of choice for treatment of enuresis in children is _____.

12. Second-generation antidepressants are called _____.

13. The uses for SSRIs include _____ and _____.

14. Clients who do not respond to TCAs or second-generation antidepressants are commonly prescribed _____.

15. Monoamine oxidase inhibitors (MAOIs) and TCAs (**should/should not**) be taken together. (Circle correct answer)

16. Examples of MAOIs include

    _____,

    _____, and

    _____.

Select the appropriate response:

Situation: P.H. is taking an MAOI for chronic anxiety and fear. The next eight questions relate to this situation.

17. P.H. is started on phenelzine (Nardil). This medication is generally scheduled to be taken:
    a. once daily.
    b. 2–3 times daily.
    c. every 4 hours.
    d. every other day.

18. The usual adult dose of Nardil is:
    a. 5 mg qid.
    b. 1 mg tid.
    c. 15 mg tid.
    d. 15 mg qd.

19. Assessment is essential with clients taking MAOIs. Frequent monitoring of which of the following is required?
    a. blood pressure
    b. pulse
    c. urine output
    d. hemoglobin

20. You assess P.H. for side effects of the drug. Which of the following is NOT a side effect of MAOIs?
    a. restlessness
    b. insomnia
    c. orthostatic hypotension
    d. urinary retention

21. You are knowledgeable about drug and/or food interactions with Nardil. Which of the following types of drugs/foods are known NOT to alter the action of Nardil?
    a. many cold medications
    b. citrus fruits
    c. vasoconstrictors
    d. cheese

22. If P.H. were to ingest drugs and/or foods that interact, which of the following is likely to occur?
    a. anaphylaxis
    b. orthostatic hypotension
    c. hypertensive crisis
    d. hallucinations

23. Health teaching for P.H. also includes the avoidance of all of the following EXCEPT:
    a. alcohol.
    b. cold preparations.
    c. antacids.
    d. tricyclics.

24. P.H. is having difficulty selecting his menu. Tyramine-rich foods to be avoided include:
    a. cheese, chocolate, and raisins.
    b. sausage, beer, and whole-grain breads.
    c. yogurt, eggs, and bananas.
    d. spinach, liver, and milk.

25. The two herbs that may be used for management of mild depression with health care provider's approval are:
    a. ephedra and garlic.
    b. St. John's wort and ginkgo.
    c. feverfew and ginger.
    d. garlic and goldenseal.

26. Prior to surgery, the use of many herbal products should be discontinued:
    a. 24 hours before surgery.
    b. 5 days before surgery.
    c. 1 to 2 weeks before surgery.
    d. 1 month before surgery.

27. The selective serotonin reuptake inhibitors (SSRIs) tend to be more popular than TCAs because they have fewer side effects. SSRIs:

   a. cause less sedation and fewer hypotensive effects.

   b. cause less hypotension and fewer circulatory changes.

   c. cause less GI distress and fewer hypotensive effects.

   d. cause less sexual dysfunction and moderate sedation.

28. Many subcategories are listed as "atypical antidepressants." Which of the following groups is NOT classified as an atypical antidepressant?

   a. NDRIs

   b. serotonin antagonists

   c. SNRIs

   d. SSRIs

Match the following drugs with their drug classification.

Drug

____ 29. mirtazapine (Remeron)

____ 30. reboxetine (Vestra)

____ 31. citalopram (Celexa)

____ 32. amitriptyline (Elavil)

____ 33. tranylcypromine (Parnate)

____ 34. Paroxetine (Paxil)

Drug Classification

a. atypical antidepressants

b. SSRIs

c. MAOIs

d. tricyclic antidepressants

Drug Chart: Complete the drug chart for sertraline HCl:

Selective Serotonin Reuptake Inhibitor (SSRI)

Drug Name Sertraline HCl (Zoloft) Pregnancy Category:	Dosage:	Assessment and Planning	Nursing Process
Contraindications:	Drug-Lab-Food Interactions:		
Pharmacokinetics: *Absorption:* *Distribution:* PB: *Metabolism:* t½: *Excretion:*	Pharmacodynamics: *PO:* Onset: Peak: Duration:	Interventions	
Therapeutic Effects/Uses: **Mode of Action:**		Evaluation	
Side Effects:	Adverse Reactions: Life-Threatening:		

Situation: R.T. is an acutely manic client prescribed lithium for the first time. The next five questions relate to this situation.

35. Nursing interventions associated with lithium carbonate in the management of bipolar disorders include all of the following EXCEPT:

    a. blood levels are drawn monthly to assure a blood level between 0.8 and 1.5 mEq/L.

    b. understanding that the drug is most effective in the depressive phase.

    c. monitoring for thirst, weight gain, and increased urination.

    d. emphasizing the importance of taking medication as ordered.

36. Specific nursing interventions with R.T. would include monitoring all of the following EXCEPT :

    a. daily weight.

    b. serum lithium level.

    c. daily EKG.

    d. intake and output.

37. Understanding R.T.'s need for hydration, you encourage him to have at least _____ ml (cc) of fluid daily.

    a. 1000

    b. 2000

    c. 3000

    d. 4000

38. After being on lithium carbonate 1200 mg/ day for five days, R.T. remains agitated and hyperactive. Today's plasma level was 0.8 mEq/L, and R.T. complains of feeling slowed down and having increased thirst. Your analysis is that the client is:

    a. still manic, with some serious signs of toxicity.

    b. toxic.

    c. still manic without serious signs of toxicity.

    d. a nonresponder.

39. Health teaching for R.T. includes all of the following EXCEPT:

    a. if medication is stopped, the depressive symptoms will reappear.

    b. avoid caffeine products that may aggravate manic phase.

    c. take medication with food.

    d. encourage client to wear/carry an ID tag indicating the drug taken.

Critical Thinking Exercises

R.C., a 65-year-old executive with the local newspaper company, has recently moved to the area. He tells you he is taking Prozac 80 mg at night because of insomnia, lack of energy, and the death of his son in a motor vehicle accident two months ago. You do a thorough nursing assessment.

1. Describe what assessments are indicated for R.C.

2. Is the dose of Prozac appropriate for R.C.? Give your rationale. What modifications, if any, might you suggest to the health care provider?

3. It usually takes _____ weeks to see the clinical effects of this drug.

4. Based on the limited information provided, does R.C. have primary or secondary depression? Provide your rationale.

5. Describe community resources that might be appropriate for R.C.

6. Identify at least six specific areas to be included in health teaching for R.C.

22 Autonomic Nervous System Agents

Study Questions

Define the following:

1. Neurotransmitter

2. Adrenergic

3. Cholinergic

4. ANS

5. CNS

6. PNS

The answers for questions 7–17 are located in the word search. Circle your responses.

```
G  I  T  F  M  L  E  I  B  G  H  M  X  Y  I  B  P  N  L  D  O  T  S  A
W  L  B  W  U  O  G  Z  H  K  L  Y  C  D  V  R  T  L  E  N  P  E  C  Q
A  R  S  T  C  E  S  Y  M  P  A  T  H  E  T  I  C  L  S  F  P  G  T  O
J  E  V  A  R  U  I  M  T  S  D  L  S  E  G  J  E  L  B  F  O  I  P  M
O  U  H  E  T  B  V  P  X  I  K  L  A  T  E  L  E  K  S  F  S  T  Y  R
P  Q  F  M  I  K  B  S  A  U  O  Y  M  A  A  C  X  D  E  M  I  L  K  D
A  C  E  T  Y  L  C  H  O  L  I  N  E  L  L  I  G  O  Y  P  T  I  B  A
M  T  E  N  I  R  H  P  E  N  I  P  E  R  O  N  R  I  E  V  E  N  E  B
K  W  J  H  I  B  N  S  C  E  Y  A  M  K  I  V  I  S  C  E  R  A  L  D
Y  H  Y  T  P  S  I  M  I  L  A  R  E  T  D  O  O  L  K  M  O  L  A  S
B  L  A  S  D  F  R  E  T  N  U  M  A  W  I  L  V  D  I  U  Q  E  R  Y
R  I  N  Y  O  E  A  T  M  J  K  L  Y  R  O  U  A  L  U  P  E  Y  U  H
S  C  B  R  P  W  L  I  Y  R  U  A  F  G  G  N  I  S  S  E  R  P  E  D
C  P  T  E  Y  B  V  R  I  M  K  L  J  C  H  T  L  D  S  O  F  W  M  N
E  O  A  G  O  D  U  L  I  U  R  A  L  B  H  A  E  S  S  C  P  O  L  Q
O  N  L  K  K  R  E  T  E  O  E  R  S  T  N  R  L  B  P  L  I  S  F  S
V  T  R  E  J  N  S  G  T  D  C  R  E  D  I  Y  I  O  B  A  L  Y  E  V
```

7. The autonomic nervous system (ANS) is referred to as the _____ system.

8. The ANS is a (**voluntary/involuntary**) nervous system. (Circle correct answer)

9. The somatic nervous system innervates _____ muscle.

10. The sympathetic and parasympathetic nervous systems act on (**the same/different**) organs. (Circle correct answer)

11. Drugs act on the nervous systems by _____ or _____.

12. The neurotransmitter in the sympathetic nervous system is _____.

13. The neurotransmitter in the parasympathetic nervous system is _____.

14. A drug that mimics the sympathetic nervous system and a drug that blocks the parasympathetic nervous system can cause (**similar/ different**) responses in an organ. (Circle correct answer)

15. Adrenalin is an example of a (**sympathetic/ parasympathetic**) stimulant. (Circle correct answer)

16. Sympathomimetics and parasympathomimetics have (**similar/opposite**) effects on organs. (Circle correct answer)

17. Sympathomimetics and parasympatholytics have (**similar/opposite**) effects on organs. (Circle correct answer)

Select the appropriate response:

18. Function of the ANS includes control and regulation of all of the following EXCEPT:
    a. heart and respiration.
    b. gastrointestinal tract and bladder.
    c. eyes and glands.
    d. skeletal muscles.

19. The action of adrenergic agonists include all of the following EXCEPT:
    a. increased blood pressure.
    b. constricted bronchioles.
    c. dilated pupils.
    d. increased blood sugar.

20. The action of cholinergic agonists include all of the following EXCEPT:
    a. increased heart rate.
    b. increased peristalsis.
    c. constriction of bronchioles.
    d. decreased blood pressure.

21. The actions of antispasmodics include all of the following EXCEPT:
    a. increased urinary retention.
    b. decreased mucous secretions.
    c. increased gastrointestinal motility.
    d. increased heart rate.

22. The actions of sympatholytics include all of the following EXCEPT:
    a. decreased blood pressure.
    b. decreased heart rate.
    c. constricted bronchioles.
    d. increased blood sugar.

23. Which autonomic nervous system groups have similar actions? _____, and _____; _____, and _____.

Complete the following chart:

Autonomic Nervous System: Sympathetic and Parasympathetic

Sympathetic Stimulants
Other Names:

_____

Action: List two

_____

_____

Sympathetic Depressants
Other Names:

_____

Action: List two

_____

_____

Parasympathetic Stimulants
Other Names:

_____

Action: List two

_____

_____

Parasympathetic Depressants
Other Names:

_____

Action: List two

_____

_____

23 Adrenergics and Adrenergic Blockers

Study Questions

Define the following:

1. Alpha blockers

2. Beta blockers

3. Selectivity

4. Sympathomimetic

5. Sympatholytic

Complete the following (word search) for questions 6–16. Circle your responses.

```
A  V  N  O  I  S  N  E  T  R  E  P  Y  H  H
D  T  A  B  P  P  G  U  H  J  X  Q  T  T  S
R  X  G  M  E  R  T  N  X  Q  F  M  O  Y  I
E  S  N  T  H  T  S  K  I  N  M  O  M  B  A
N  P  J  B  K  T  A  M  O  T  M  P  H  G  L
E  U  C  E  X  D  S  B  U  S  A  Z  P  T  P
R  G  Y  T  K  F  B  A  L  T  R  W  H  F  H
G  N  X  A  L  Q  P  B  H  O  O  G  X  X  A
I  I  O  1  Z  Z  R  O  A  1  C  P  U  J  2
C  T  W  L  X  S  L  B  Q  Y  A  K  P  Q  Y
A  T  G  C  2  Y  I  M  H  T  L  H  E  G  E
V  I  S  A  T  I  B  I  O  F  F  X  P  R  Z
Y  S  T  I  Y  N  I  Z  D  T  L  D  O  L  S
P  E  C  Z  O  E  N  I  T  I  G  E  R  D  A
B  S  M  H  M  W  S  S  E  R  P  I  N  I  M
```

6. Adrenergic receptors are located on the cells of _____ muscle.

7. The four types of adrenergic receptors are _____, _____, _____, and _____.

8. Urinary retention may occur with high doses of _____ drugs.

9. Nasal sprays should be used with the client (**sitting up/lying down**). (Circle correct answer)

10. Sympathomimetics (**do/do not**) pass into the breast milk. (Circle correct answer)

11. Adrenergic blockers are the same as _____.

12. The antidote for the intravenous infiltration of the alpha- and beta-adrenergic drugs such as norepinephrine and dopamine is _____.

13. The alpha blocker that may cause impotence or a decrease in libido is _____.

14. Mood changes such as depression and suicidal tendencies are possible when taking which type of adrenergic blocker? _____.

15. Abruptly stopping a beta blocker can cause rebound _____.

16. Nonselective beta blockers such as Inderal are contraindicated in clients with _____ and _____.

17. What is most likely to occur if a client is taking an adrenergic agonist with an adrenergic blocker? _____

Match the letter of the receptor with the associated adrenergic response.

Adrenergic Response		Adrenergic Receptor
____ 18. increases gastrointestinal relaxation	a.	alpha$_1$
	b.	alpha$_2$
____ 19. increases force of heart contraction	c.	beta$_1$
	d.	beta$_2$
____ 20. dilates pupils		
____ 21. decreases salivary secretions		
____ 22. inhibits release of norepinephrine		
____ 23. dilates bronchioles		
____ 24. increases heart rate		
____ 25. promotes uterine relaxation		
____ 26. dilates blood vessels		

Select the appropriate response:

Situation: N.F. has asthma and is taking isoproterenol (Isuprel) for control of this condition. The next four questions refer to this situation.

27. The desired effect of this drug is:
    a. decreased heart rate.
    b. bronchodilation.
    c. increased urinary output.
    d. increased state of alertness.

28. Isoproterenol also stimulates beta$_1$ receptors resulting in:
    a. increased heart rate.
    b. bronchospasm.
    c. acute heart block.
    d. nasal congestion.

29. You assess N.F. for all of the following common side effects of adrenergic drugs EXCEPT:
    a. tachycardia.
    b. palpitations.
    c. tremors.
    d. decreased blood pressure.

30. You advise N.F. that adrenergic drugs should be administered _____ to avoid nausea and vomiting.
    a. at bedtime
    b. with food
    c. two hours after meals
    d. with extra fluids

31. Over-the-counter drugs for cold symptoms have sympathetic properties and are contraindicated in clients with:
    a. hypertension.
    b. diabetes mellitus.
    c. coronary artery disease.
    d. all of the above.

32. (See Table 23-2.)The adrenergic drug used to treat acute hypertension which does NOT decrease renal function is:
    a. epinephrine.
    b. norepinephrine bitartrate.
    c. metaraminol bitartrate.
    d. dopamine HCl.

33. For an asthmatic, beta$_2$ adrenergic drugs are more desirable than those that have beta$_1$ and beta$_2$ properties. The advantage of a beta$_2$ (selective) adrenergic agonist is that the drug:
    a. increases heart rate.
    b. increases blood pressure.
    c. dilates bronchial tubes.
    d. increases urine output.

34. Which of the following is NOT a beta$_2$ adrenergic agonist?
    a. albuterol
    b. dopamine
    c. terbutaline
    d. isoetharine chloride

Situation: K.R., 64 years old, is receiving prazosin (Minipress) for dysrhythmias. The next three questions refer to this situation.

35. You assess K.R. for all of the following common side effects of Minipress EXCEPT:
    a. dysrhythmias.
    b. flushing.
    c. headache.
    d. hypotension.

36. The usual dose of Minipress is:
    a. 0.5–1 mg tid.
    b. 1–5 mg tid.
    c. 6–10 mg tid.
    d. 10–15 mg tid.

37. Which of the following would NOT be included in K.R.'s teaching plan?
    a. Warning signs of hypoglycemia may be masked.
    b. Arise slowly to avoid orthostatic hypotension.
    c. Increase fluid intake.
    d. Report "stuffy nose" and/or dizziness.

38. Which of the following is NOT included in health teaching specific to diabetes mellitus?
    a. Warning signs of hypoglycemia may be masked.
    b. Add two snacks to the daily diet.
    c. Monitor blood sugar monthly and follow the diet.
    d. The insulin dose may need to be adjusted.

39. (See Table 23–4 if necessary.) A beta blocker used to decrease blood pressure and pulse (heart) rate in asthmatic clients with little effect on bronchial tubes is:
    a. propranolol HCl.
    b. nadolol.
    c. pindolol.
    d. atenolol.

40. List four nursing implications associated with adrenergic medications:
    a.

    b.

    c.

    d.

41. List four nursing implications associated with adrenergic blocker medications:
    a.

    b.

    c.

    d.

Critical Thinking Exercises

K.S. is taking propranolol (Inderal) 40 mg tid for angina pectoris and cardiac dysrhythmias. During the nursing assessment, the nurse records that the client stated, "I'm troubled at times with asthma." Vital signs (VS): BP 126/84; P 62; R 24.

1. Propranolol HCl blocks which receptor site(s)?

2. Is K.S.'s drug dose within safe range? Explain.

3. Could propranolol affect K.S.'s asthma? Explain.

4. What effect could propranolol have on K.S.'s heart rate? Why?

5. K.S. may experience certain side effects when using propranolol over a long period. What are the client teaching aspects that should be explained to K.S.?

6. If K.S. abruptly stopped taking propranolol, would rebound tachycardia or rebound hypertension occur? Explain.

7. If K.S. were a diabetic, what affect might this drug have on his blood sugar?

8. What other beta blockers might K.S. take that might cause fewer side effects?

24 Cholinergics and Anticholinergics

Study Questions

Define the following:

1. Acetylcholine

2. Anticholinergic

3. Cholinergic

4. Cholinesterase

5. Muscarinic receptors

6. Adrenergic receptors

7. Parasympathomimetics

8. Parasympatholytics

Complete the following:

9. Cholinergic drugs and anticholinergic drugs have (**similar/opposite**) effects. (Circle correct answer)

10. The receptor that stimulates smooth muscle and slows the heart rate is

    _____.

11. Nicotinic receptors affect the

    _____

    muscles.

12. List four purposes of cholinergic drugs.
    a.

    b.

    c.

    d.

13. The cholinergic drug used primarily to increase urination is

    _____.

14. Indirect-acting cholinergic drugs inhibit the release of

    _____.

15. Anticholinesterases are used to produce pupillary

    _____.

16. The classic anticholinergic drug is

    _____.

17. Anticholinergic drugs are contraindicated for clients having what disease of the eye?

    _____

18. Four major effects of anticholinergics are
_____, _____,
_____, and
_____.

Select the appropriate response:

Situation: J.R. has difficulty urinating. He was prescribed bethanechol chloride (Urecholine) 25 mg, tid. The next six questions relate to this client situation.

19. Bethanechol is a:
    a. cholinergic agonist.
    b. anticholinergic.
    c. cholinesterase inhibitor.
    d. sympatholytic.

20. The mode of action of bethanechol is to:
    a. stimulate nicotinic receptors.
    b. stimulate muscarinic receptors.
    c. inhibit muscarinic receptors.
    d. inhibit nicotinic receptors.

21. J.R.'s drug dose is:
    a. higher than therapeutic range.
    b. lower than therapeutic range.
    c. within suggested therapeutic range.
    d. extremely low daily therapeutic dose.

22. The action of bethanechol to correct J.R.'s clinical problem of urinary retention is to:
    a. promote contraction of the bladder.
    b. inhibit bladder contraction.
    c. stimulate kidney secretion.
    d. decrease bladder tone.

23. Which of the following is NOT a clinical action of bethanechol?
    a. increased gastrointestinal peristalsis
    b. increased gastrointestinal secretion
    c. increased pulse (heart) rate
    d. pupillary constriction

24. List four nursing interventions associated with bethanechol:
    a.

    b.

    c.

    d.

25. Which of the following is NOT a tissue response to large doses of cholinergic drugs?
    a. increased bronchial secretions
    b. increased salivation
    c. urinary retention
    d. decreased heart rate

26. The drug used to treat myasthenia gravis by increasing muscle strength is:
    a. bethanechol (Urecholine).
    b. pilocarpine (Pilocar).
    c. neostigmine bromide (Prostigmine).
    d. edrophonium chloride (Tensilon).

27. Which of the following is NOT an effect of anticholinergic drugs?
    a. diarrhea
    b. urinary retention
    c. mydriasis
    d. dilated bronchi

28. Atropine is frequently prescribed in all of the following situations EXCEPT:
    a. preoperative medication.
    b. as an antispasmodic.
    c. to treat bradycardia.
    d. to treat urinary retention.

29. Atropine-like drugs are contraindicated in clients with:
    a. parkinsonism.
    b. peptic ulcer.
    c. glaucoma.
    d. cirrhosis.

Situation: C.G., 70 years old, is admitted for evaluation of peptic ulcers. She is taking propantheline (Pro-Banthine) three times a day. The next four questions relate to this situation.

30. The usual dose of Pro-Banthine is:
    a. 0.5–15 mg tid.
    b. 7.5–15 mg tid.
    c. 75–150 mg tid.
    d. 150–250 mg tid.

31. You would encourage C.G. to eat foods that are:
    a. high in fiber.
    b. high in protein.
    c. low in fat.
    d. low in salt.

32. Your health teaching plan for C.G. would include all of the following EXCEPT:
    a. avoid alcohol.
    b. use artificial tears.
    c. decrease fluids.
    d. avoid constipation.

33. Anticholinergic drugs are contraindicated in clients with all of the following conditions EXCEPT:
    a. asthma.
    b. urinary retention.
    c. gastrointestinal obstruction.
    d. heart block.

34. List four nursing implications associated with anticholinergic medications:
    a.

    b.

    c.

    d.

35. A specific group of anticholinergics may be prescribed in the early treatment of which of the following neuromuscular disorders?
    a. myasthenia gravis
    b. Parkinson's disease (parkinsonism)
    c. multiple sclerosis
    d. muscular dystrophy

36. Which of the following is NOT an action of this group of anticholinergics?
    a. suppressing tremors
    b. decreasing muscular rigidity
    c. increasing gastrointestinal peristalsis
    d. decreasing salivation and drooling

37. Which of the following drugs is used to treat an overdose of organophosphate pesticides that cause paralysis?
    a. neostigmine
    b. edrophonium Cl
    c. pralidoxime Cl
    d. tacrine HCl

38. Advice for the client taking anticholinergic drugs would include which of the following?
    a. increased vitamins A and C
    b. increased fluids and foods high in fiber
    c. increased caffeine intake
    d. avoidance of organic meats

Critical Thinking Exercises

G.P., age 62, complains of frequent lower abdominal cramps. She has intermittent diarrhea and constipation. The clinical problem is irritable bowel syndrome. G.P. was prescribed dicyclomine HCl (Bentyl) 20 mg, tid.

1. What type of drug is dicyclomine HCl? What other drug is similar to dicyclomine?

2. Is the dose within suggested therapeutic range?

3. What are the contraindications for use of dicyclomine?

5. Is the daily dose of trihexyphenidyl within safe therapeutic range?

6. How many ml should F.M. receive per day?

4. What are three side effects of this drug?

G.P.'s next-door neighbor, F.M., has been diagnosed recently with Parkinson's disease. In treating her early parkinsonism, she was prescribed trihexyphenidyl (Artane) 1 mg/d for one week, and then the dose was increased over several weeks to 6 mg/d.

Trihexyphenidyl is available as:

7. What type of drug is trihexyphenidyl, and how are its actions similar or opposite to dicyclomine?

Lederle   NDC 0005-4440-65

Artane®
Trihexyphenidyl
Hydrochloride
Elixir

This package not for household dispensing.
EACH TEASPOONFUL (5 mL)
CONTAINS:
Trihexyphenidyl HCl 2 mg
Alcohol 5%
Preservatives:
Methylparaben 0.08%
Propylparaben 0.02%
AVERAGE DOSAGE:
3 to 5 teaspoonfuls (15-25 mL)
daily for maintenance.
See Accompanying Literature.
CAUTION: Federal law prohibits dispensing without prescription.
Store at Controlled Room Temperature 15-30°C (59-86°F).
DO NOT FREEZE
Dispense in tight containers as defined in the USP.
Control No.   Exp. Date

22819 D5
LEDERLE LABORATORIES DIVISION
American Cyanamid Company
Pearl River, NY 10965 Made in U.S.A.

1 Pint (473 mL)

25 Drugs for Neuromuscular Disorders: Parkinsonism, Myasthenia Gravis, Multiple Sclerosis, Alzheimer's Disease, and Muscle Spasms

Study Questions

Define the following:

1. Acetylcholinesterase inhibitor

2. Cholinergic crisis

3. Dopamine agonist

4. Muscle relaxant

5. Myasthenic crisis

Complete the following:

6. The two neurotransmitters within the neurons of the striatum of the brain that have opposing effects are _____ and _____.

7. Which of the neurotransmitters is deficient in Parkinson's disease? _____

8. The drug prescribed to treat parkinsonism by replacing the neurotransmitter is _____.

9. The substance that inhibits the enzyme dopa decarboxylase and allows more levodopa to reach the brain is _____.

10. Recently FDA approved anticholinergic drugs are _____ and _____.

11. Acetylcholinesterase inhibitors are used for control of _____.

12. The drug used to diagnose myasthenia gravis is _____.

13. MS is characterized by multiple lesions forming plaques on the _____.

14. Muscle relaxants relieve spasms and pain associated with _____ injuries and _____ debilitating disorders.

15. The drug that is most effective in reducing spasticity in clients with MS is _____.

16. Muscle relaxants are usually contraindicated during _____.

17. Side effects related to peripherally acting muscle relaxants include _____, _____, _____, _____, and _____.

18. The newest acetylcholinesterase inhibitor is _____.

19. Acetylcholinesterase inhibitors _____ transmission at the cholinergic synapses, both peripheral and central.

20. Two common side effects of acetylcholinesterase inhibitors are _____ and _____.

21. The drug _____ prolongs action of levodopa and can decrease "on-off" fluctuations in clients with parkinsonism.

22. Entacapone (Comtan) is the newest FDA-approved COMT inhibitor which does not affect _____ funtion.

Select the appropriate response:

Situation: C.H., 51 years old, has Parkinson's disease and is receiving levodopa. The next eight questions refer to this situation.

23. The usual maintenance dose of levodopa is:
    a. 0.3–0.6 g/d.
    b. 1–3 g/d.
    c. 3–6 g/d.
    d. 6–9 g/d.

24. You monitor C.H. for all of the following side effects of the drug EXCEPT:
    a. gastrointestinal disturbances.
    b. dyskinesia.
    c. fever.
    d. orthostatic hypotension.

25. Your health teaching plan for C.H. would include which of the following?
    a. Take medications before meals.
    b. Urine will darken with exposure to air.
    c. Take vitamin B$_6$.
    d. All of the above.

26. You are knowledgeable about drug and food interactions with levodopa. All of the following types of drugs and foods are known to alter the action of levodopa EXCEPT:
    a. antipsychotics.
    b. vitamin B$_6$.
    c. monoamine oxidase inhibitors.
    d. antacids.

27. You would recommend that C.H. avoid which of the following foods?
    a. leafy green and yellow vegetables
    b. beans and cereals
    c. cheese
    d. citrus fruits

28. Anticholinergics are contraindicated for clients with any of the following EXCEPT:
    a. glaucoma.
    b. emphysema.
    c. shingles.
    d. renal disorders.

29. C.H.'s medication regimen is changed due to intolerance of the side effects of levodopa. Which drug is most likely to be combined with levodopa to decrease the side effects and the drug's action?
    a. amantadine
    b. carbidopa
    c. Cogentin
    d. Artane

30. Which of the following statements is NOT true?
    a. Entacapone turns urine yellow/orange.
    b. Tolcapone turns urine bright yellow.
    c. Entacapone and tolcapone intensify adverse reactions to levodopa.
    d. Entacapone and tolcapone shorten the effects of levodopa.

31. List four nursing implications for administering drugs to treat clients with parkinsonism:
    a.

    b.

    c.

    d.

Situation: M.W., age 62, is receiving treatment for myasthenia gravis with an acetylcholinesterase inhibitor. The next three questions refer to this situation.

32. You assess M.W. for the common side effects of the drug, including:
    a. gastrointestinal disturbances.
    b. miosis.
    c. increased salivation.
    d. all of the above.

33. You observe changes in M.W. She is drooling, and she has increased tearing and sweating. M.W. is experiencing a/an:
    a. cholinergic crisis.
    b. myasthenic crisis.
    c. vascular spasm.
    d. anaphylaxis.

34. The antidote for the episode that M.W. is experiencing is:
    a. edrophonium.
    b. atropine.
    c. Valium.
    d. pyridostigmine.

35. Which of the following is NOT a centrally acting muscle relaxant?
    a. chlorphenesin (Maolate)
    b. orphenadrine (Norflex)
    c. dantrolene sodium (Dantrium)
    d. baclofen (Lioresal)

36. Which of the following does NOT cause drug dependence?
    a. carisoprodol (Soma)
    b. metaxalone (Skelaxin)
    c. cyclobenzaprine (Flexeril)
    d. methocarbamol (Robaxin)

Situation: S.Q., age 32, was recently diagnosed with MS. S.Q. has muscle weakness in the right extremity and complains of diplopia. S.Q. was given 80 units of adrenocorticotropic hormone (ACTH) in 500 mL of D_5W per day for five days. The next three questions relate to this situation.

37. MS is difficult to diagnose. A diagnostic test useful in identifying MS and new lesions is:
    a. magnetic resonance imaging (MRI).
    b. computed tomography (CT).
    c. x-ray.
    d. angiography.

38. ACTH is used to:
    a. increase blood flow.
    b. increase exacerbations.
    c. increase demyelinating axons.
    d. decrease the acute inflammatory process.

39. The nurse should instruct S.Q. to avoid all of the following drugs EXCEPT:
    a. histamine$_2$ blockers.
    b. beta blockers.
    c. cephalosporins.
    d. certain nonsteroidal antiinflammatory drugs (NSAIDs).

Situation: T.R. has had MS for several years, during which he has had many remissions and exacerbations. He has been prescribed Imuran and Betaseron. The next two questions relate to this situation.

40. Biological response modifiers (BRM) and immunosuppressant drugs are prescribed for all of the following purposes EXCEPT to:
    a. reduce spasticity.
    b. increase muscular movement.
    c. decrease steroid (glucocorticoids) use.
    d. form new neurons and axons.

41. T.R. had an acute attack of MS. The following drugs may be used to alleviate the acute attack with the exception of:
    a. immunosuppressant (cyclophosphamide).
    b. ACTH.
    c. glucocorticoid (prednisone).
    d. 6-alpha methylprednisolone.

42. The actions of centrally acting muscle relaxants include which of the following?
    a. decrease pain and do not affect range of motion
    b. decrease pain and increase range of motion
    c. increase range of motion and no effect on pain
    d. decrease pain and decrease range of motion

43. List four nursing interventions for administering drugs to clients with myasthenia gravis:

    a.

    b.

    c.

    d.

44. List four points to be included in a health teaching plan for clients taking muscle relaxants:

    a.

    b.

    c.

    d.

Critical Thinking Exercises

D.G., 76 years old, was diagnosed having Parkinson's disease six years ago, for which he took levodopa 750 mg, tid. Because of side effects, levodopa was discontinued and carbidopa-levodopa was started.

1. What are three characteristic symptoms of parkinsonism?

2. How does parkinsonism differ from myasthenia gravis?

3. How effective is levodopa in alleviating symptoms of parkinsonism? Explain.

4. What are some of the side effects D.G. may have encountered while taking levodopa?

5. Why is carbidopa-levodopa more effective and desirable for treatment of Parkinson's disease than levodopa only?

6. When would an anticholinergic antiparkinsonism drug be used for parkinsonism? Is D.G. a candidate for this group of drugs? Explain.

7. What type of drug is amantadine, and when is it used for parkinsonism?

9. What are four client teaching strategies that the nurse may include in D.G.'s care?

   a.

   b.

8. What are the similarities of amantadine, bromocriptine, and pergolide?

   c.

   d.

26 Antiinflammatory Drugs

Study Questions

Define the following:

1. DMARDs

2. Immunosuppressives

3. NSAIDs

4. Prostaglandins

5. Uricosuric

Complete the following:

6. Inflammation is a response to tissue
   _____
   and _____.

7. *Inflammation* and *infection* are terms that
   (**should/should not**) be used interchangeably.
   (Circle correct answer)

8. The five cardinal signs of inflammation are
   _____,
   _____,
   _____, _____,
   and _____.

9. The oldest antiinflammatory drug is
   _____.

10. Leukocyte infiltration of the inflamed tissue
    occurs during the _____ phase
    of inflammation.

11. The half-life of each NSAID (**does/does not**)
    differ greatly. (Circle correct answer)

12. When using NSAIDs for the pain relief only,
    the dosage must be _____
    than for antiinflammatory purposes.

13. The half-life of corticosteroids is greater than
    _____ hours.

14. The first injectable NSAID is
    _____.

Select the appropriate response:

15. The vascular phase of inflammation is associated with:
    a. vasoconstriction and fluid influx to interstitial space.
    b. vasodilation with increased capillary permeability.
    c. leukocyte and protein infiltration to inflamed tissue.
    d. vasoconstriction with leukocyte infiltration to inflamed tissue.

16. The following are among the eight groups of NSAIDs, with which exception?
    a. macrolides
    b. fenamates
    c. indoles
    d. oxicams

17. Which of the following is NOT a property of antiinflammatory agents?
    a. analgesic
    b. antipyretic
    c. anticoagulant
    d. antihypertensive

18.   A common side effect of NSAIDs is:

    a.   tachycardia.

    b.   heartburn.

    c.   gastrointestinal distress.

    d.   polyuria.

19.   The mechanism of action of nonsteroidal and antiinflammatory drugs includes:

    a.   enhancement of the inflammatory process.

    b.   inhibition of synthesis of prostaglandins.

    c.   inhibition of phagocytic activity.

    d.   decrease in red and white blood cells.

20.   Your client is taking large doses of aspirin for an arthritic condition. The nurse needs to know all the following information EXCEPT that:

    a.   tinnitus is a common symptom of early toxicity.

    b.   the half-life of aspirin in large doses is approximately 15–30 hours.

    c.   aspirin can lower blood sugar in diabetics, causing hypoglycemia.

    d.   aspirin taken at mealtime or with food will reduce gastrointestinal distress.

21.   The analgesic drug to give a child with a virus or flu is:

    a.   aspirin.

    b.   acetaminophen.

    c.   ibuprofen.

    d.   Indocin.

22.   The medication for a child with a virus should be one that prevents:

    a.   gastric distress.

    b.   clot formation.

    c.   osteoarthritis.

    d.   Reye's syndrome.

Situation: J.W. is taking ibuprofen. The next five questions relate to this situation.

23.   Ibuprofen is a rapid-acting NSAID that inhibits prostaglandin synthesis. This agent/drug is classified as a:

    a.   para-aminophenol derivative.

    b.   indoles/indenes derivative.

    c.   propionic acid derivative.

    d.   anthranilic acid derivative.

24.   Ibuprofen is generally scheduled to be taken:

    a.   daily.

    b.   2–3 times per day.

    c.   3–4 times per day.

    d.   every two hours.

25.   The usual adult dose of ibuprofen is:

    a.   30–80 mg.

    b.   300–800 mg.

    c.   2 g.

    d.   4 g.

26.   Ibuprofen (Motrin, Advil, Nuprin) is a frequently taken antiinflammatory, analgesic, and antipyretic agent. Which of the following is true about ibuprofen?

    a.   It causes less gastrointestinal upset than other NSAIDs.

    b.   It should be taken between meals with water.

    c.   It has a long half-life of 20–30 hours.

    d.   It has severe side effects, including hypertension, deafness, and renal insufficiency.

27.   J.W.'s health teaching plan would include all of the following EXCEPT:

    a.   explaining common side effects.

    b.   suggesting decreasing fluid intake.

    c.   avoiding use of ibuprofen 1–2 days prior to menstruation.

    d.   not to take concurrently with aspirin.

28. Piroxicam (Feldene) is a relatively new NSAID. Its advantage over other agents is which of the following?

    a. well-tolerated

    b. low incidence of toxic problems

    c. long half-life

    d. fast-acting

29. Nursing strategies related to administering NSAIDs include all of the following EXCEPT:

    a. reporting epigastric distress.

    b. advising the client that alcohol can be taken with NSAIDs.

    c. observing for tarry stools, bleeding gums, and bruising, while taking NSAIDs over an extended time.

    d. advising those with heavy menstrual flow to take NSAIDs 1–2 days before menstruation and not during heavy flow.

30. Ketorolac is recommended for pain management. All of the following statements are true EXCEPT that it:

    a. is effective for short-term pain management.

    b. has an efficacy equal to morphine.

    c. can be administered intramuscularly.

    d. has a usual adult dose of 30–60 mg q6h.

31. What characteristics are associated with celecoxib (Celebrex)?

    a. not to be used for cardiac precautions like ASA

    b. avoid during third trimester of pregnancy

    c. relieves pain and inflammation without causing GI distress

    d. all of the above

32. Clients receiving gold therapy for advanced arthritic conditions may receive a corticosteroid as part of the early multiple-dosage regimen. The client may ask about the reason for the combination of a steroid and a DMARD. Your best reply would be that the:

    a. health care provider usually combines these drugs.

    b. combination of drugs improves the outcome.

    c. gold takes time to achieve its effects; the steroid assists immediately in the alleviation of arthritic symptoms.

    d. combination of drugs causes an absence of symptoms.

33. Client teaching for those on gold therapy includes all of the following EXCEPT:

    a. desired clinical effect may take 3–4 months.

    b. adherence to scheduled lab tests is essential.

    c. meticulous dental hygiene is required.

    d. measures to control constipation are needed.

34. The antigout drug colchicine acts by:

    a. inhibiting migration of leukocytes to the inflamed area.

    b. inhibiting the final steps of uric acid biosynthesis.

    c. blocking reabsorption of uric acid excretion.

    d. reabsorbing uric acid from distal tubules of the kidney.

35. Client teaching related to antigout drugs includes all of the following EXCEPT:

    a. taking large doses of vitamin C.

    b. increasing fluid intake.

    c. avoiding alcohol and caffeine.

    d. avoiding foods high in purine.

36. Uricosuric agents such as probenecid (Benemid) are used in the treatment of gout. Benemid promotes:

    a. retention of urate crystals in the body.

    b. uric acid excretion via the kidney.

    c. reabsorption of urates from the kidney.

    d. uric acid excretion via the sweat glands.

37. Side effects of Benemid include:
    a. sore gums and headache.
    b. flushed skin and oliguria.
    c. constipation and edema.
    d. blurred vision and urinary retention.

38. A client is taking corticosteroids for an arthritic condition. You would include which of the following in your health teaching plan?
    a. Corticosteroids are used to control arthritic flare-ups in severe cases.
    b. Corticosteroids have a short half-life and are taken several times a day.
    c. Corticosteroid dosage must be tapered when discontinuing therapy.
    d. a and c only

39. When discontinuing steroid therapy, the dosage should be tapered over a period of how many days?
    a. 1–3
    b. 4–6
    c. 5–10
    d. > 10

40. Available:

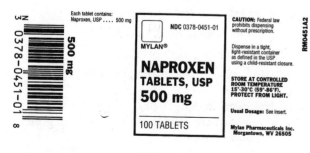

    B.J. has ordered Naproxen 500 mg bid for moderate arthritic pain. What is the correct number of tablets to give B.J. per dose? Per 24 hrs?

41. Which tablet concentration is preferred? Provide a rationale.

42. B.J. asks if he can take this medication on an empty stomach. What correct instructions would you give B.J.?

Critical Thinking Exercises

M.B., 37 years old, comes to the clinic for treatment of an inflammatory condition. She reports taking 975 mg of aspirin q4h for the past week.

1. What is the usual adult dosage of aspirin? What recommendations are indicated for this client?

2. What is the serum therapeutic range for aspirin? What is the toxicity level?

3. What laboratory tests are influenced by aspirin?

4. What is the mode of action of aspirin?

M.B. also complains of anorexia and stomach pains and wonders, "What else is wrong with me?"

5.   How should the nurse respond?

6.   Identify at least three adverse reactions to aspirin.

7.   Identify at least four health teaching points for this client.

27 Antibacterials: Penicillins and Cephalosporins

Study Questions

Define the following:

1. Acquired resistance

2. Antibacterials

3. Antimicrobials

4. Bactericidal

5. Bacteriostatic

6. Broad-spectrum antibiotic

7. Immunoglobulins

8. Nosocomial infections

9. Superinfection

Complete the following:

10. Bacteriostatic drugs such as tetracycline (**inhibit/kill**) the growth of bacteria. (Circle correct answer)

11. Bactericidal drugs such as penicillin (**inhibit/kill**) bacteria. (Circle correct answer)

12. The four mechanisms of action of antibacterial drugs are:

    a.

    b.

    c.

    d.

13. Antibacterials with a longer half-life usually maintain a (**greater/lesser**) concentration at the binding site. (Circle correct answer)

14. Most antibiotics (**are/are not**) highly protein-bound. (Circle correct answer)

15. The steady state of an antibacterial drug occurs after the ____ to ____ half-life.

16. An antibacterial drug is eliminated from the body after the _____ half-life.

17. Bacterial resistance may be natural or caused by previous exposure to the drug. The latter is known as _____ resistance.

134

18. Infections acquired while the client is hospitalized are known as _____ infections.

19. The three major adverse effects related to antibacterial drugs are:

    a.

    b.

    c.

20. The organism continues to grow when the bacteria is (**sensitive/resistant**) to the drug. (Circle correct answer)

21. Drugs with similar actions, such as penicillins and cephalosporins, can result in _____ .

22. The minimum effective concentration (MEC) depends on the following four processes:

    a.

    b.

    c.

    d.

23. When minimum bactericidal concentration (MBC) is needed, a greater concentration of the drug is required, so the client should be monitored for _____ .

24. A continuous infusion regimen is recommended for severe infections because of need for _____ drug concentration and _____ exposure.

25. List at least four factors related to the host's defense mechanisms:

    a.

    b.

    c.

    d.

26. List at least six nursing interventions related to the administration of penicillin:
    _____ ,
    _____ ,
    _____ ,
    _____ ,
    _____ , and
    _____ .

27. List at least four areas to include in teaching for clients taking penicillin:

    a.

    b.

    c.

    d.

28. Second-generation cephalosporins have the same effectiveness as first-generation with the addition of organisms such as _____ and _____ .

29. Third-generation cephalosporins extend effectiveness to gram-negative bacteria such as _____ and _____ .

30. Most cephalosporins are administered by the _____ and _____ routes.

Select the appropriate response:

31. A condition that occurs when the normal flora is disturbed during antibiotic therapy is known as:

    a. organ toxicity.

    b. superinfection.

    c. hypersensitivity.

    d. allergic reaction.

32. All of the following statements are true about the pharmacokinetics of penicillin derivatives amoxicillin and cloxacillin EXCEPT:

    a. amoxicillin is 20% protein-bound and cloxacillin is about 90% protein-bound.

    b. both drugs have short half lives.

    c. amoxicillin is excreted in the urine and cloxacillin is excreted in bile and urine.

    d. both drugs are absorbed well from the gastrointestinal tract.

33. Allergic effects occur in what percentage of persons receiving penicillin compounds?

    a. 1–4%

    b. 5–10%

    c. 11–15%

    d. over 15%

34. A drug interaction occurs with cephalosporins and which of the following?

    a. alcohol

    b. anticonvulsants

    c. antacids

    d. antihypertensives

35. Aztreonam (Azactam) is effective against which of the following?

    a. *H. influenzae*

    b. *E. coli*

    c. Proteus

    d. Pseudomonas

36. When probenecid is administered with cefazolin (Ancef) or cefamandole (Mandol), which of the following results?

    a. hypersensitivity is common

    b. glucosuria

    c. drug action is decreased

    d. drug action is increased

Situation: S.W., age 40, is suffering from an *E. coli* infection. She is unable to swallow pills, so oral suspension of cephalexin 250 mg is ordered. The next seven questions refer to this situation.

37. S.W. is taking cephalexin (Keflex). This medication is generally scheduled to be taken:

    a. q2h.

    b. q4h.

    c. q6h.

    d. q12h.

38. The usual dose of Keflex is:

    a. 250–500 mg q6h.

    b. 250 mg–1 g q6h.

    c. 1–2 g q6h.

    d. 2–3 g q6h.

39. Available:

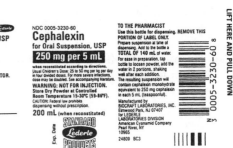

    How many ml of the drug should S.W. receive per dose, and per 24 hours?

40. You assess S.W. for all of the following side effects EXCEPT:

    a. nausea.

    b. vomiting.

    c. tinnitus.

    d. diarrhea.

41. Which of the following drugs/foods are known to change the action of Keflex?

    a. laxatives

    b. antacids

    c. alcohol

    d. uricosurics

42. Specific nursing interventions for S.W. would include all of the following EXCEPT:
    a. taking culture for C & S (culture and sensitivity).
    b. assessing for allergic reaction.
    c. monitoring urinary output.
    d. restricting fluids.

43. The health teaching plan for S.W. would include all of the following EXCEPT:
    a. taking total amount of prescribed antibiotic.
    b. resting.
    c. finishing antibiotics from a previous prescription.
    d. being alert for signs and symptoms of superinfection.

44. The drug that may be used as a substitute for penicillin is:
    a. erythromycin.
    b. amoxicillin.
    c. cephalosporin.
    d. tetracycline.

45. The broad-spectrum penicillins may decrease the effectiveness of which of the following?
    a. antacids
    b. oral contraceptives
    c. anticonvulsants
    d. cholinergics

46. Quinupristin/dalfopristin (Synercid) is marketed for IV use against life-threatening infection caused by which of the following?
    a. vancomycin-resistant *Enterococcus faecium*
    b. Streptococcus
    c. *Escherichia coli*
    d. *Proteus mirabilis*

Critical Thinking Exercises

J.L., 25 years old, is hospitalized for treatment of a severe penicillin G-resistant *Staphylococcus aureus* infection. He is receiving nafcillin parenterally.

1. What is nafcillin's drug classification?

2. What is the usual adult dose for this drug?

3. What are the preferred routes of administration?

4. Available:

   How many ml are required to administer 500 mg IM of the drug?

5. What drug should be readily available in the event of severe allergic reaction?

6. What are the differences between the penicillin groups?

7. List four nursing interventions related to the administration of the drug to J.L.

28 Antibacterials: Macrolides, Tetracyclines, Aminoglycosides, and Fluoroquinolones

Study Questions

Define the following:

1. Bacteriostatic

2. Bactericidal

3. Pathogen

4. Superinfection

Complete the following:

5. Vancomycin is a (**bactericidal/bacteriostatic**) drug. (Circle correct answer)

6. The drug frequently prescribed for clients with hypersensitivity to penicillin is _____.

7. Erythromycin is effective against most gram-negative and -positive bacterias except _____.

8. Erythromycin acts by interfering with bacterial _____ synthesis.

9. List four nursing interventions related to administration of erythromycin (macrolides):

a.

b.

c.

d.

10. A drug usually effective against drug-resistant *Staphylococcus aureus* in clients with penicillin allergy is _____.

11. Two adverse reactions of vancomycin are _____ and _____.

12. It is necessary to draw serum peak and trough levels for vancomycin to minimize _____ effects.

13. The newest aminoglycoside with a decreased occurrence of toxicity is _____. Its pregnancy category is _____.

14. Serious adverse reactions to aminoglycosides include _____ and _____.

15. List four specific nursing interventions for administration of aminoglycosides:

    a.

    b.

    c.

    d.

16. Fluoroquinolones are (**bactericidal/bacteriostatic**). (Circle correct answer)

17. Due to the adverse reaction of blood dyscrasias, fluoroquinolones are used only for treatment of serious infections with drugs such as _____.

18. Spectinomycin (Trobicin) is the single IM dose treatment for _____.

19. Aztreonam (Azactam) is effective against the organism _____.

20. Which of the following is NOT a fluoroquinolone with daily dosing?
    a.   levofloxacin (Levaquin)
    b.   ofloxacin (Floxin)
    c.   sparfloxacin (Zagam)
    d.   trovafloxacin (Trovan)

Select the appropriate response:

Situation: J.T. is taking tetracycline for a respiratory tract infection. The next seven questions refer to this situation.

21. The usual dose of tetracycline is:
    a.   250–500 mg q6h.
    b.   250–500 mg q4h.
    c.   500 mg–1 g q4h.
    d.   1–2 g q4h.

22. You assess J.T. for side effects, which include all of the following EXCEPT:
    a. rash.
    b. photosensitivity.
    c. nausea.
    d. constipation.

23. A laboratory test influenced by tetracycline is:
    a.   blood urea nitrogen.
    b.   serum calcium level.
    c.   prothrombin time.
    d.   white blood cell count.

24. For best results, it is recommended that tetracycline be taken:
    a.   with meals.
    b.   with extra fluids.
    c.   on an empty stomach.
    d.   one-half hour after meals.

25. You know that all of the following drugs modify the action of tetracycline EXCEPT:
    a.   antacids.
    b.   beta blockers.
    c.   milk products.
    d.   iron.

26. Specific nursing interventions for J.T. include all of the following EXCEPT:
    a.   storing the drug out of light.
    b.   monitoring laboratory test results.
    c.   obtaining specimen for culture and sensitivity.
    d.   restricting fluids.

27. The health teaching plan for J.T. would NOT include which of the following?
    a.   Outdated tetracycline breaks down into toxic byproducts and must be discarded.
    b.   Observe for superinfection.
    c.   Avoid tetracycline during pregnancy.
    d.   Anticipate urinary urgency.

28. Available:

J.W.'s health care provider has ordered Zithromax (azithromycin) for his mild-moderate strep infection. How many ml of this suspension are required for the first dose and for each of the daily doses for the next four days?

29. You know that food **(increases/decreases)** absorption of the drug by 50%. (Circle correct answer) Therefore, what instructions would you give J.W.?

Critical Thinking Exercises

A.B. comes to the health care provider complaining of a productive cough, fever, and feeling flu-like. Ciprofloxacin (Cipro) is prescribed.

1. Is Cipro a reasonable choice of drug? Give your rationale. What specific nursing assessments are indicated?

2. What are the usual adult dosages for mild/moderate and severe infections?

3. Under what circumstances is this drug used with caution?

4. What laboratory tests require monitoring?

6. List three recommendations for client teaching for A.B.

5. List three specific nursing interventions related to the administration of fluoroquinolones.

29 Antibacterials: Sulfonamides

Study Questions

Define the following:

1. Cross sensitivity

2. Photosensitivity

3. Synergistic effect

Complete the following. Refer to word search for questions 4–12. Circle your responses.

```
P E N I C I L L I N T F T Q I
F O L I C A C I D K U I P C U
L K Z Q I S Y E N D I K I I H
M R I B O S S B S Z T T B N L
M I E U S S R R E O A N R C G
C R R V O A A D N T I I T R N
A P C P I P C S S Z I M S E O
F P V W O L I O X G T D P A L
X Q B A U H I T S L Q J A S Y
F W S P L R T T V E S H Y E M
C J X G E U U E O X N W Z M A
W S X T G X A Q M N D Y W Z F
F E C K P M F L N I E U L U L
X A N H Q C C W U G R R Q Y U
B C B Q P I B E N Z O T A D S
```

4. Sulfonamides inhibit bacterial synthesis of
   _____.

5. Clinical use of sulfonamides has decreased due to the availability and effectiveness of
   _____.

6. The new antibacterial drug that has a synergistic effect with the sulfonamide is
   _____.

7. Sulfonamides (**are/are not**) effective against viruses and fungi. (Circle correct answer)

8. Anaphylaxis (**is/is not**) common with the use of sulfonamides. (Circle correct answer)

9. Sulfonamide drugs are metabolized in the _____ and excreted by the _____.

10. Sulfonamides are (**bacteriostatic/bactericidal**). (Circle correct answer)

11. The use of warfarin with sulfonamides (**increases/decreases**) the anticoagulant effect. (Circle correct answer)

12. A sulfonamide derivative for the treatment of second- and third-degree burns is

    _____.

13. The drug used to treat seborrheic dermatitis is

    _____.

Select the appropriate response:

Situation: P.J., 45 years old, is admitted for treatment of a severe urinary tract infection. His current medications include Septra (trimethoprim/ sulfamethoxazole) and digoxin. The next four questions refer to this situation.

14. The usual adult dose of Septra (also ordered for P. J.) is which of the following?
    a. 160 mg TMP/800 mg SMZ q6h
    b. 160 mg TMP/800 mg SMZ q12h
    c. 40 mg TMP/60 mg SMZ q6h
    d. 40 mg TMP/60 mg SMZ q12h

15. Available:

    Septra tablets: each scored tablet contains 80 mg trimethoprim and 400 mg of sulfameth-oxazole

    How many tablets should P. J. take for each dose and per 24 hours?

16. As the nurse, you would:
    a. administer medications and extra fluids.
    b. monitor urinary output.
    c. observe for allergic response.
    d. do all of the above.

17. Advise the client of all of the following possible side effects EXCEPT:
    a. photosensitivity.
    b. constipation.
    c. decreased WBC and platelets.
    d. anorexia.

18. Digoxin and all EXCEPT which of the following drugs will displace sulfonamides from protein-binding sites?
    a. NSAIDs
    b. phenytoin
    c. Kayexalate
    d. aspirin

19. Displacement of the sulfonamides from the protein-binding sites results in:
    a. increased free drug in blood.
    b. decreased free drug in blood.
    c. no change in free drug in blood.
    d. synergistic effect of drug.

Critical Thinking Exercises

Y.M., 11 years old, complains of "pain when I go to the bathroom." Gantrisin is prescribed with a loading dose of 3.75 grams. Y.M. weighs 110 pounds.

1. What is the recommended dose? Is Y.M.'s loading dose within safe parameters?

2. Why is this drug so effective in treating urinary tract infections?

3. List three nursing interventions related to the administration of sulfonamides.

5. Explain why it is advisable that Y.M. increase her fluid intake.

4. List four areas for client teaching related to the drug.

30 Antitubercular Drugs, Antifungal Drugs, Peptides, and Metronidazole

Study Questions

Define the following:

1. First-line drugs

2. Opportunistic infections

3. Peptides

4. Prophylaxis

5. Second-line drugs

Complete the following:

6. The first and also current drug prescribed to treat tuberculosis is
    _____.

7. Single-drug therapy for tuberculosis (**is/is not**) more effective than multiple drug therapy. (Circle correct answer)

8. First-line drugs are (**less/more**) effective and less toxic than second-line drugs in treating tuberculosis. (Circle correct answer)

9. Vitamin _____ is frequently given with isoniazid.

10. A serious adverse effect of streptomycin is
    _____.

11. A contraindication for prophylactic treatment of tuberculosis is _____.

12. Prophylactic doses of isoniazid are given to family members of a person newly diagnosed with tuberculosis for a period of _____ to _____ months.

13. Second-line tuberculosis drugs may be used in combination with first-line drugs in clients with _____ tuberculosis.

14. The drug of choice to prevent disseminated *Mycobacterium avium* complex (MAC) disease in clients with advanced HIV infection is
    _____.

15. List four groups of antifungal drugs:
    a.

    b.

    c.

    d.

16. Systemic fungal infections usually involve the _____ or
    _____.

17. Fungi are normal flora of the following four organs/cavities: _____,
    _____,
    _____, and
    _____.

18. To treat severe systemic fungal infections, the drug of choice is _____, administered in low doses via the
    _____ route.

19. Excretion of amphotericin B (**is/is not**) affected by renal disease. (Circle correct answer)

20. The action of Nystatin (**increases/decreases**) the permeability of the fungal cell membrane. (Circle correct answer)

21. Two common oral antifungal agents are _____ and _____.

22. Many early polymyxins were discontinued due to toxicity causing _____ and _____; lab values for _____ and _____ require monitoring.

23. Polymyxins are (**bactericidal/bacteriostatic**). (Circle correct answer)

24. Polymyxins are effective against most (**gram-negative/gram-positive**) bacteria. (Circle correct answer)

25. The preferred route of administration for polymyxins is _____.

26. When the polymyxin is discontinued, neurotoxicity (**is/is not**) usually reversible. (Circle correct answer)

Select the appropriate response:

Situation: R.T. is a 21-year-old admitted with gastroenteritis. He is receiving colistin-S. The next five questions refer to this situation.

27. The usual dose of colistin-S is:
    a. 5–15 mg/kg/d.
    b. 3–5 mg/kg/d.
    c. 40,000 U/d.
    d. 60,000–100,000 U/d.

28. During the time R.T is taking colistin-S, all of the following must be frequently monitored EXCEPT:
    a. BUN.
    b. creatinine.
    c. pulse.
    d. urinary output.

29. Colistin-S is excreted via which of the following?
    a. lungs
    b. feces
    c. urine
    d. liver

30. Common side effects of peptides include all of the following EXCEPT:
    a. nephrotoxicity.
    b. tingling/numbness of the extremities.
    c. dizziness.
    d. neurotoxicity.

31. R.T. is now receiving the medication intramuscularly. Special considerations include:
    a. using Z-track technique.
    b. using 18 gauge needle.
    c. adding 1% lidocaine to medication.
    d. using vastus lateralis site.

Situation: B.T., 69 years old, is taking isoniazid (INH). The next five questions refer to this situation.

32. During the admission interview, you should obtain which of the following?
    a. history of TB
    b. last PPD, chest x-ray and results
    c. drug allergies
    d. all of the above

33. The usual dose of INH for active treatment is:
    a. 1–4 mg/kg/d.
    b. 5–10 mg/kg/d.
    c. 11–15 mg/kg/d.
    d. 16–20 mg/kg/d.

34. When the client is on INH, frequent monitoring of which of the following is required?
    a. liver enzymes
    b. WBC
    c. creatinine
    d. BUN

35. Which of the following drugs/foods change the action of INH?:
    a. laxatives
    b. cheese
    c. antacids
    d. digoxin

36. Health teaching for B.T. would include all the following EXCEPT:
    a. possible need to take vitamin B_6 to avoid peripheral neuritis.
    b. increase fluid intake; avoid alcohol.
    c. urine and saliva may be red-orange.
    d. daily weights.

37. List at least three specific nursing interventions related to the administration of INH:
    a.

    b.

    c.

38. Which of the following is/are true about the drug rifapentine?
    a. newest drug for treating tuberculosis
    b. has twice-weekly dosing
    c. taken with another antitubercular drug to avoid resistance
    d. all of the above

Situation: B.G., age 67, is being treated for histoplasmosis. The next five questions relate to this situation.

39. B.G. is receiving amphotericin B. This medication is generally administered:
    a. rectally.
    b. topically.
    c. intramuscularly.
    d. intravenously.

40. The usual dose of amphotericin B is:
    a. 0.25–1 mg/kg/d.
    b. 1–2 mg/kg/d.
    c. 2–3 mg/kg/d.
    d. 3–4 mg/kg/d.

41. During the time B.G. is receiving this drug, frequent monitoring of which of the following is required?
    a. WBC
    b. BUN
    c. platelets
    d. eosinophils

42. You assess for side effects of the drug, which may include all of the following EXCEPT:
    a. hypertension.
    b. hypotension.
    c. flushing.
    d. thrombophlebitis.

43. The health teaching plan for B.G. would include all of the following EXCEPT to:
    a. avoid operating hazardous equipment.
    b. report weakness.
    c. obtain lab testing as ordered.
    d. consume no alcohol.

44. Metronidazole is primarily used for treatment of disorders caused by organisms in which of the following?
    a. respiratory tract
    b. urinary tract
    c. gastrointestinal tract
    d. peripheral nervous system

45. In combination with other agents, metronidazole is commonly used to treat *H. pylori* associated with recurrent:
    a. peptic ulcers.
    b. urinary retention.
    c. adenomas.
    d. gastric-esophageal reflux disease (GERD).

46. Side effects of metronidazole may include:
    a. urinary retention.
    b. photophobia.
    c. abdominal cramps and diarrhea.
    d. headache and depression.

47. List five conditions that metronidazole is prescribed to treat:

   a.

   b.

   c.

   d.

   e.

48. Available:

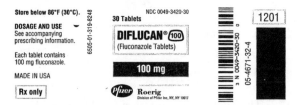

   M.M.'s prescription is for a maintenance dose of Diflucan (fluconazole), 150 mg/d. How many tablets should M.M. take per dose?

Critical Thinking Exercises

C.J., a 22-year-old, has come to the health maintenance organization (HMO) complaining of "white spots in my mouth." She has been taking multiple antibiotics during the past month for a severe lower respiratory tract infection. Mycostatin is ordered, 250,000 U oral swish and swallow qid.

   Available:

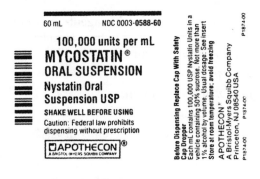

1. Is C.J.'s dose within the recommended adult dose range?

2. What is the most likely cause of these "white spots?"

3. What is the most likely causative organism?

4. What are specific instructions related to the correct administration of this drug?

5. List at least four general areas for health teaching related to antifungal drugs.

6. Compare and contrast nystatin and amphotericin B.

31 Antiviral, Antimalarial, and Anthelmintic Drugs

Study Questions

Define the following:

1. Erythrocytic phase

2. Opportunistic infection

3. Tissue phase

Complete the following (word search) for questions 4–9. Circle your responses.

```
S  R  A  L  L  E  C  I  R  A  V  K  R  H  H
D  U  E  A  U  I  S  Z  Q  K  W  E  E  O  E
I  A  R  N  C  O  Y  K  J  A  W  R  D  T  R
D  Y  C  I  A  V  R  K  B  O  P  A  S  C  P
A  B  P  E  V  L  M  I  L  E  X  U  E  Y  E
N  K  R  Y  V  O  T  S  S  P  V  U  S  T  S
O  D  C  S  W  T  L  S  R  U  J  U  G  I  Z
S  L  P  W  C  I  I  A  H  I  D  M  J  C  O
I  P  S  L  S  M  U  Z  G  E  F  K  L  I  S
N  A  R  C  P  T  J  A  Q  E  P  A  W  X  T
E  A  K  L  V  T  M  O  G  U  M  A  W  O  E
H  X  E  C  X  K  O  S  H  W  O  O  T  T  R
M  X  X  I  E  L  M  J  X  U  V  K  T  I  J
I  R  E  P  L  I  C  A  T  I  O  N  B  Y  C
R  I  M  A  N  T  I  D  I  N  E  H  C  L  C
```

4. Antiviral drugs prevent _____ of the virus.

5. AZT (**is/is not**) the only FDA-approved antiviral drug for treating persons with AIDS. (Circle correct answer)

6. Antiviral drug development has been (**slower/faster**) than antibacterial drug development in part due to _____ of some antivirals. (Circle correct answer)

7. A new drug to treat influenza A is _____. When a client is taking this drug, two organ functions that require monitoring are _____ and _____.

8. The drug Vidarabine, introduced as an antineoplastic for the treatment of leukemia, is now known to have effects against which four organisms? _____, _____, _____, and _____.

9. A new drug for treatment of advanced HIV infection in clients who do not tolerate zidovudine is _____ (_____).

10. Amantadine hydrochloride (Symmetrel) and rimantadine hydrochloride (Flumadine) were used to treat Type _____ influenza.

11. Chills, fever, and sweating are symptoms of the _____ phase of malaria.

12. The most common site for helminthiasis is in the _____.

13. The pork roundworm can cause _____, which is diagnosed by a _____.

Select the appropriate response:

Situation: M.I., 17 years old, is receiving treatment for herpes simplex I. Acyclovir sodium 200 mg q2h is prescribed. The next four questions refer to this situation.
    Available:

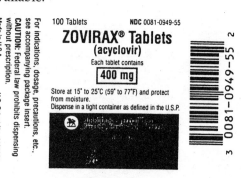

14. Is the prescribed dose within safe parameters? How many tablets should M.I. take at each dose?

15. Acyclovir is effective against the herpes virus. It was first introduced as an:
    a. antiviral.
    b. antineoplastic.
    c. antimalarial.
    d. antidepressant.

16. You tell the client on acyclovir that all of the following are associated with this drug EXCEPT:
    a. headache.
    b. hypertension.
    c. decreased BUN.
    d. nausea.

17. A drug interaction occurs between acyclovir and which of the following drugs?
    a. primaquine
    b. amantadine
    c. probenecid
    d. flucytosine

18. Which of the following drugs are effective in combating herpes simplex viruses (HSV-1, HSV-2)?
    a. famiciclovir (Famvir)
    b. ganciclovir sodium (Cytovene)
    c. valacyclovir (Valtrex)
    d. all of the above

19. Which of the following is/are true about Relenza and Tamiflu?
    a. promote activity of neuraminidase
    b. are a substitute for "flu shots"
    c. to be taken within 48 hours of flu symptoms
    d. all of the above

20. Today, malaria is a common disease caused by:
    a. fungus.
    b. virus.
    c. bacteria.
    d. protozoa.

21. The drug of choice for treatment of chloroquine-resistant malaria is:
    a. combination of antimalarials.
    b. quinidine.
    c. Aralen.
    d. primaquine.

22. Chloroquine increases the effects of all of the following drugs EXCEPT:
    a. digoxin.
    b. anticoagulants.
    c. anticonvulsants.
    d. neuromuscular blockers.

23. Chloroquine affects all of the following laboratory test results EXCEPT:
    a. BUN.
    b. RBC.
    c. hemoglobin.
    d. hematocrit.

24. The client taking chloroquine needs to know about which of the following possible side effects?

    a.   anorexia

    b.   fatigue

    c.   pruritus

    d.   all of the above

25. Nursing interventions during antimalarial drug therapy include:

    a.   monitoring urinary output and liver function.

    b.   assessing hearing; drugs may be oto-toxic.

    c.   assessing for visual changes; chloroquine may cause retinopathy.

    d.   all of the above.

26. What is the recommended schedule for taking chloroquine in preparation for a visit to a country infested with malaria?

    a.   during the visit

    b.   during the visit and after the visit

    c.   before the visit and during the visit

    d.   before, during, and after the visit

27. Assessment of clients for treatment with anthelmintics includes which of the following?

    a.   history of food intake

    b.   collect stool specimen

    c.   determining if other household members have same signs and symptoms

    d.   all of the above

28. Which of the following drugs is commonly used in the treatment of giant roundworms and pinworms?

    a.   bithional (Actamer)

    b.   pyrantel pamoate (Antiminth)

    c.   mebendazole (Vermox)

    d.   oxamninquine (Vansil)

29. Neurological problems related to anthelmintics include all of the following EXCEPT:

    a.   dizziness.

    b.   headache.

    c.   urinary retention.

    d.   drowsiness.

30. Long-term therapy with anthelmintics is required with all of the following drugs EXCEPT:

    a.   niclosamide

    b.   mebendazole

    c.   piperazine

    d.   thiabendazole

31. Client teaching for anthelmintics includes:

    a.   importance of washing hands after toileting and before eating

    b.   showering rather than bathing

    c.   changing towels, underwear, and bed clothes daily

    d.   all of the above

Critical Thinking Exercises

K.B., age 35, has been attending the HIV clinic for several years. One of his medications is didanosine (Videx).

1. This drug belongs to which class of antivirals?

2. What are specific instructions for when to take this medication?

3. Which laboratory test results require monitoring when taking Videx?

4. What adverse reactions should clients report to the health care provider?

5. Describe recommended oral hygiene. Give your rationale.

32 Drugs for Urinary Tract Disorders

Study Questions

Define the following:

1. Bacteriostatic

2. Bactericidal

3. Urinary analgesics

4. Urinary antiseptics/antiinfectives

5. Urinary antispasmodics

6. Urinary stimulants

Complete the following:

7. The therapeutic action of urinary antiseptics occurs in the renal _____ and _____.

8. Urine cultures should be done (**before/after**) starting drug treatment? (Circle correct answer)

9. *Pseudomonas aeruginosa* is resistant to the drug _____.

10. Cranberry juice (**decreases/increases**) urine pH. (Circle correct answer)

11. Inform clients that the drug nitrofurantoin changes the color of urine to _____ and it also may stain the _____.

12. Health teaching includes that the color of urine changes to red-orange when taking the drug _____.

13. Drug dosage of quinolones should be (**decreased/increased**) in clients with renal dysfunction. (Circle correct answer)

14. Parasympathomimetics are used to stimulate _____.

15. Urinary antispasmodics are (**recommended/contraindicated**) for use in clients with urinary obstruction. (Circle correct answer)

16. To be an effective antiseptic, the urine pH should be below _____.

17. Methenamine (Mandelamine) should not be used with sulfonamides because of the risk of _____.

18. The urinary stimulant drug that is frequently prescribed is _____.

19. One of the drugs of choice for uncomplicated urinary tract infections is the sulfonamide _____.

20. A drug, taken as a single dose, for the treatment of uncomplicated urinary tract infections in women is _____.

Select the appropriate response:

21. The groups of urinary antiseptics include all of the following EXCEPT:

    a. nitrofurantoin.

    b. phenothiazide.

    c. methenamine.

    d. quinolones.

22. All of the following substances can be taken to decrease urine pH EXCEPT:

    a. ammonium chloride.

    b. cranberry juice.

    c. potassium chloride.

    d. ascorbic acid.

Situation: L.P. is 53 years old and is receiving nalidixic acid (NegGram) for a chronic urinary tract infection. The next three questions relate to this situation.

23. The dose of NegGram for long-term use is:

    a. 1 g qd.

    b. 1 g bid.

    c. 1 g tid.

    d. 1 g qid.

24. Your assessment of L.P. for signs and symptoms of side effects of the drug would include all of the following EXCEPT:

    a. headache and rash.

    b. syncope and visual disturbance.

    c. chest pain and fever.

    d. peripheral neuritis.

25. Your health teaching plan for L.P. would include all of the following EXCEPT:

    a. urine may turn orange.

    b. protection against photosensitivity.

    c. increase fluid intake.

    d. avoid operating hazardous machinery.

26. Common urinary antiseptic drug-drug interactions include all of the following EXCEPT that:

    a. nalidixic acid increases effects of warfarin.

    b. antacids increase nitrofurantoin absorption.

    c. antiseptics cause false-positive Clinitest results.

    d. sodium bicarbonate inhibits action of methenamine.

27. Clients taking nitrofurantoin should report which of the following to the health care provider?

    a. chest pain

    b. fever

    c. cough

    d. all of the above

28. A specific adverse effect from nitrofurantoin is:

    a. superinfection.

    b. peripheral neuropathy.

    c. anorexia.

    d. drowsiness.

29. Urinary analgesics are used to relieve all of the following EXCEPT:

    a. burning sensation.

    b. frequency.

    c. urgency.

    d. retention.

30. A commonly prescribed urinary analgesic is:

    a. phenazopyridine HCl (Pyridium).

    b. trimethoprim (Trimpex).

    c. flavoxate (Urispas).

    d. bethanechol (Urecholine).

31. Nursing interventions associated with administering urinary analgesics include all of the following EXCEPT:

    a. administering drug with food or milk.

    b. instructing that chewable tablets are to be chewed.

    c. observing for side effects.

    d. monitoring blood pressure.

32. Clients taking bethanechol should report all of the following to the health care provider EXCEPT:

    a.   abdominal discomfort.

    b.   headache.

    c.   increased salivation.

    d.   urgency.

33. Urinary tract spasms are commonly treated with which of the following drugs?

    a.   trimethoprim (Trimpex)

    b.   phenazopyridine HCl (Pyridium)

    c.   flavoxate (Urispas)

    d.   bethanechol (Urecholine)

34. The drug used to control an overactive bladder and contraindicated in clients with narrow-angle glaucoma is which of the following?

    a.   tolterodine tartrate (Detrol)

    b.   bethanechol chloride (Urecholine)

    c.   flavoxate HCl (Urispas)

    d.   phenazopyridine HCl (Pyridium)

35. List four nursing interventions related to administering drugs for urinary tract disorders:

    a.

    b.

    c.

    d.

Critical Thinking Exercises

J.B., 11 years old, is taking urinary antispasmodic for treatment of an injury to his urinary tract causing spasms of the smooth muscle. Ditropan 5 mg, tid, has been prescribed.

1.   What drug classification is Ditropan?

2.   What is the recommended dosage range for J.B.? Describe nursing responsibilities, if any.

3.   What are the side effects of this drug to include in client teaching?

4.   What are the contraindications for the use of this drug? Is this an appropriate drug for J.B. based on the information provided?

5.   What are the drug-food and drug-laboratory effects of this drug?

6.   Compare the side effects of Ditropan and Pro-Banthine.

33 Human Immunodeficiency Virus–Related Agents

Study Questions

Define the following:

1. Antibody

2. Antigen

3. Antiretroviral

4. HAART

5. Postexposure prophylaxis

Multiple choice:

6. The leading AIDS indicator as of 1996 is:
   a. *Pneumocystis carinii* pneumonia.
   b. severe HIV-related immunosuppression.
   c. Kaposi's sarcoma.
   d. *Mycobacterium avium* complex.

7. Potential benefits of early initiation of antiretroviral therapy in the asymptomatic HIV-infected client include all of the following EXCEPT:
   a. control of viral replication.
   b. decreased risk of drug toxicity.
   c. earlier development of drug resistance.
   d. prevention of progressive immunodeficiency.

8. Potential risks of early initiation of antiretroviral therapy in asymptomatic HIV clients include all of the following EXCEPT:
   a. unknown long-term toxicity.
   b. reduction in quality of life from adverse effects.
   c. earlier development of drug resistance.
   d. decreased risk of selection of resistant virus.

9. The goal of combination antiretroviral therapy is to:
   a. increase the CD4 count, decrease the viral load, and have the client clinically well.
   b. decrease the viral load to undetectable in all patients.
   c. replace the memory cells within the immune system.
   d. decrease the CD4 count and increase the viral load.

10. The decision to treat asymptomatic individuals with detectable HIV RNA in plasma should include which of the following?
    1. client's age and support
    2. amount of time since diagnosis
    3. client's willingness to accept therapy
    4. probability of adherence to therapy
    a. 1, 2
    b. 1, 2, 3, 4
    c. 1, 3, 4
    d. 3, 4

11. Combination therapy (HAART):
    a. targets three enzymes in the HIV life cycle.
    b. offers a cure to AIDS-defined patients.
    c. offers a cure to pediatric patients.
    d. provides prophylaxis—treatment of major secondary infections.

Match the descriptors with the letter of the class of agents.

Descriptor		**Class of Agents**
___ 12.	block protease	a. nucleoside analogues
___ 13.	act by inhibiting HIV reverse transcriptase	b. nonnucleoside analogues
		c. protease inhibitors
___ 14.	suppress virions in infected cell populations	
___ 15.	prevent infection of new cells	

Situation: The following five questions relate to J.C., who is taking zidovudine.

16. Zidovudine received FDA approval in which of the following years?
    a. 1987
    b. 1991
    c. 1994
    d. 1996

17. Zidovudine is generally scheduled to be taken at which of the following frequencies?
    a. daily
    b. q 12 hours
    c. q 4–6 hours
    d. q 1–3 hours

18. The usual adult dose of zidovudine is which of the following?
    a. 300 mg bid
    b. 200 mg q12h
    c. 300 mg qd
    d. 1.5 mg/kg q3h

19. During the time that J.C. is taking zidovudine, frequent monitoring of which of the following is/are required?
    a. CBC
    b. renal function
    c. hepatic function
    d. all of the above

20. You assess J.C. for the side effects of zidovudine, which may include all of the following EXCEPT:
    a. numbness and pain in lower extremities.
    b. headache.
    c. seizures.
    d. difficulty swallowing.

Situation: The following five questions relate to Z.B., who is taking nevirapine.

21. Nevirapine received FDA approval in which of the following years?
    a. 1987
    b. 1991
    c. 1994
    d. 1996

22. Z.B. is taking nevirapine, which is generally initially scheduled to be taken at which of the following intervals?
    a. 14-day lead-in, give one 200 mg tablet daily, then one 200 mg tablet twice a day with an NRTI
    b. q 12 hours
    c. q 4–6 hours
    d. q 1–3 hours

23. The usual adult dose of nevirapine is which of the following?
    a. 100 mg
    b. 200 mg bid
    c. 300 mg
    d. none of the above

24. During the time that Z.B. is taking nevirapine, frequent monitoring of which of the following is/are required:
    a. CBC and platelets.
    b. renal function.
    c. hepatic function.
    d. all of the above.

25. You assess Z.B. for the side effects of nevirapine, which may include all of the following EXCEPT:
   a. diarrhea.
   b. stomatitis.
   c. difficulty swallowing.
   d. rash.

Situation: The following five questions relate to J.T., who is taking saquinavir (Invirase).

26. Invirase received FDA approval in which of the following years?
   a. 1987
   b. 1991
   c. 1995
   d. 1997

27. Invirase is generally scheduled to be taken at which of the following intervals?
   a. daily
   b. twice a day
   c. three times a day
   d. four times a day

28. The usual adult dose of Invirase is which of the following?
   a. 600 mg
   b. 800 mg
   c. 1 g
   d. 2 g

29. Frequent monitoring of which of the following is/are required while J.T. is taking Invirase?
   a. blood sugar
   b. triglycerides
   c. cholesterol
   d. all of the above

30. You assess J.T. for the side effects of Invirase, which may include all of the following EXCEPT:
   a. mouth ulcers.
   b. urinary retention.
   c. diarrhea.
   d. itching.

31. Which of the following drugs is the traditional treatment for sickle cell anemia and is now used as rescue/salvage therapy for the treatment of AIDS?
   a. Preveon
   b. vitamin B_{12} injections
   c. Hydrea
   d. ferrous gluconate

32. Prophylaxis for *Mycobacterium avium* complex might include all EXCEPT which of the following?
   a. Bactrim DS one po qd
   b. azithromycin 1200 mg po q week
   c. rifabutin 300 mg po qd
   d. clarithromycin 500 mg po bid

33. First choice of drugs for prophylaxis for PCP is:
   a. Dapsone 50 mg po bid.
   b. Atovaquone 750 mg po bid.
   c. Bactrim DS 1 tab po g/d.
   d. aerosolized pentamidine by mouth.

34. Postexposure prophylaxis includes all of the following EXCEPT 4 weeks (28 days) of:
   a. ritonavir and ddI.
   b. ZDV + 3TC and nelfinavir.
   c. ZDV + 3TC and indinavir.
   d. both zidovudine and lamivudine.

35. In the pregnant client, zidovudine monotherapy is begun at how many weeks gestation?
   a. 6
   b. 10
   c. 12
   d. 14

36. The dose of zidovudine for the pregnant client is which of the following?
   a. 100 mg tid
   b. 100 mg 5x/d or 300 mg bid
   c. 200 mg daily
   d. 200 mg 5x/d

37. Identify at least six areas for assessment of clients with HIV or AIDS:

   a.

   b.

   c.

   d.

   e.

   f.

38. List at least four potential nursing diagnoses for the client with AIDS:

   a.

   b.

   c.

   d.

39. List at least six specific nursing interventions related to antiretroviral agents:

   a.

   b.

   c.

   d.

   e.

   f.

40. A health teaching plan for a client with HIV would likely include the following six factors:

   a.

   b.

   c.

   d.

   e.

   f.

41. All EXCEPT which of the following are nursing interventions to increase adherence to therapeutic regimen?
   a. pill organizers
   b. pill counting
   c. timers/beepers
   d. scheduled pill holidays

42. Combivir and Trizivir are fixed combinations of which of the following?
   a. NRTIs
   b. NNRTIs
   c. PIs
   d. NSAIDs

34 Vaccines

Study Questions

Define the following:

1. Anaphylaxis

2. Seroconversion

3. Toxoids

4. Antibodies

5. Antigen

Complete the following:

6. Active natural immunity is often present for **(several months/the remainder of an individual's life).** (Circle correct answer).

7. Attenuated vaccines contain **(weakened/killed)** microorganisms. (Circle correct answer).

8. Newborn infants naturally have passive immunity via transfer of maternal antibodies across the _____.

9. Rubella is commonly known as _____.

10. Susceptible individuals ≥13 years of age receive _____ doses of varicella vaccine spaced _____ weeks apart.

11. List the three viruses contained in the MMR vaccine:

    a.

    b.

    c.

12. DTaP vaccine **(is/is not)** administered to individuals ≥ seven years of age. (Circle the correct answer).

13. The following vaccines are routinely administered to adults 65 years of age and older:

    a.

    b.

14. _____ is defined as the acquisition of detectable levels of antibodies in the bloodstream.

15. If measles-mumps-rubella vaccine is not given the same day as varicella vaccine, their administration should be spaced at least _____ apart.

16. A healthy 11-year-old girl receiving no medications presents to the clinic for measles-mumps-rubella (MMR) vaccine given she lives in a state where a second dose is required at sixth-grade entrance. The nurse would also assess the need for the following vaccines:

    a.

    b.

    c.

    d.

Select the appropriate response:

17. The type of immunity conferred by Td vaccine would best be described as:

    a. active.

    b. passive.

    c. natural.

    d. inactive.

18. Examples of live, attenuated vaccines include:

    a. measles-mumps-rubella (MMR) and Haemophilus influenzae type B (Hib).

    b. varicella and tetanus-diphtheria (Td).

    c. measles-mumps-rubella (MMR) and varicella.

    d. influenza and hepatitis B.

19. Symptoms of influenza include:

    a. vomiting and diarrhea.

    b. abdominal pain and cough.

    c. fever and diarrhea.

    d. fever, myalgias, and cough.

20. A physically and medically neglected 15-month-old child has recently been placed in foster care. The foster parents present with this child today for immunization update. They have no idea what, if any, vaccines he has previously received. Today the nurse would most likely administer:

    a. no vaccines because it is assumed he is up to date.

    b. DTaP #4, Hib #4, and MMR #1.

    c. DTaP, Hib, hepatitis B, MMR, and IPV.

    d. MMR and IPV.

Situation: Andy, a four-month-old boy, was seen in the emergency room of the local hospital three days ago and was diagnosed with a cold and an ear infection. He is taking amoxicillin, an antibiotic, as prescribed for his ear infection and is generally improved. The next five questions refer to this situation.

21. His mother is concerned that he should not receive vaccines today because of his illness and medication usage. Which of the following is the BEST response to this mother's concern?

    a. You empathize with her concern but suggest that neither a mild acute illness nor antibiotic usage are contraindications to immunizing her son today.

    b. You agree that Andy should not receive immunizations today and suggest that his mom return in two weeks after he has completed the amoxicillin.

    c. The cold is a contraindication to immunizing Andy today, but the medication he is taking is not.

    d. Amoxicillin is a contraindication to immunizing Andy today, but his cold is not.

22. Andy's immunization record shows he received hepatitis B vaccine on day two of life. At two months of age, he received hepatitis B, DTaP, Hib, and IPV vaccines. If you elected to immunize him today, what vaccines would you administer?

    a. pneumococcal and influenza

    b. hepatitis B, DTaP, Hib, and IPV

    c. DTaP, Hib, and influenza

    d. DTaP, Hib, and IPV

23. Andy's mother reports that after his first dose of DTaP he experienced some redness and tenderness at the injection site in his left thigh. With this in mind you would administer:

    a. DTaP again as these are common side effects of but not contraindications to further use of DTaP.

    b. DT in the right thigh.

    c. DTaP subcutaneously instead of intramuscularly to prevent muscle soreness.

    d. half the usual dose of DTaP to reduce the likelihood of a reaction.

24. Following today's visit you would recommend that Andy return for immunizations:
    a. in 2 weeks after he has recovered from his cold and ear infection.
    b. at 9 months of age.
    c. at 6 months of age.
    d. at 12 months of age.

25. Prior to leaving the clinic today, the nurse appropriately provides Andy's mother with:
    a. Vaccine Information Statements (VISs) for all vaccines administered.
    b. an immunization record.
    c. an appointment card for the next immunization clinic visit.
    d. all of the above.

26. A source of health and immunization information for nurses assisting clients prior to foreign travel is:
    a. the U.S. embassy in the destination country.
    b. the Centers for Disease Control and Prevention.
    c. the client's travel agent.
    d. not necessary because there are no special immunization needs for travelers.

27. In the case of an anaphylactic reaction to a vaccine, which of the following should the nurse have readily available?
    a. epinephrine
    b. acetaminophen
    c. pseudoephedrine
    d. diphenhydramine

28. It is a federal law to provide a client who is to receive vaccines with:
    a. an immunization record.
    b. no more than four immunizations on any given day.
    c. Vaccine Information Statements (VISs).
    d. no more than two immunizations at any given visit.

Critical Thinking Exercises

A 70-year-old man presents to the clinic on Halloween after having stepped on a nail. He has suffered a puncture wound to the sole of his right foot. He wonders whether he needs a "lock jaw" shot. He says he has not had any shots since he was in the army for a four-year stint "straight out of high school." He is on atenolol for hypertension but otherwise does not "go to the doctor much." He has no known medication allergies.

1. What is another name for "lock jaw?"

2. What are the symptoms of tetanus?

3. What vaccine would routinely be administered in this circumstance?

4. What is the route of administration for the above vaccine?

5. Given this man's age and the time of year, name the two vaccines for which he would also likely be eligible.

6. What are contraindications to the administration of influenza vaccine?

35 Anticancer Drugs

Study Questions

Define the following:

1. Androgens

2. Antiestrogens

3. Cell-cycle nonspecific

4. Cell-cycle specific

5. Corticosteroids

6. Progestins

7. Tumoricidal

8. Vesicants

9. Mitotic inhibitors

Complete the following:

10. The classification of drugs that act on a specific phase of the cell cycle is
_____.

11. Doubling time (**is/is not**) related to the growth fraction. (Circle correct answer)

12. The term *doubling time* is defined as
_____
_____.

13. (**Single/multiple**) drug therapy is the preferred method in treatment settings. (Circle correct answer)

14. What is the major difference between the actions of antineoplastics and antibiotics?
_____.

15. Malignant cells (**do/do not**) have definite cell walls. (Circle correct answer)

16. Most anticancer drugs (**do/do not**) cross the blood/brain barrier. (Circle correct answer)

17. Most anticancer drugs (**are/are not**) administered orally. (Circle correct answer)

18. Antitumor antibiotics are classified as
_____ drugs.

19. An adverse reaction to many antitumor antibiotics is _____, blistering of tissue.

20. The hormone used as palliative treatment for prostatic cancer is _____.

21. Masculine symptoms appear with use of
_____ such as Nolvadex.

22. Avoidance of the following types of foods helps to reduce nausea: _____
and _____.

23. Clients taking Cytoxan should increase fluid intake to avoid the development of
_____.

24. It is recommended that pregnancy be postponed for both males and females for _____ years after neoplastic treatment is completed.

25. The most common toxic effect of antineoplastics is _____.

Select the appropriate response:

26. Tumors that respond best to chemotherapy are those with:
    a. long doubling times.
    b. very large mass.
    c. high growth fraction.
    d. low growth fraction.

27. As tumors age and enlarge, which of the following is a true statement? Growth fraction:
    a. increases and doubling time increases.
    b. increases and doubling time decreases.
    c. decreases and doubling time increases.
    d. decreases and doubling time decreases.

28. The cellular system *most seriously* affected by most cancer chemotherapy agents is the:
    a. bone marrow.
    b. cells of the gastrointestinal tract.
    c. hair follicles.
    d. cardiac muscle.

29. A cell-cycle nonspecific (CCNS) agent effective in inhibiting any phase of the cancer cell cycle is:
    a. methotrexate (antimetabolite).
    b. Cytoxan (alkylating agent).
    c. 5-fluorouracil (5-FU).
    d. vincristine.

30. General adverse effects of anticancer drugs include all of the following EXCEPT:
    a. bone marrow suppression.
    b. infertility.
    c. stomatitis.
    d. urinary retention.

31. Combinations of chemotherapeutic agents are frequently used today for all of the following purposes EXCEPT:
    a. preventing drug resistance.
    b. providing a synergistic action.
    c. decreasing cost of treatment.
    d. providing a shortened and intensified therapy regimen.

32. When your client is receiving cyclophosphamide (Cytoxan), he/she should be advised to drink plenty of water/fluids to:
    a. prevent renal failure.
    b. prevent hemorrhagic cystitis.
    c. prevent liver dysfunction.
    d. increase the red blood cell count.

33. The antitumor antibiotic used to decrease serum calcium levels is:
    a. bleomycin.
    b. plicamycin.
    c. dactinomycin.
    d. vincristine.

34. Which of the following alkylating drugs may be used to prepare the client for bone marrow transplantation (BMT)?
    a. bleomycin
    b. Platinol
    c. methotrexate
    d. Myleran

35. An antineoplastic drug also used for immunosuppression following organ transplant is:
    a. bleomycin.
    b. Platinol.
    c. methotrexate.
    d. dactinomycin.

36. Stomatitis is a common adverse effect of most antineoplastics due to superinfection. The antifungal commonly ordered is:
    a. rifampin.
    b. tetracycline.
    c. pyridoxine.
    d. nystatin.

37. Leucovorin is required as a rescue for normal cells with administration of higher doses of:
    a. bleomycin.
    b. Platinol.
    c. methotrexate.
    d. dactinomycin.

Situation: E.B. is receiving the MOPP regimen. The next four questions refer to this situation.

38. The MOPP regimen is used in the treatment of:
    a. advanced prostatic cancer.
    b. metastatic breast cancer.
    c. ovarian cancer.
    d. Hodgkin's disease.

39. During the time E.B. is taking MOPP, frequent monitoring of all of the following laboratory tests is required EXCEPT:
    a. CBC.
    b. BUN.
    c. creatinine.
    d. SGOT.

40. The cortisone component of E.B.'s treatment contributes to all of the following EXCEPT:
    a. fluid retention and risk of infection.
    b. increase in blood sugar.
    c. sense of well-being and euphoria.
    d. decrease in bleeding tendency.

41. In addition to the general adverse effects of antineoplastics, most antitumor antibiotics also cause which of the following side effects?
    a. leukopenia
    b. vesication
    c. nausea and vomiting
    d. stomatitis

Situation: R.M. is 25 years old and is receiving vinblastine. The next three questions refer to this situation.

42. Vinblastine belongs to which group of antineoplastic drugs?
    a. antitumor antibiotics
    b. hormones
    c. mitotic inhibitors
    d. antimetabolites

43. This drug is frequently used in the treatment of:
    a. leukemia.
    b. testicular tumors.
    c. pancreatic tumors.
    d. colon tumors.

44. Vinblastine is classified as:
    a. cell-cycle specific.
    b. cell-cycle nonspecific.
    c. antimetabolite.
    d. none of the above.

45. Where is the action of vinblastine?
    a. G_1
    b. G_2
    c. all phases
    d. M phase

46. The maximum initial dose of this drug for R.M. is:
    a. $3.7 \ mg/m^2$.
    b. $5.7 \ mg/m^2$.
    c. $7.7 \ mg/m^2$.
    d. $9.7 \ mg/m^2$.

47. In addition to side effects common to antineoplastics, what is a specific effect of vinblastine for which R.M. requires monitoring?
    a. urinary retention
    b. hypotension
    c. diarrhea
    d. neurotoxicity

48. Available:

A.B., a 26-year-old, 110-pound female, is on a maintenance dose of Cytoxan of 2 mg/kg/d. What is A.B.'s daily dose, and how many tablets/day?

49. What instructions would you review with A.B. about storage of this medication?

50. The most important laboratory test to order prior to the initiation of drug therapy is:

    a. pancreatic enzymes.

    b. blood lipids.

    c. complete blood count (CBC).

    d. coagulation time.

51. Which of the following is a hormonal antagonist drug to treat advanced metastatic prostatic carcinoma?

    a. bicalutamide (Casodex)

    b. trastuzuma (Herceptin)

    c. valrubicin (Valstar)

    d. berarotene (Targretin)

52. Which of the following drugs is for the treatment of node-positive breast cancer and has adverse effects of bone marrow depression, cardiotoxicity, and extravasation necrosis?

    a. anastrozole (Arimidex)

    b. methotrexate

    c. epirubicin (Ellence)

    d. cisplatin (Platinol)

53. List four general adverse effects of antineoplastic therapy and a specific nursing intervention for each:

Adverse Effect	Nursing Intervention
a.	a.
b.	b.
c.	c.
d.	d.

Critical Thinking Exercises

D.H. is 70 years old and was recently diagnosed with lung cancer. She also has a history of cardiac problems and is taking digoxin. She reports feeling tired, "Just not right," and asks the health care provider about smoking. Cyclophosphamide is one of the drugs prescribed.

1. Does cyclophosphamide belong to CCS or CCNS category? Explain.

2. To what group of antineoplastic drugs does cyclophosphamide belong?

3.   Describe the nursing interventions and client teaching related to D.H.'s care.

6.   When would you expect to see the peak effect of the drug on D.H.'s blood count?

4.   D.H. is started on IV preparation of cyclophosphamide of 50 mg/kg in divided doses over the next three days. Is this dosage within the recommended range? List nursing responsibilities, if any.

7.   In what ways does cyclophosphamide (Cytoxan) differ from 5-fluorouracil (5-FU)?

5.   Would you be concerned about any drug-drug interaction with her digoxin? If yes, why?

36 Biologic Response Modifiers

Study Questions

Define the following:

1. Nadir

2. Absolute neutrophil count

3. Thrombocytopenia

4. Interferons

5. Myelosuppressives

Complete the following:

6. Two advances that led to mass production of BRMs were _____ and _____.

7. The three primary functions of BRMs are _____, _____, and _____.

8. There are three types of interferons: alpha, beta, and gamma. To date, only _____ interferon is FDA-approved for commercial use.

9. The major side effects of alpha interferon is _____ syndrome.

10. Women of childbearing age (**should/should not**) use contraceptives while receiving alpha interferon. (Circle correct answer)

11. The dose of erythropoietin (EPO) should be reduced when the hematocrit reaches the _____ % to _____ % range or increases by > _____ points in a two-week period.

12. Filgrastin administration results in a _____ neutrophil response.

13. A consistent client reaction to GCSF therapy is _____ _____.

14. A GMCSF product is _____.

15. It is recommended that special attention be given to the _____ system during and/or immediately after GMCSF infusions.

Match the description in Column I with the appropriate term in Column II.

Column I		Column II
_____ 16. colony-stimulating factors (CSFs)	a.	glycoprotein that regulates the production of neutrophils within the bone marrow
_____ 17. erythropoietin		
_____ 18. granulocyte colony-stimulating factor (GCSF)	b.	proteins that stimulate growth and maturation of bone marrow stem cells
_____ 19. granulocyte macrophage colony stimulating factor (GMCSF)	c.	glycoprotein produced by kidneys in response to hypoxia
_____ 20. Neumega (Oprelvekin)	d.	supports survival, clonal expression, and differentiation of hematopoietic progenitor cells
	e.	indicated for prevention of severe thrombocytopenia

Select the appropriate response:

Situation: F.F., 64 years old, has hairy cell leukemia, which is being treated with the alpha IFN, Roferon. The next 10 questions relate to this situation.

21. The usual dose of Roferon for this diagnosis is:
    a.   3 million IU daily for 16–24 weeks.
    b.   3 million IU daily for 4 weeks.
    c.   8 million IU weekly.
    d.   32 million IU monthly.

22. The dose-limiting side effect is:
    a.   malaise.
    b.   chills.
    c.   fever.
    d.   fatigue.

23. F.F. reports all the following gastrointestinal side effects. Which is considered to be the dose-limiting toxicity for this system?
    a.   taste alteration
    b.   anorexia
    c.   xerostomia
    d.   diarrhea

24. F.F. also reports neurologic side effects. The most appropriate response to F.F.'s questions would be that:
    a.   these side effects occur rarely.
    b.   they are reversible after the drug is stopped.
    c.   they are not reversible.
    d.   the worst effect is the mild confusion.

25. To assess renal and hepatic effects of the drugs, all of the following laboratory studies are monitored EXCEPT:
    a.   BUN.
    b.   creatinine.
    c.   transaminase.
    d.   bilirubin.

26. Dermatologic effects of the alpha IFN include all of the following EXCEPT:
    a.   vesicle formation.
    b.   alopecia.
    c.   irritation at injection site.
    d.   pruritus.

27. The best time to administer BRM is:
    a.   at bedtime.
    b.   two hours after meals.
    c.   with meals.
    d.   one hour before meals.

28. Nursing interventions to provide some relief from the side effects of BRM include all of the following EXCEPT:
    a.   checking client temperature at onset of chills.
    b.   administering meperidine 25–50 mg as ordered to decrease rigors.
    c.   covering client with blankets to promote warmth.
    d.   ambulating client every 2–4 hours.

29. Health teaching for F.F. and significant others would include all of the following EXCEPT:
    a.   that most BRM side effects disappear within 72–96 hours after discontinuation of therapy.
    b.   provision for return demonstration of drug administration techniques.
    c.   reporting weight gain.
    d.   providing information of the effect of BRM-related fatigue on sexuality.

30. F.F. asks how long this treatment is going to continue. An appropriate response would be that treatment usually continues for at least _____ month(s) before deciding if the client is a responder or nonresponder.

 a. 1

 b. 3

 c. 6

 d. 12

Situation: R.K. is a 47-year-old dialysis client. One of his many medications is erythropoietin (EPO). The next three questions relate to this situation.

31. You assess R.K. for the side effects of this drug including all of the following EXCEPT:

 a. chest pain.

 b. seizures.

 c. headache.

 d. constipation.

32. Some dialysis clients will require the initiation of or increase in which of the following therapies?

 a. cardiac glycoside

 b. antihypertensive

 c. antacid

 d. anticonvulsant

33. Special preparation and administration of EPO is recommended, including all of the following EXCEPT:

 a. inject <3 ml volume/injection.

 b. do not reenter the vial.

 c. discard unused portion; no preservatives.

 d. warm vial to room temperature.

34. E.K. is receiving GCSF for an ANC of 300. The client's platelet count is 5000. Will GCSF increase this count? Why or why not?

35. Describe the nursing interventions for clients receiving EPO three times per week with a hemoglobin of 21 and hematocrit of 42.

36. The client described in #34 is at high risk for:

 a. bleeding.

 b. CVA.

 c. chest pain.

 d. hypertension.

 e. a, c, d.

 f. all of the above.

37. GMCSF should be administered to clients with which of the following conditions?

 a. ANC < 500

 b. autologous BMT recipient

 c. allogenic BMT recipient

 d. two weeks post-high–dose chemo-therapy administration

 e. all of the above

38. List three differences between GCSF and GMCSF:

 a.

 b.

 c.

39. Name the major side effect of Neumega:

Critical Thinking Exercises

J.G. is a 67-year-old client diagnosed with metastatic renal cell carcinoma. His medical oncologist has prescribed interleukin-2 (IL-2). J.G. weighs 150 pounds, and he will receive 600,000 IU/kg (0.037 mg/kg) intravenously every 8 hours for 5 days (total of 14 doses) of IL-2. He will have a 9-day rest after the initial 14 doses and then receive another 14 doses. Pretreatment laboratory work will include CBC, serum electrolytes, and renal and liver function tests. Client education will focus on review of treatment schedule, side effect profile, and postinfusion management.

1.   What mg dose of IL-2 should J.G. receive?

2.   In addition to his cancer, J.G. also has congestive heart failure (CHF). How should this underlying condition affect nursing care?

3.   J.G. calls his oncology nurse three days after receiving the last dose of IL-2. He is complaining of dizziness, pruritus, and urinary retention. What should the nurse advise?

4.   Eight days after receiving IL-2, J.G. experiences confusion and lethargy. Are these symptoms related to the IL-2? How should the client be treated?

37 Drugs for Common Upper Respiratory Infections

Study Questions

Define the following:

1. Antihistamines

2. Antitussives

3. Decongestants

4. Expectorants

5. Rebound nasal congestion

Complete the following word search for questions 6–11. Circle your responses.

```
L  Q  A  D  P  R  U  O  F  O  T  O  W  T  A
A  N  Q  C  L  Z  I  Z  D  B  O  P  P  R  S
R  Q  K  S  U  X  Z  N  O  S  L  Z  E  T  L
Y  S  R  G  K  T  H  A  P  P  D  N  A  M  V
N  I  R  A  L  S  E  P  H  E  O  W  O  G  R
G  T  H  Y  D  T  A  R  T  T  F  N  D  J  P
I  I  A  I  P  T  B  C  H  Q  O  C  P  G  A
T  S  U  P  E  W  I  F  Y  I  J  E  P  A  N
I  U  P  K  F  R  V  S  C  R  N  E  J  K  K
S  N  I  K  T  L  U  B  B  J  A  I  I  Z  H
R  I  U  S  D  M  G  W  P  B  U  N  T  Q  L
I  S  N  P  K  V  G  N  U  G  H  G  I  I  N
L  O  E  L  F  L  E  F  M  R  U  X  V  R  S
C  C  O  M  M  O  N  C  O  L  D  G  B  K  U
N  C  E  Q  S  I  T  I  L  L  I  S  N  O  T
```

6. Upper respiratory infections include the following five conditions:

    _____, _____,

    _____, _____,

    and _____.

7. The most common cause of upper respiratory infections (URIs) is

    _____.

8. On the average, adults have _____ to
    _____ colds per year.

9. When the H_1 receptor is stimulated, smooth muscle lining the nasal cavity is

    _____.

10. Antihistamines **(are/are not)** used to treat anaphylaxis. (Circle correct answer)

11. Clients taking antihistamines need to be monitored for signs and symptoms of
    _____ dysfunction.

12. After constant use of a nasal spray, _____ congestion is likely to occur.

13. Do NOT use nasal sprays for children less than _____ years of age.

14. The drug group that acts on the cough control center in the medulla is _____.

15. A nondrug expectorant available to everyone is _____.

16. In emergency situations such as anaphylaxis, antihistamines (**are/are not**) helpful. (Circle correct answer)

17. Drug therapy for acute laryngitis has (**minimal/optimal**) impact on the condition. (Circle correct answer)

Select the appropriate response:

18. The groups of drugs to treat cold symptoms include all of the following EXCEPT:
    a. decongestants.
    b. antitussives.
    c. expectorants.
    d. indoles.

19. Antihistamines, another group of drugs used for the relief of cold symptoms, have _____ properties that result in decreased secretions.
    a. cholinergic
    b. anticholinergic
    c. analgesic
    d. antitussive

20. The second-generation antihistamines have a lower incidence of which of the following than first-generation?
    a. vomiting
    b. tinnitus
    c. drowsiness
    d. headache

21. The FDA has ordered removal of all cold remedies containing which of the following drugs?
    a. propranolol
    b. dextromathorphan
    c. guaifenesin
    d. phenylpropanolamine

Situation: R.T., age 20, is experiencing acute rhinitis, and diphenhydramine (Benadryl) has been prescribed. The next five questions refer to this situation.

22. The recommended dose of Benadryl is:
    a. 25–50 mg q4–6h.
    b. 25–50 mg qd.
    c. 50–100 mg q4–6h.
    d. 100 mg qd.

23. Benadryl also has which of the following effects?
    a. antihypertensive
    b. anticoagulant
    c. antitussive
    d. anticonvulsant

24. Benadryl, an _____ blocker, competes with histamine for the receptor site.
    a. H_1
    b. H_2
    c. B_1
    d. B_2

25. Since R.T. is breastfeeding her daughter, you would advise her that:
    a. large amounts of the drug pass into milk; breastfeeding is not recommended.
    b. drug does not affect breastfeeding.
    c. small amounts of the drug pass into breast milk; breastfeeding is not recommended.
    d. breastfeeding is not recommended.

26. R.T.'s health teaching plan would include the side effects of Benadryl. Which of the following is NOT a side effect?
    a. drowsiness
    b. disturbed coordination
    c. urinary retention
    d. tinnitus

27. The advantage of systemic decongestants over nasal sprays and drops is that they:
    a. are less costly.
    b. provide longer relief.
    c. have fewer side effects.
    d. are preferred by elders.

28. Decongestants are contraindicated for clients with all of the following EXCEPT:

    a. hyperthyroidism.

    b. cardiac disease.

    c. obesity.

    d. diabetes mellitus.

29. An expectorant that is frequently an ingredient in cold remedies is:

    a. guaifenesin.

    b. ephedrine.

    c. hydrocodone.

    d. promethazine.

30. Nursing interventions for the common cold include:

    a. monitoring vital signs.

    b. observing color of bronchial secretions; antibiotics may be needed.

    c. monitoring reaction; codeine preparations for cough suppression can lead to physical dependence.

    d. all of the above.

31. List four health teaching points for individuals with the common cold:

    a.

    b.

    c.

    d.

Critical Thinking Exercises

S.Y. is 80 years old and complains, "My head is all filled up. I need something to open it up." A decongestant, Afrin, is ordered. She reports having lots of medications in the bathroom cabinet.

1. What is the recommended dose and schedule for administration of this drug?

2. What is the recommended length of time for use?

3. What possible side effects would you discuss with the client? Are they expected to increase or decrease with use of the drug?

4. Describe rebound nasal congestion. What preventive measures would you advise?

5. What are the dietary restrictions, if any?

6. What would you advise S.Y. About the use of OTC cold preparations?

38 Drugs for Acute and Chronic Lower Respiratory Disorders

Study Questions

Define the following:

1. Bronchodilator

2. Bronchospasm

3. Glucocorticoids

4. Mucolytic

Complete the following:

5. The substance responsible for maintaining bronchodilation is _____.

6. In acute bronchospasm due to anaphylaxis, the drug administered subcutaneously to promote bronchodilation and elevate the blood pressure is _____.

7. The first line of defense in an acute asthmatic attack are the drugs categorized as _____.

8. Isuprel, one of the first drugs to treat broncho-spasm, is a (**selective/nonselective**) beta$_2$ agonist. (Circle correct answer)

9. The drug of choice, administered intrave-nously, for the treatment of acute asthma is _____.

10. Theophylline (**increases/decreases**) the risk of digitalis toxicity. (Circle correct answer)

11. When theophylline and beta$_2$ adrenergic agonists are given together, a _____ effect can occur.

12. The half-life of theophylline is (**shorter/longer**) for smokers than for nonsmokers.

13. Aminophylline, theophylline, and caffeine are _____ derivatives used to treat _____.

14. The drug commonly prescribed to treat unresponsive asthma is _____.

15. Cromolyn (Intal) is used as _____ treatment for bronchial asthma. It acts by inhibiting the release of _____.

16. A serious side effect of cromolyn is _____.

17. Leukotriene modifiers (**are/are not**) recom-mended for treatment of an acute asthmatic attack. (Circle correct answer)

18. The new leukotriene receptor antagonist considered safe for use in children six years and older is _____.

19. The preferred time of day for the administra-tion of Singulair is _____.

20. The usual dose of Singulair for an adult is _____ and for a child is _____ administered without food.

21. A group of drugs used to liquefy and loosen thick mucous secretions is _____.

22. With infection resulting from retained mucous secretions, a _____ may be prescribed.

Select the appropriate response:

Situation: E.B., 54 years old, is under treatment for chronic obstructive pulmonary disease (COPD). The next four questions refer to this situation.

23. E.B.'s medication is delivered via a metered dose inhaler. Related health teaching would include which one of the following?
    a. Test the inhaler first to see if spray works.
    b. Shake the inhaler well just prior to use.
    c. Refrigerate the inhaler.
    d. Hold the inhaler upside down.

24. E.B. has questions about the inhaler. Your review includes all EXCEPT which of the following?
    a. Keep lips secure around mouthpiece and inhale while pushing top of canister once.
    b. Hold breath for a few seconds, remove mouth piece and exhale slowly.
    c. Wait five minutes and repeat the procedure if a second inhalation is required.
    d. Cleanse mouthpiece.

25. Which of the following is NOT true about inhaler drug dose?
    a. lower than an oral dose
    b. higher than an oral dose
    c. fewer side effects than an oral dose
    d. onset of action is more rapid than that of an oral dose

26. Remind E.B. to wait _____ minutes after using a bronchodilator before using the glucocorticoid preparation.
    a. one
    b. three
    c. five
    d. ten

27. Health teaching for E.B. also includes that frequent use of bronchodilators may lead to all of the following side effects EXCEPT:
    a. increased heart rate.
    b. nervousness.
    c. tremors.
    d. blurred vision.

Situation: M.M. is brought to the emergency room with an acute asthmatic attack. The next seven questions relate to this situation.

28. M.M. was given an IV loading dose of aminophylline. He is now on oral Theo-Dur. This medication is generally scheduled to be taken:
    a. q2h.
    b. q3–4h.
    c. q6–12h.
    d. qd.

29. The usual adult dose of Theo-Dur is:
    a. 100–200 mg q8–12h.
    b. 200–300 mg q8–12h.
    c. 300–400 mg q8–12h.
    d. 400–500 mg q8–12h.

30. You know that it is essential to keep the serum theophylline level within which of the following ranges?
    a. 10–20 µg/ml
    b. 20–30 µg/ml
    c. 30–40 µg/ml
    d. 40–50 µg/ml

31. Which one of the following side effects is NOT associated with Theo-Dur?
    a. tachycardia
    b. insomnia and restlessness
    c. cardiac dysrhythmias
    d. urinary retention

32. All of the following drugs are known to change the action of Theo-Dur EXCEPT:
    a. antacids.
    b. digitalis.
    c. Colace.
    d. lithium.

33. Dietary influences for M.M. include all of the following EXCEPT:

    a. increase metabolism with low-carbohydrate diet.

    b. decrease elimination with high-carbohydrate diet.

    c. increase elimination with high-carbohydrate diet.

    d. increase metabolism with high-protein diet.

34. Which one of the following is NOT a contraindication for the use of Theo-Dur?

    a. hypertension

    b. severe cardiac dysrhythmias

    c. peptic ulcer disease

    d. uncontrolled seizure disorder

35. Specific nursing interventions for Theo-Dur include all of the following EXCEPT:

    a. provide hydration.

    b. monitor vital signs.

    c. observe for confusion.

    d. weigh daily.

36. M.M.'s health teaching plan includes avoidance of all of the following EXCEPT:

    a. smoking.

    b. fluid intake.

    c. OTC products.

    d. caffeine products.

37. Which one of the following is NOT a side effect of long-term use of glucocorticoids?

    a. hypoglycemia

    b. impaired immune response

    c. fluid retention

    d. hyperglycemia

38. The new anticholinergic drug _____ has few systemic effects and is administered by aerosol.

    a. Amcort

    b. Aristocort

    c. Atrovent

    d. Theo-Dur

39. Drug selection and dosage for older adults with an asthmatic condition need to be considered. The use of large, continuous doses of a beta$_2$ adrenergic agonist may cause which side effect in the older adult?

    a. urinary retention

    b. bronchoconstriction

    c. constipation

    d. tachycardia

40. Which of the following herbs should be avoided by clients taking theophylline products?

    a. feverfew

    b. ephedra

    c. ginkgo

    d. garlic

Critical Thinking Exercises

Sarah, age 15, has severe asthma. She is being treated with theophylline and an inhaled glucocorticoid.

1. Are inhaled glucocorticoids the treatment of choice for severe asthmatic attacks? Explain.

2. When should theophylline be taken in relation to food?

3. What are the possible side effects associated with oral inhalers? What may prevent or diminish these side effects?

5. List at least three nursing interventions associated with bronchodilators.

4. Steroid use for prolonged periods is likely to cause which side effects?

6. List at least three points to be included in Sarah's health teaching.

39 Drugs for Cardiac Disorders

Study Questions

Crossword puzzle: Use the definitions in questions 1–13 (next page) to determine the pharmacologic/physiologic term.

Crossword puzzle:

Across

1. Peripheral vascular resistance
3. Amount of blood in the ventricle at the end of diastole
6. Pulse rate below 60
10. Increased carbon dioxide in the blood
12. Low serum potassium level
13. Lack of blood supply to the (heart) muscle

Down

2. Drug category used to treat angina pectoris
4. Drug group used to treat disturbed heart rhythm
5. Drug group used to control angina pain by relaxing coronary vessels
7. Myocardium at rest
8. Myocardial contraction
9. Cardiac _____ causes cardiac muscles to contract more efficiently
10. Lack of oxygen to body tissues
11. Pulse rate above 100

Complete the following:

1. Digitalis is obtained from the _____ plant and can be poisonous.

2. The digitalis drug with a short half-life is _____.

3. Many drugs (**have/do not have**) drug interactions with digitalis preparations. (Circle correct answer)

4. Antacids (**decrease/increase**) absorption of digitalis. (Circle correct answer)

5. The action of antianginal drugs is to _____ blood flow and either to (**increase/decrease**) oxygen supply or to (**increase/decrease**) oxygen demand by the myocardium. (Circle correct answers).

6. Beta blockers and calcium channel blockers (**decrease/increase**) the workload of the heart. (Circle correct answer)

7. Nitroglycerin (NTG) is not swallowed because _____, thereby decreasing it effectiveness.

8. NTG sublingually acts within _____ minutes. It may be repeated _____ times.

9. The most common side effect of NTG is _____.

10. The drug group that may be used as an antianginal, antidysrhythmic, and antihypertensive is _____.

11. A calcium channel blocker that is effective in the long-term treatment of angina and has the side effect of bradycardia is _____.

12. Beta blockers and calcium channel blockers should not be discontinued without health care provider approval. Withdrawal symptoms may include _____ and _____.

13. Quinidine and procainamide are used for (**short-term/long-term**) use in the treatment of dysrhythmias. (Circle correct answer)

14. Quinidine was the first drug developed to treat dysrhythmias. It has many side effects, including _____ and _____.

15. Clients taking antidysrhythmics should avoid _____ and _____.

16. A specific side effect of the drug amiodarone is _____.

17. Classic angina occurs when the client is _____.

18. Unstable angina (preinfarction) has the following pattern of occurrence: _____

19. Variant angina (Prinzmetal's angina) occurs when the client _____.

20. Prinzmetal's angina is due to _____ of the vessels.

21. The major systemic effect of nitrates is
    _____.

22. Dexamethasone (Decadron), a corticosteroid, produces an antiinflammatory response, and (**is/is not**) useful during severe shock and persistent unresponsive hypotension. (Circle correct answer)

23. List four nonpharmacological means to decrease anginal attacks:

    a.

    b.

    c.

    d.

Situation: S.W. tells the nurse that she is taking Procardia XL daily. She said she heard that this drug can be harmful.

24. Nifedipine (Procardia), the immediate-release form (doses that are taken several times a day), has been associated with:
    a.   renal failure.
    b.   sudden cardiac death.
    c.   liver failure.
    d.   severe GI distress.

25. What would be the most appropriate response to S.W.'s question about Procardia XL being harmful?
    a.   "Procardia of all types may be harmful, please check with your health care provider."
    b.   "There are no cases where Procardia has caused harm."
    c.   "Procardia XL is considered safe if it is taken as directed."
    d.   "Do not worry, the health care provider would not prescribe the drug if it would be harmful."

Select the appropriate response:

26. An antidysrhythmic drug used during life-threatening situations to convert ventricular fibrillation to normal sinus rhythm when lidocaine and procainamide are ineffective is:
    a.   phenytoin (Dilantin).
    b.   tocainide.
    c.   atropine.
    d.   bretylium.

27. The antidysrhythmic drug lidocaine/Xylocaine is used primarily for the treatment of:
    a.   bradycardia.
    b.   ventricular arrhythmias.
    c.   atrial arrhythmias.
    d.   heart block.

28. Vasopressors are effective in increasing blood pressure during shock. They act on alpha-adrenergic receptors in smooth muscle of all vessels. Vasopressors are:
    a.   sympatholytics.
    b.   sympathomimetics.
    c.   parasympathomimetics.
    d.   parasympatholytics.

29. An example of a vasopressor that does not constrict renal vessels and is effective in increasing blood pressure during shock is:
    a.   dobutamine (Dobutrex).
    b.   dopamine (Intropin).
    c.   levarterenol (Levophed).
    d.   metaraminol (Aramine).

30. Your client is receiving the vasopressor norepinephrine (Levarterenol/Levophed). Nursing responsibility includes all of the following EXCEPT:
    a.   check blood pressure every 2–3 minutes.
    b.   reduce IV flow rate if systolic blood pressure is > 100.
    c.   remain with the client.
    d.   reduce IV flow rate if systolic blood pressure is > 120.

31. A drug used to correct metabolic acidosis during shock is:
    a.   sodium nitroprusside.
    b.   dexamethasone (Decadron).
    c.   sodium bicarbonate.
    d.   calcium gluconate.

32. A common problem with the use of verapamil is:
    a.   tachycardia.
    b.   bradycardia.
    c.   headache.
    d.   nausea.

33. The most potent calcium blocker is:
    a. nicardipine (Cardene).
    b. diltiazem (Cardizem).
    c. verapamil (Calan).
    d. nifedipine (Procardia).

34. Clients taking calcium blockers need to have which of the following laboratory values monitored?
    a. BUN
    b. creatinine
    c. liver enzymes
    d. urinary output

Situation: J.H., 80 years old, is taking digoxin daily along with several other medications. The next eight questions refer to this situation.

35. Digitalis preparations are effective in treating all of the following conditions EXCEPT:
    a. congestive heart failure.
    b. atrial flutter.
    c. emphysema.
    d. atrial fibrillation.

36. The usual maintenance dose of digoxin is:
    a. 0.125–0.5 mg/d.
    b. 0.5–1 mg/d.
    c. 0.04–0.06 mg/d.
    d. 0.4–0.6 mg/d.

37. J.H.'s serum digoxin level should be within the range of:
    a. 0.15–0.5 ng/ml.
    b. 0.5–2.0 ng/ml.
    c. 2–3.5 ng/ml.
    d. 3.5–4 ng/ml.

38. You assess J.H. for all of the following signs and symptoms of digitalis toxicity EXCEPT:
    a. anorexia.
    b. diarrhea.
    c. bradycardia.
    d. visual disturbances.

39. An antidote for digitalis toxicity is:
    a. protamine.
    b. vitamin K.
    c. digoxin immune Fab.
    d. gamma globulin.

40. The drugs that alter the action of digoxin include all of the following EXCEPT:
    a. furosemide (Lasix).
    b. cortisone.
    c. nitroglycerin.
    d. potassium-wasting diuretics.

41. Specific nursing interventions include taking J.H.'s pulse at the:
    a. radial rate for 30 seconds.
    b. radial rate for 60 seconds.
    c. apical rate for 30 seconds.
    d. apical rate for 60 seconds.

42. You would NOT advise J.H. to include which of the following foods in his diet?
    a. fruits
    b. potatoes
    c. fruit juice
    d. sausage

43. J.H.'s teaching plan may NOT include:
    a. take blood pressure daily.
    b. read drug labels carefully.
    c. eat foods high in potassium.
    d. report pulse < 60.

44. Other drugs that may be used to treat heart failure include all of the following EXCEPT:
    a. vasodilators.
    b. angiotensin-converting enzyme (ACE) inhibitors.
    c. beta blockers.
    d. diuretics.

The nurse should obtain a history of herbs the client is taking. This is especially true for clients taking digoxin. Match the herbs with their effects on digoxin.

Herb	Effect on Digoxin
____ 45. St. John's wort	a. increased risk of digitalis toxicity
____ 46. Ephedra	b. decreased digoxin absorption
____ 47. Metamucil	
____ 48. Aloe	c. decreased effects of digoxin
____ 49. Goldenseal	d. falsely elevated digoxin levels
____ 50. Ginseng	

51. Phosphodiesterase inhibitors are used to treat CHF by inhibiting the enzyme phosphodiesterase. These agents promote:
    a. positive inotropic response.
    b. negative inotropic response.
    c. vasoconstriction.
    d. increased serum sodium and potassium levels.

52. An example of a phophodiesterase inhibitor is:
    a. digoxin.
    b. isosorbide dinitrate (Isordil).
    c. amlodipine (Norvasc).
    d. amrinone lactate (Inocor).

Give the rationale for the nursing interventions related to digoxin administration.

Nursing Interventions	Rationale
53. Check the apical pulse rate before administering digoxin.	53.
54. Check the serum digoxin level.	54.
55. Instruct the client to report side effects of digoxin.	55.
56. Advise a client who is taking a potassium-wasting diuretic to eat foods rich in potassium.	56.
57. What type(s) of edema is/are associated with heart failure?	57.

Situation: B.A. is receiving NTG sublingually for anginal pain. The next four questions refer to this situation.

58. You monitor B.A.'s vital signs. Which of the following is associated with antianginal drugs?
    a. hypotension
    b. hypertension
    c. increased heart rate
    d. decreased heart rate

59. You assess B.A. for the most common side effect of NTG, which is:
    a. faintness.
    b. dizziness.
    c. headache.
    d. weakness.

60. Health teaching for B.A. includes all of the following EXCEPT:
    a. biting sensation indicates that NTG tablet is fresh.
    b. store NTG away from light.
    c. contents of opened bottle of NTG remains effective for approximately six months.
    d. if pain persists after five tablets, notify the health care provider immediately.

61. Later, a Nitro transdermal patch was prescribed for B.A. How often is the patch applied?
    a. every 6 hours
    b. every 12 hours
    c. every 24 hours
    d. every 48 hours

62. The action of antidysrhythmics includes all of the following EXCEPT:
    a. block adrenergic stimulation of the heart.
    b. increase myocardial contractility.
    c. decrease myocardial contractility.
    d. increase recovery time of the myocardium.

Give the rationale for the nursing interventions related to antianginal agents.

Nursing Interventions   **Rationale**

63. Monitor vital signs.   63.

64. Offer sips of water before giving sublingual (SL) tablets.   64.

65. Give nitroglycerin SL for chest pain and repeat in 5 minutes if pain persists.   65.

66. Instruct client not to ingest alcohol while taking a nitrate drug.   66.

67. Instruct client on how to apply a transdermal Nitro-patch.   67.

68. Inform client that headaches may occur when first taking a nitrate product.   68.

69. Instruct client not to discontinue taking the antianginal drug, beta blocker, or calcium blocker. Drug doses are usually tapered.   69.

Critical Thinking Exercises

J.B., 61 years old, has had several attacks of angina pectoris. J.B. has nitroglycerin gr 1/150 sublingual tablets to relieve acute attacks, and metoprolol (Lopressor) 25 mg, bid, was prescribed. Vital signs: BP 154/88, P. 82, R. 26. (See Case Study, Chapter 20.)

1.   From which of the following nitroglycerin bottles should J.B. take his medication?

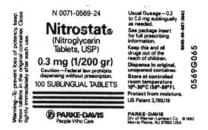   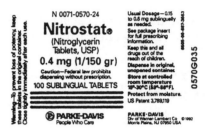

2.   What are the nursing interventions for J.B. regarding the use of nitroglycerin tablets?

3.   Why should J.B.'s vital signs be monitored?

4.   What are the similarities and differences of metoprolol tartrate and propranolol HCl? Which drug should a client with asthma take? Why?

5.   Metoprolol tartrate and propranolol HCl can be prescribed for what other cardiac conditions?

6. What nonpharmacologic measures should the nurse include in the health teaching for J.B.?

J.B.'s antianginal drug was changed to diltiazem 60 mg, tid.

7. How does this drug compare to other calcium channel blockers?

8. Is the diltiazem dose within normal range? What is the maximum daily dose?

40 Diuretics

Study Questions

Indicate which diuretic group acts on the segment of the renal tubule on the figure below:

a. _____

b. _____

c. _____

d. _____

e. _____

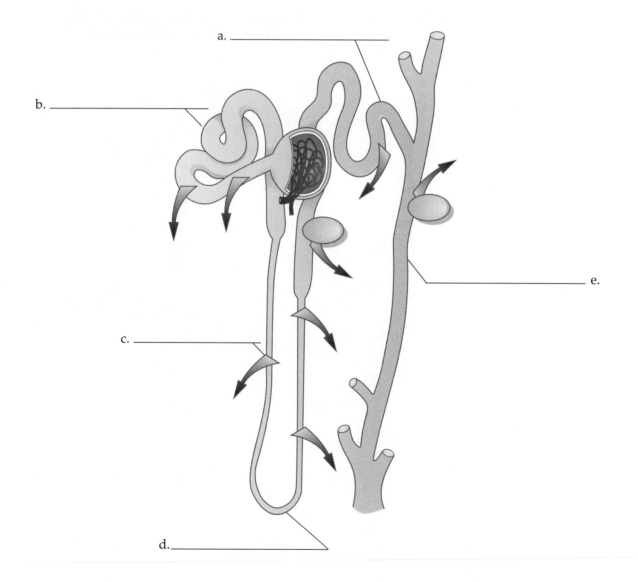

Define the following:

1. Diuresis

2. Hyperglycemia

3. Hyperkalemia

4. Natriuresis

5. Oliguria

6. Osmolality

7. Potassium-wasting diuretics

Complete the following:

8. The two main purposes for the use of diuretics are _____ and _____.

9. Diuretics act by inhibiting sodium and water (**retention/reabsorption**) from the kidney (**ureters/tubules**). (Circle correct answer)

10. Five groups of diuretics are
    _____,
    _____,
    _____,
    _____, and
    _____.

11. Thiazide and loop (high-ceiling) diuretics cause the loss of the cellular electrolyte _____.

12. The most serious thiazide drug interaction occurs with the digitalis preparation, _____. It may result in _____ _____.

13. Loop diuretics have (**little/much**) effect on blood sugar. (Circle correct answer)

14. Diuretics that promote potassium retention are called potassium _____ diuretics.

15. Potassium-sparing diuretics are (**weaker/ stronger**) than thiazides and loop diuretics. (Circle correct answer)

16. Potassium-sparing diuretics interfere with the sodium-potassium pump that is controlled by the mineralocorticoid hormone _____.

17. The main side/adverse effect of potassium-sparing diuretics is (**hypokalemia/hyperkalemia**). (Circle correct answer)

18. Currently, a combination drug of potassium-wasting and potassium-sparing agents is frequently prescribed, such as _____.

19. When a combination of diuretics is used, the dosage of each is usually (**less/more**) than the dose of one drug. (Circle correct answer)

20. Mannitol is the most frequently prescribed _____ diuretic.

21. Carbonic anhydrase inhibitors (**decrease/ increase**) intraocular pressure in clients with glaucoma. (Circle correct answer)

List the possible abnormal serum chemistry test results associated with thiazides.

Laboratory Tests	Abnormal Results
22. Potassium	22.
23. Magnesium	23.
24. Calcium	24.
25. Chloride	25.
26. Bicarbonate	26.
27. Uric acid	27.
28. Blood sugar	28.
29. Blood lipids	29.

Select the appropriate response:

30. Which of the following groups of diuretics is NOT frequently prescribed to treat hypertension and congestive heart failure?
    a. osmotic
    b. potassium-sparing
    c. loop
    d. thiazides

31. Loop (high-ceiling) diuretics, when compared with thiazides, are:
    a. more effective as antihypertensives.
    b. more potent as diuretics.
    c. promote potassium absorption.
    d. cause calcium reabsorption.

32. You would encourage clients on loop diuretics to include all of the following foods in their diets EXCEPT:
    a. fresh and dry fruits.
    b. ice cream.
    c. potato skins.
    d. peanut butter.

33. B.T. is taking spironolactone (Aldactone). He requests assistance with his diet. Which of the following foods would you NOT recommend?
    a. lean meat
    b. bananas
    c. apples
    d. squash

34. Acetazolamide (Diamox) is NOT effective for treating:
    a. diuresis.
    b. epilepsy.
    c. emphysema.
    d. high-altitude sickness.

35. Diuretics, as the first line of antihypertensive drugs, are generally ordered for clients with systolic pressures greater than:
    a. 130 mm Hg.
    b. 140 mm Hg.
    c. 150 mm Hg.
    d. 160 mm Hg.

36. Herb-diuretic interaction should be assessed by the nurse. An herb that may increase the blood pressure when it is taken with thiazide diuretics is:
    a. St. John's wort
    b. licorice.
    c. ginkgo.
    d. ginger.

37. Clients taking spironolactone (Aldactone) should have their serum potassium level monitored periodically. If the serum potassium level is 5.5 mEq/L, what intervention should be considered?
    a. The Aldactone dose should be reduced or stopped and instruct the client to decrease foods rich in polassium.
    b. The Aldactone dose should be continued and client encouraged to eat fruits, vegetables, and meats.
    c. The Aldactone dose should be increased and client instructed to decrease foods rich in potassium.
    d. Instruct the client to continue the prescribed Aldactone dose and report any signs or symptoms of hypokalemia.

38. The pharmacologic action of Aldactone is to:
    a. increase potassium and sodium excretion.
    b. promote potassium retention and sodium excretion.
    c. promote potassium, sodium, and calcium retention.
    d. promote potassium excretion and sodium retention.

Situation: J.H., 80 years old, is under treatment for hypertension and congestive heart failure. Hydrochlorothiazide (HydroDIURIL) is one of his medications. The next 11 questions refer to this situation.

39. HydroDIURIL is generally scheduled to be taken:
    a. q2h.
    b. q4h.
    c. q6h.
    d. qd.

40. The usual dose of HydroDIURIL is:
    a. 25–100 mg/d.
    b. 100–150 mg/d.
    c. 150–200 mg/d.
    d. 200–250 mg/d.

41. The optimal time to administer diuretics is:
    a. at bedtime.
    b. with meals.
    d. on an empty stomach.
    d. in the morning.

42. While J.H. is taking HydroDIURIL, monitoring of all of the following laboratory values are required EXCEPT:
    a. serum calcium.
    b. uric acid.
    c. blood sugar.
    d. alkaline phosphatase.

43. Monitoring which of the following laboratory values is also recommended when taking HydroDIURIL?
    a. serum cholesterol
    b. BUN
    c. low-density lipoprotein
    d. triglycerides

44. You assess J.H. for side effects, which include all of the following EXCEPT:
    a. electrolyte imbalances.
    b. dizziness.
    c. diarrhea.
    d. headache.

45. Thiazides can cause all of the following drug-lab interactions EXCEPT:
    a. enhance action of lithium.
    b. enhance hypertensive state when used with alcohol.
    c. potentiate other antihypertensives.
    d. cause hypokalemia.

46. You would recommend that J.H. include all of the following fruits in his diet EXCEPT:
    a. oranges.
    b. dates.
    c. apples.
    d. bananas.

47. Specific nursing interventions include all of the following EXCEPT:

    a. assess extremities for pitting edema.

    b. monitor lung sounds.

    c. monitor lab results.

    d. encourage fluids.

48. The health teaching plan for J.H. includes all of the following EXCEPT:

    a. maintenance of nutrition.

    b. advise the client to arise slowly to standing position.

    c. monitor pulse and respiratory rates

    d. weigh daily.

49. Thiazides are contraindicated for use in clients with which of the following?

    a. emphysema

    b. arteriosclerotic cardiovascular disease

    c. renal failure

    d. liver failure

Critical Thinking Exercises

A.D., age 56, is hypertensive. She has maturity-onset diabetes mellitus. Vital signs: BP. 162/90, P. 90, R. 24. A.D. was prescribed hydrochlorothiazide (HydroDIURIL) 50 mg, daily.

1. Hydrochlorothiazide is available as follows:

How many tablet(s) should A.D. receive per day? _____

2. A.D. is on an oral antidiabetic (hypoglycemic) drug. Why should A.D.'s blood glucose level be closely monitored?

3. What are the similarities and differences in the actions of thiazide diuretics and loop diuretics?

4. What are the similarities and differences of thiazide diuretics and loop diuretics in their blood chemistry (i.e., electrolytes, uric acid, and blood glucose)?

5. If A.D.'s serum calcium was 12.5 mg/dL, which diuretic should she avoid? Why?

6.   What are four client teaching strategies that should be included in A.D.'s care?

a.

b.

c.

d.

Digoxin 0.25 mg, daily, was added to her drug regimen. Her serum potassium is 3.7 mEq/L.

7.   What is the average serum potassium range? Why should A.D.'s serum potassium be closely monitored?

8.   What are the signs and symptoms of digitalis toxicity?

9.   What groups of diuretics can affect electrolyte balance?

10.   When is it a benefit to use the combination of potassium-wasting and potassium-sparing diuretics?

41 Antihypertensive Drugs

Study Questions

Define the following:

1. Alpha-adrenergic blockers

2. Beta-adrenergic blockers

3. Calcium channel blockers

4. Angiotensin-converting enzyme (ACE) inhibitors

5. Angiotensin II receptor antagonists (A-II blockers)

Complete the following:

6. Four causes of essential hypertension include
   _____,
   _____,
   _____, and
   _____.

7. Nonpharmacologic measures to decrease blood pressure include: _____,
   _____,
   _____,
   and _____.

8. When hypertension cannot be controlled by nonpharmacologic means, antihypertensive drugs may be prescribed. Three of the sympatholytic groups are
   _____,
   _____, and
   _____.

9. Three additional categories of antihypertensives in addition to the sympatholytics are
   _____,
   _____, and
   _____.

10. The Joint National Committee on Detection, Evaluation, and Treatment of Hypertension of the American Heart Association recommended a _____
    _____ approach to the treatment of high blood pressure.

11. There is movement toward a more (**generic/ individualized**) approach to treatment of high blood pressure and the use of fewer numbers of drugs given at the lowest effective doses. (Circle correct answer)

12. Modified Pharmacologic Approach is another method for managing hypertension. The first step is lifestyle changes which include increasing _____, and decreasing
    _____, _____,
    _____, and _____.

13. Many antihypertensive drugs can cause fluid retention. To decrease body fluid, what drug group is often administered with antihypertensive drugs? _____

14. Thiazide diuretics may be combined with other antihypertensive agents such as
    _____ and _____.

15. ACE inhibitors may be combined with the antihypertensive agent _____.

16. A step I drug from the stepped-care approach categories is used to control stage 1 hypertension. A client with a blood pressure of 182/105 has what stage of hypertension?
    _____

17. Beta-adrenergic blockers reduce cardiac output by diminishing the sympathetic nervous system response. With continued use of beta blockers, vascular resistance is (**increased/diminished**) and blood pressure is (**lowered/increased**). (Circle correct answers)

18. The cultural group that does not respond well to beta blockers or ACE inhibitors is

_____.

19. Atenolol and metoprolol are examples of (**cardioselective/noncardioselective**) antihypertensive drugs. (Circle correct answer)

20. The generic names for beta blockers end with which four letters? _____

21. The alpha blockers are useful in treating hypertensive clients with lipid abnormalities. The effect they have on lipoproteins include

_____

_____.

22. An example of a cardioselective alpha blocker is _____.

23. Two direct-acting arteriolar vasodilators for treating acute hypertensive emergencies are _____ and

_____.

24. A new group of antihypertensive drugs is

_____.

Match the generic drug name with the group category of antihypertensives.

	Drug		Antihypertensive Category
____	25. captopril	a.	beta blocker
____	26. verapamil	b.	selective alpha blocker
____	27. prazosin		
____	28. methyldopa	c.	angiotensin antagonist (ACE inhibitor)
____	29. hydralazine		
____	30. candesartan	d.	calcium blocker
		e.	centrally acting sympatholytic
		f.	direct-acting vasodilator
		g.	angiotensin II receptor antagonist (A-II blocker)

Select the appropriate response:

31. The advantages of a cardioselective beta-adrenergic blocker for its antihypertensive effect include all of the following EXCEPT that it:
    a. minimizes hypoglycemic effect.
    b. helps prevent bronchoconstriction.
    c. maintains renal blood flow.
    d. can be abruptly discontinued without causing rebound symptoms.

32. The nonselective alpha-adrenergic blockers are useful for:
    a. treating mild to moderate hypertension.
    b. treating severe hypertension due to adrenal medulla tumor.
    c. preventing hyperlipidemia.
    d. administration with all drugs.

33. Direct-acting vasodilators to treat hypertension act on:
    a. smooth muscles of the blood vessels.
    b. skeletal muscles.
    c. renal tubules.
    d. cardiac valves.

34. The direct-acting vasodilators are in which step of the "stepped-care approach" in treating hypertension?
    a. step I
    b. step II
    c. step III
    d. step IV

35. With use of direct-acting vasodilators, sodium and water are retained, and peripheral edema occurs. A drug category that is given to avoid fluid retention is:
    a. anticoagulants.
    b. antidysrhythmics.
    c. cardiac glycosides.
    d. diuretics.

36. Which of the following is NOT an action of A-II blockers?
    a. blocks the angiotensin II
    b. increases sodium retention
    c. causes vasodilation
    d. decreases peripheral resistance

37. Angiotensin II blocker can be combined with the thiazide diuretic HydroDIURIL. The purpose for combining these two drugs is to:
    a. decrease rapid blood pressure drop.
    b. promote potassium retention.
    c. enhance the antihypertensive effect by promoting sodium and water loss.
    d. increase sodium and water retention for controlling blood pressure.

38. An increased number of A-II blocker drugs are being marketed today. Which one of the following drugs is NOT an angiotensin II blocker?
    a. irbesartan (Avapro)
    b. losartan potassium (Cozaar)
    c. valsartan (Diovan)
    d. lisinopril (Prinzide)

39. The use of ACE inhibitors is NOT effective for treating hypertension in the African-American population. This is because African-Americans:
    a. are susceptible to low-renin hypertension.
    b. respond mostly to loop and thiazide diuretics.
    c. are susceptible to high-renin hypertension.
    d. have increased sodium and water retention.

40. ACE inhibitors can be effective for treating hypertension in African-Americans if the ACE inhibitor is given with which other drug?
    a. beta blocker
    b. calcium blocker
    c. angiotensin II blocker
    d. diuretic

41. Herb-drug interactions may occur if the client is taking certain herb supplements. An herb history should be obtained. Ma-huang or ephedra with an antihypertensive drug may:
    a. increase the hypertensive state.
    b. decrease or counteract the effects of the antihypertensive drug.
    c. increase the hypotensive effects of the antihypertensive drug.
    d. not have any effect on the antihypertensive drug.

Situation: D.D., age 59, has essential hypertension. He is taking captopril 25 mg, tid. D.D. tells the health care provider that he feels fine, his blood pressure is within normal range, and he feels he does not need the drug. The next 11 questions relate to this situation.

42. Captopril is from which group of antihypertensives?
    a. beta blocker
    b. calcium blocker
    c. direct-acting vasodilator
    d. angiotensin antagonist (ACE inhibitor)

43. The action of captopril is to:
    a. dilate the arteries.
    b. inhibit angiotensin II (a vasoconstrictor).
    c. increase sodium and water excretion.
    d. inhibit the alpha receptors.

44. The protein-binding power of captopril is:
    a. highly protein-bound.
    b. moderately to highly protein-bound.
    c. moderately protein-bound.
    d. low protein-bound.

45. If D.D. takes captopril with a highly protein-bound drug, what might occur?
    a. No drug displacement, because captopril is not highly protein-bound.
    b. A moderate drug displacement of captopril, which is moderately to highly protein-bound.
    c. Captopril and the highly protein-bound drug compete for protein sites.
    d. Concentration of captopril is increased.

46. What drug interaction could occur if D.D. takes captopril with nitrates, diuretics, or adrenergic blockers?
    a. hypertensive reaction
    b. hypotensive reaction
    c. no effect
    d. hypoglycemic reaction

47. Captopril may not be as effective with which of the following group(s) of people?

    a. children

    b. middle-aged adults

    c. elderly

    d. Caucasian

48. If D.D. takes captopril with a potassium-sparing diuretic, what might occur?

    a. hypokalemia

    b. hyperkalemia

    c. hypocalcemia

    d. hypercalcemia

49. D.D. states that he wishes to stop taking the drug. How might the nurse respond?

    a. "Yes, you could stop taking captopril because your blood pressure has been normal."

    b. "Stop taking the drug for a month and see what happens."

    c. "Captopril is controlling your blood pressure and should not be stopped until you discuss this with the health care provider."

    d. "Stop taking captopril, exercise, and avoid salt."

50. D.D.'s antihypertensive drug was changed to nifedipine (Procardia) 10 mg, tid. What type of antihypertensive drug is nifedipine?

    a. beta blocker

    b. calcium blocker

    c. angiotensin antagonist

    d. centrally-acting sympatholytic

51. The protein-binding power of nifedipine (Procardia) is:

    a. highly protein-bound.

    b. moderately to highly protein-bound.

    c. moderately protein-bound.

    d. low protein-bound.

52. Side effects that D.D. may encounter with the use of nifedipine include all of the following EXCEPT:

    a. dizziness.

    b. lightheadedness.

    c. headache.

    d. increased blood pressure.

Give the rationale for the nursing interventions related to ACE inhibitors.

Nursing Interventions	**Rationale**
53. Monitor vital signs.	53.
54. Monitor WBC, BUN, serum creatinine, protein, potassium, and blood glucose levels.	54.
55. Inform client that dizziness and lightheadedness may occur during the first week.	55.
56. Instruct the client not to discontinue ACE inhibitor abruptly without notifying health care provider.	56.
57. Instruct the client to report bruising, petechiae, and/or bleeding.	57.
58. Instruct the client to take the drug 20 minutes to 1 hour before meals.	58.

59. Zebeta is classified as a:
    a. diuretic.
    b. beta blocker.
    c. calcium blocker.
    d. ACE inhibitor.

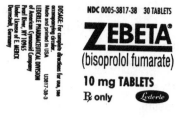

60. Procardia is classified as a:
    a. diuretic.
    b. beta blocker.
    c. calcium blocker.
    d. ACE inhibitor.

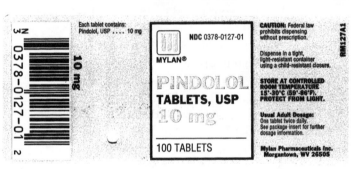

61. Pindolol is classified as a:
    a. diuretic.
    b. beta blocker.
    c. calcium blocker.
    d. ACE inhibitor.

Critical Thinking Exercises

S.H., 82 years old, has essential hypertension. He is taking methyldopa 250 mg, bid, and hydrochlorothiazide 25 mg, daily. His vital signs are: BP. 138/88, P. 74, R. 22. He lives by himself and has a care person who is with him for four hours in the morning and four hours in the evening. The care person assists him with his medication and food.

1. What type of antihypertensive agent is methyldopa? Is the drug dosing for S.H. within normal range?

2. What is the pharmacologic action of methyldopa?

3. From what drug group is hydrochlorothiazide? Why would this drug be ordered for S.H.?

4. What type of electrolyte imbalance may occur with the use of hydrochlorothiazide? Why?

5. With his blood pressure within normal range, should the drug be discontinued or the drug dose be reduced?

6. What important client teaching points should the nurse discuss with S.H.'s care person?

7. What are the similarities and differences between methyldopa and beta blockers?

8. What are some of the side effects of methyldopa?

9. What laboratory tests should be monitored?

42 Drugs for Circulatory Disorders

Study Questions

Word search:
Locate and circle the abbreviations for:

a.   High-density lipoprotein

b.   International normalized ratio

c.   Low-density lipoprotein

d.   Low molecular weight heparin

e.   Partial thromboplastin time

f.   Very low-density lipoprotein

Identify the terms according to the definitions.
Circle the term in the word search puzzle.

g.   Clumping together of platelets to form a clot

h.   Inhibits blood clot formation

i.   Decreases the blood lipid concentration

j.   Breakdown of fibrin for preventing clot formation

k.   High levels of blood lipids

l.   Lack of blood supply to tissues

m.   Death of tissues

n.   Drug category used to destroy blood clot formation

```
V  H  C  G  S  I  S  O  R  C  E  N  A  A  U
G  L  Y  J  L  F  G  K  R  J  H  N  B  N  L
R  Z  D  P  T  R  M  I  R  W  T  Y  Z  T  N
K  Y  A  L  E  T  H  G  M  I  O  P  D  I  O
Z  K  O  M  D  R  P  L  C  E  M  X  O  L  I
O  Z  F  K  I  V  L  O  P  G  X  A  K  I  T
S  E  L  Z  D  H  A  I  E  N  I  W  G  P  A
Z  K  S  R  D  G  M  P  P  G  X  V  I  E  G
H  B  L  L  U  I  A  U  I  I  X  N  B  M  E
L  U  L  L  K  X  Q  R  F  I  D  F  Q  I  R
G  D  A  S  V  Z  X  A  L  F  F  E  B  C  G
L  N  X  H  U  I  J  F  L  O  U  R  M  J  G
T  I  S  C  H  E  M  I  A  G  X  T  R  I  A
F  C  I  T  Y  L  O  B  M  O  R  H  T  N  A
M  L  S  I  S  Y  L  O  N  I  R  B  I  F  I
```

Complete the following:

1. A thrombus can form in a(n)
   _____ and
   _____.

2. Anticoagulants are used to inhibit
   _____.

3. Anticoagulants and thrombolytics (**have/do not have**) the same action. (Circle correct answer)

4. The most frequent use of heparin is to prevent
   _____
   _____.

5. Heparin can be given (**orally/subcutaneously/ intravenously**). (Circle correct answers)

6. The new low molecular weight heparins (LMWH) are derivatives from
   _____.
   The advantage of the use of LMWHs is to
   _____.

7. The international normalized ratio (INR) is a new laboratory test to monitor the therapeutic effect of (**warfarin/heparin**). (Circle correct answer)

8. Heparin can (**decrease/increase**) the platelet count, causing thrombocytopenia. (Circle correct answer)

9. A thrombus disintegrates when a thrombolytic drug is administered within _____ hours following an acute myocardial infarction.

10. The action of the thrombolytic drugs streptokinase and urokinase is the conversion of
    _____
    to _____.

11. The major complication with the use of thrombolytic drugs is
    _____.

12. "Friendly" lipoproteins are the _____.

13. Clients should fast for _____ hours prior to a lipid profile.

14. The most common discomfort (side effect) of many antilipemics is
    _____.

15. An antilipemic medication may take several (**days/weeks**) to decrease the blood lipid levels. (Circle correct answer)

16. The desired cholesterol level is
    _____.

17. Some clients report a decreased libido with the drug _____.

18. Peripheral dilators are more effective in disorders resulting from vasospasms than
    _____.

19. The hemorrheologic group such as pentoxifylline (Trental) increases
    _____
    blood flow.

Match the drug with its drug group:

	Drug		**Drug Group**
___ 20.	gemfibrozil (Lopid)	a.	anticoagulant: LMWH
___ 21.	warfarin	b.	antilipidemic
___ 22.	fluvastatin (Lescol)	c.	Coumarin
___ 23.	aspirin	d.	antiplatelet
___ 24.	enovaparin (Lovenox)	e.	anticoagulant antagonist
___ 25.	vitamin K	f.	thrombolytic
___ 26.	streptokinase		
___ 27.	simvastatin (Zocor)		
___ 28.	protamine sulfate		
___ 29.	reteplase (Retavase)		

Select the appropriate response:

30. Anticoagulants will:
    a. dissolve blood clots.
    b. be administered with thrombolytics to dissolve blood clots.
    c. prevent new clot formation.
    d. promote clot formation.

31. Anticoagulants are recommended for use in all of the following arterial disorders EXCEPT:
    a. coronary thrombosis.
    b. valvular prosthetic devices.
    c. pulmonary embolism.
    d. cerebrovascular accidents.

32. Clients on warfarin therapy have their INR maintained at:
    a. 1.3 to 2.0.
    b. 2.0 to 3.5.
    c. 3.0 to 4.5.
    d. >5.0.

33. More low molecular weight heparins (LMWHs) are being prescribed today. Which one of the following is NOT true regarding LMWHs' use?
    a. can be taken orally
    b. have a lower risk of bleeding than heparin
    c. overdose of LMWH is rare
    d. can be administered by the client at home

34. LMWHs are frequently prescribed to:
    a. prevent cerebral vascular acident or stroke.
    b. enhance the action of warfarin.
    c. prevent deep vein thrombosis following knee or hip replacement.
    d. prevent GI bleeding caused by peptic ulcer.

35. Recently three new LMWHs were approved by the FDA. The one drug that is NOT a LMWH is:
    a. ardeparin (Normiflo).
    b. danaparoid (Organan).
    c. tinzaparin sodium (Innohep).
    d. clopidogrel (Plavix).

36. An example of an antiplatelet agent for angioplasty and acute coronary syndrome is:
    a. abciximab.
    b. protamine sulfate.
    c. warfarin.
    d. aminocaproic acid.

Situation: R.B. was given heparin for early treatment of deep vein thrombophlebitis. Later, warfarin (Coumadin) was prescribed. The next nine questions relate to this situation.

37. Effects of heparin are monitored by which of the following laboratory test(s)?
    a. CBC, WBC
    b. PTT and APTT
    c. PT, INR
    d. BUN

38. Enoxaparin sodium is an anticoagulant used to prevent and treat deep vein thrombosis and pulmonary embolism. This drug is in which drug group?
    a. standard heparin
    b. low molecular weight heparin (LMWH)
    c. oral anticoagulant
    d. thrombolytic

39. In the event of hemorrhage, which of the following medications is most likely to be administered intravenously?
    a. urea
    b. cimetidine
    c. phenytoin
    d. protamine sulfate

40. The protein-binding power of warfarin is:
    a. highly protein-bound.
    b. moderately to highly protein-bound.
    c. moderately protein-bound.
    d. low protein-bound.

41. If R.B. was taking a highly protein-bound drug with warfarin, what might occur?

    a. no drug displacement of warfarin or the highly protein-bound drug

    b. a moderate drug displacement of warfarin, which is moderately protein-bound

    c. drug displacement of warfarin, which is also highly protein-bound

    d. drug displacement of the highly protein-bound drug but not displacement of warfarin

42. Which of the following medications is administered to decrease bleeding and increase clotting for bleeding resulting from excess free Coumadin?

    a. vitamin E

    b. vitamin K

    c. glucagon

    d. calcium gluconate

43. Of the following drugs/foods, which does NOT alter the action of heparin?

    a. aspirin

    b. oral hypoglycemics

    c. phenytoin

    d. Maalox

44. List four specific nursing interventions related to clients receiving anticoagulants:

    a.

    b.

    c.

    d.

45. Your health teaching plan for R.B. would include all of the following EXCEPT:

    a. comply with ongoing laboratory test regimen.

    b. report bleeding.

    c. take aspirin for headache.

    d. use an electric razor.

Situation: E.Z., a 51-year-old in the emergency room, is receiving streptokinase. The next three questions refer to this situation.

46. Assessment for an allergic reaction to streptokinase includes all of the following EXCEPT:

    a. nausea.

    b. hives.

    c. dyspnea.

    d. bronchospasm.

47. Which drug would you have readily available as an antidote?

    a. aminocaproic acid (Amicar)

    b. Apsac

    c. TPA

    d. calcium gluconate

48. Nursing care for E.Z. would include all of the following EXCEPT:

    a. record vital signs and report changes.

    b. observe for signs and symptoms of bleeding.

    c. monitor liver enzymes.

    d. assess for reperfusion dysrhythmias.

Situation: E.B. is 54 years old and is taking isoxsuprine HCl (Vasodilan) for peripheral vascular disease. The next two questions relate to this situation.

49. Vasodilan is also prescribed for treatment of all of the following conditions EXCEPT:

    a. transient ischemic attack.

    b. Raynaud's disease.

    c. Buerger's disease.

    d. Paget's disease.

50. The usual dose of Vasodilan is:

    a. 10–20 mg, tid.

    b. 20–30 mg, tid.

    c. 30–40 mg, tid.

    d. 40–50 mg, tid.

51. You are assessing for signs of adequate blood flow to the extremities. Which one of the following is NOT a sign of impaired blood flow?

    a. pallor

    b. coolness of extremities

    c. heat

    d. pain

52. List four points you would include in E.B.'s health teaching plan:

    a.

    b.

    c.

    d.

Situation: A.B.'s lipid levels are as follows: cholesterol: 258 mg/dl; LDL: 160 mg/dl; and HDL: 38 mg/dl. A.B.'s diet consisted of <30% total daily fat intake and <300 mg of cholesterol daily intake. After 2 months A.B.'s cholesterol was 246 mg/dl, LDL was 150 mg, and the HDL was 42 mg/dl.

What are the desired lipid levels?

53. Cholesterol _____

54. Low-density lipoprotein (LDL) _____

55. High-density lipoprotein (HDL) _____

56. Why did A.B.'s serum lipids not drop after two months of a low-fat and -cholesterol diet?

    a. A.B. most likely did not adhere to the diet.

    b. Diet modification will usually lower cholesterol levels by only 10 to 30%.

    c. A.B. was too obese and lost only 10 pounds.

    d. A.B.'s exercise program should have been increased.

A.B. was prescribed simvastatin (Zocor) 10 mg, daily to take in the evening.

57. A.B. asked if she could eat whatever she wanted because of the Zocor. Your response could be:

    a. "Yes, as long as you take Zocor."

    b. "Diet is not important if you take Zocor and exercise."

    c. "You should maintain a low-fat and low-cholesterol diet and exercise."

    d. "With Zocor, diet is not important but you should lose weight and exercise."

58. There are other antilipemics than the "statins" for reducing cholesterol and LDL levels. Which one of the following is NOT an antilipemic?

    a. cholestyramine resin (Questran)

    b. tolazoline HCl (Priscoline)

    c. gemfibrozil (Lopid)

    d. nicotinic acid (Niacin)

Give the rationale for the nursing interventions related to antilipemics.

	Nursing Interventions	**Rationale**
59.	Monitor the client's blood lipid levels.	59.
60.	Monitor laboratory tests for liver function.	60.
61.	Advise the client to take the antilipemic with sufficient water or with meals.	61.
62.	Instruct the client to have an annual eye examination.	62.
63.	Instruct the client to maintain a low-fat diet.	63.
64.	Inform the client that it may take several weeks for the blood lipid levels to decline.	64.

Critical Thinking Exercises

B.C., age 63, had a myocardial infarction (heart attack). While hospitalized, he received heparin 5000 units subcutaneously q6h for 5 days. On the fifth day, warfarin 5 mg daily was started. His INR is 2.7. His serum cholesterol is 274 mg/dl. Atorvastatin (Lipitor) 10 mg daily was prescribed.

1. How many ml of heparin should B.C. receive per dose?

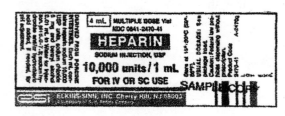

2. Can heparin be given orally? Explain.

3. What laboratory test is used to monitor heparin doses? What is the normal range?

4. How many tablet(s) of warfarin (Coumadin) should the nurse administer to B.C. per day?

NDC 0056-0176-90

DU PONT PHARMACEUTICALS
DUPONT COUMADIN®   **2½ mg**
(crystalline warfarin sodium, U.S.P.)*

HIGHLY POTENT ANTICOAGULANT
WARNING: Serious bleeding results from overdosage. Do not use or dispense before reading directions and warnings in accompanying product information.
USUAL ADULT DOSAGE:
Read accompanying product information.
CAUTION: Federal law prohibits dispensing without prescription.
*Present as crystalline sodium warfarin isopropanol clathrate.
Dispense in a tight, light-resistant container as defined in the U.S.P.
RESEAL CAP TIGHTLY.
PROTECT FROM LIGHT. STORE IN CARTON UNTIL CONTENTS HAVE BEEN USED.
Store at controlled room temperature (59°-86°F, 15°-30°C)
1000 TABLETS

Lot:
Exp:

DuPont Pharmaceuticals
E.I. duPont de Nemours & Co.
Wilmington, Delaware 19898
Made and Printed in U.S.A.   7584/CB

5. What is INR? For what drug is INR ordered? How does INR compare with prothrombin time (PT)?

6. What side effects might occur with the use of warfarin?

7. What is the protein-binding power and half-life of warfarin?

8. A desired serum cholesterol level is _____. Is B.C.'s serum cholesterol level within desired range? Explain.

9. What is atorvastatin? For what reason would B.C. receive the drug?

10. What is the protein-binding power of atorvastatin? What effect is likely to occur when taking warfarin with atorvastatin?

11. What laboratory tests should be monitored while B.C. is taking atorvastatin?

12. What client teaching is essential for B.C.'s drug therapy?

43 Drugs for Gastrointestinal Tract Disorders

Study Questions

Define the following:

1. Adsorbents

2. Cannabinoids

3. Chemoreceptor trigger zone (CTZ)

4. Emetics

5. Opiates

6. Osmotics

7. Purgatives

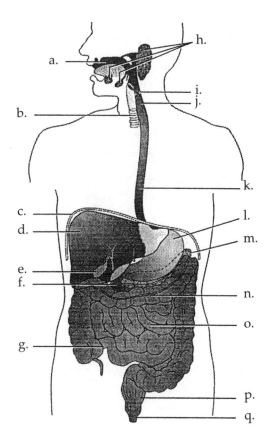

8. Match the following parts of the GI system to the figure above.

    _____ pancreas

    _____ trachea

    _____ salivary glands

    _____ duodenum

    _____ esophagus

    _____ diaphragm

    _____ ileocecal valve (junction)

    _____ anus

    _____ liver

    _____ oral cavity

    _____ superior esophageal sphincter

    _____ stomach

    _____ esophagus

    _____ large intestine (colon)

    _____ gallbladder

    _____ rectum

    _____ small intestine

Complete the following:

9. The two main centers that cause vomiting when stimulated are

_____ and _____ in the medulla.

10. The five groups of prescriptive antiemetics are

_____,

_____,

_____,

_____, and

_____.

11. Many antiemetics act as _____ to dopamine, histamine, and acetylcholine, which are associated with vomiting.

12. Which group of drugs should NOT be used until the cause of vomiting is identified?

_____

13. Nonpharmacologic methods to decrease nausea and vomiting include:

a.

b.

c.

d.

e.

14. Over-the-counter (OTC) antihistamines such as Dramamine and the prescribed scopolamine transderm patch used for motion sickness are best taken _____ minutes before travel.

15. Antiemetic drugs (**are/are not**) recommended for use during pregnancy. (Circle correct answer)

16. Drugs from the _____ group are most commonly used in the treatment of motion sickness.

17. The major ingredient of the cannabinoids is

_____.

18. Diphenidol (Vontrol) is recommended for nausea, vomiting, and vertigo due to _____ disease.

19. In addition to antiemetic effects, Benzquinamide also (**increases/decreases**) cardiac output and blood pressure.

20. The mode of action of charcoal is

_____.

21. The four groups of antidiarrheals are:

_____,

_____,

_____, and

_____.

22. The primary action of the opiates is to

_____.

23. A common side effect of opium preparations is

_____.

24. Use of opiates and opiate-related drugs may lead to drug _____ and

_____.

25. Laxatives promote a _____ stool; cathartics result in a

_____ stool with cramping.

26. The four laxative/cathartic groups are

_____,

_____,

_____, and

_____.

27. Contact laxatives/cathartics increase peristalsis by _____. This group is frequently prescribed prior to _____ and

_____.

28. Emollients act by promoting

_____ in the intestine.

29. Saline cathartics are contraindicated for clients with _____.

30. Bulk-forming laxatives (**do/do not**) cause laxative dependence. (Circle correct answer)

31. Mineral oil absorbs essential _____ soluble vitamins _____, _____, _____, and _____.

Select the appropriate response:

32. Contraindications for the use of laxatives/cathartics include all of the following EXCEPT:
    a. inflammatory disease of the gastrointestinal (GI) tract.
    b. undiagnosed severe pain.
    c. cirrhosis.
    d. bowel obstruction.

Situation: R.T., 50 years old, is receiving prochlorperazine (Compazine) for nausea and vomiting. The next four questions refer to this situation.

33. The usual dose of Compazine varies with form and includes all of the following EXCEPT:
    a. 5–10 mg q3–4h IM PRN.
    b. 10 mg SR q12h po.
    c. 5–25 mg supp PRN.
    d. 25 mg q3h PRN.

34. You assess R.T. for the following side effects of Compazine EXCEPT:
    a. hypotension.
    b. rash.
    c. agitation.
    d. urinary retention.

35. Specific nursing interventions for R.T. would include all of the following EXCEPT:
    a. obtaining history of vomiting.
    b. monitoring vital and bowel signs.
    c. encouraging fluids.
    d. maintaining oral hygiene.

36. R.T.'s health teaching plan would include all of the following EXCEPT:
    a. suggest nonpharmacologic methods.
    b. stay busy to "keep your mind off" the nausea.
    c. avoid driving or operating hazardous machinery.
    d. avoid alcohol.

37. E.P. is taking dronabinol (Marisol) for nausea and vomiting due to cancer chemotherapy. It is recommended that this drug be administered:
    a. 1–3 h before and for 24 h after chemotherapy.
    b. 12 h before and for 24 h after chemotherapy.
    c. q3–4h PRN.
    d. q6h PRN.

38. The usual adult dose of dronabinol is:
    a. 1–2 mg/m^2.
    b. 3–4 mg/m^2.
    c. 5–7 mg/m^2.
    d. 8–10 mg/m^2.

39. Prolonged use of opiate-related drugs may cause all of the following EXCEPT:
    a. tachycardia.
    b. paralytic ileus.
    c. rash.
    d. physical dependence.

40. Antidiarrheals are contraindicated in clients with all of the following EXCEPT:
    a. congestive heart failure.
    b. narcotic dependence.
    c. ulcerative colitis.
    d. liver disease.

41. With severe diarrhea, it is important to monitor all of the following EXCEPT:
    a. electrolytes.
    b. vital signs.
    c. bowel sounds.
    d. white blood count.

42. Which of the following drugs is a somatostatin analogue frequently prescribed for metastatic cancer-related severe diarrhea?

    a. loperamide

    b. octreotide (Sandostatin)

    c. docusate potassium (Dialose)

    d. psyllium

Situation: P.J., age 3, has reportedly ingested about 10 aspirin tablets. He is brought to the emergency room, where ipecac syrup is ordered for P.J. The next four questions refer to this situation.

43. The usual dose of ipecac for P.J. is:

    a. 5 ml.

    b. 10 ml.

    c. 15 ml.

    d. 20 ml.

44. It is best to administer ipecac syrup to P.J. with which of the following?

    a. milk

    b. a carbonated beverage

    c. water

    d. lemonade

45. You anticipate that P.J. will vomit within _____ minutes after taking the medication.

    a. 5–20

    b. 15–30

    c. 30–45

    d. 60

46. Ipecac can be toxic in all of the following situations EXCEPT if:

    a. it does not produce vomiting.

    b. it is absorbed.

    c. it treated with activated charcoal, gastric lavage, and support cardiovascular symptoms.

    d. an extract is administered.

47. It was essential to identify what P.J. ingested because ipecac is contraindicated with all of the following EXCEPT:

    a. ammonia.

    b. paint thinner.

    c. lighter fluid.

    d. phenothiazides.

48. You recommend that a client with diarrhea avoid all of the following foods EXCEPT:

    a. fried foods.

    b. clear liquids.

    c. spiced foods.

    d. hot liquids.

49. Bulk-forming laxatives should be mixed in at least _____ ounces of fluid.

    a. 4

    b. 8

    c. 12

    d. 16

50. You would advise a client with constipation to eat all of the following foods EXCEPT:

    a. cheese.

    b. bran.

    c. grains.

    d. fruit.

51. List four points to include in health teaching plans for clients experiencing constipation:

    a.

    b.

    c.

    d.

Critical Thinking Exercises

L.B., age 85, comes to your clinic complaining, "I can't move my bowels." L.B. lives independently in a studio apartment in housing for the elderly. Two months ago she fell and fractured her hip. She is currently taking digoxin, an antacid, and a narcotic PRN for pain.

1. You know that constipation is a major problem in the elderly. Identify at least six possible contributing factors to L.B.'s problem.

It is determined that L.B. does not have a fecal impaction and bisacodyl 10 mg, po, is ordered.

2. Is this dose within the therapeutic range? At what time of day should this be taken?

3. What is the mode of action of bisacodyl?

4. What is the mode of action of bulk-forming laxatives?

5. What are the contraindications for use of bisacodyl?

6. Describe at least two drug-lab-food interactions. Relate these interactions to L.B.'s current drug regimen.

7. What specific instructions would you discuss with L.B. related to taking bisacodyl?

8. Describe at least six health teaching points to be included in L.B.'s care.

44 Antiulcer Drugs

Study Questions

Define the following:

1. Gastric mucosal barrier (GMB)

2. Gastroesophageal reflux disease (GERD)

3. Histamine$_2$ receptor antagonists

Complete the following:

4. Gastric secretion in the stomach attempts to maintain a pH of _____.

5. The gastric mucosal barrier is a defense against _____ substances.

6. Predisposing factors of peptic ulcers include the following:
   a.

   b.

   c.

   d.

7. The classic symptom of peptic ulcers is
   _____
   _____ pain.

8. The seven groups of antiulcer drugs are:
   a.

   b.

   c.

   d.

   e.

   f.

   g.

9. Antacids neutralize hydrochloric acid; they (**do/do not**) coat the ulcer. (Circle correct answer)

10. Bromo-Seltzer® and Alka-Seltzer® (**are/are not**) recommended for treatment of peptic ulcers. (Circle correct answer)

11. A combination of magnesium and aluminum salts neutralize the gastric acid without causing _____ or _____.

12. Sucralfate (Carafate) is a mucosal _____ drug.

13. All proton pump inhibitors (**can/cannot**) be combined with antibiotics to treat *H. pylori*. (Circle correct answer)

Match the descriptor in Column I with the drugs/ factor in Column II. Use each term only once.

Column I	Column II
____ 14. risk factor for the development of PUD	a. Pepto-Bismol®
____ 15. neutralizes gastric acid	b. magnesium hydroxide
____ 16. inhibition of gastric acid secretion	c. *Helicobacter pylori*
____ 17. associated with recurrence of PUD	d. sucralfate
	e. cimetidine
____ 18. used as mucoprotective in conjunction with NSAIDs	f. omeprazole
	g. misoprostol
	h. smoking
____ 19. binds free protein in base of ulcer	i. antacids
____ 20. eradication rates require addition of this antimicrobial	j. metronidazole
____ 21. causes antidiarrheal effect of some antacids	
____ 22. OTC agent used in combination to eradicate *H. pylori*	
____ 23. H₂ antagonist with multiple drug interactions	

Select the appropriate response:

24. Ideal dosing for antacids is:
    a. with meals and one hour after.
    b. one hour before meals.
    c. one and three hours after meals.
    d. with meals.

25. For best results, antacids should be taken with _____ ounces of water.
    a. 2–4
    b. 4–6
    c. 6–8
    d. at least 8

26. The most popular drugs in the treatment of gastric and duodenal ulcers are:
    a. histamine blockers.
    b. antacids.
    c. pepsin inhibitors.
    d. tranquilizers.

27. The group of drugs used to prevent reflux acid in the esophagus is:
    a. antacids.
    b. pepsin inhibitors.
    c. antacids.
    d. histamine blockers.

Situation: D.Z. is under treatment for peptic ulcers. She is taking Pro-Banthine. The next four questions refer to this situation.

28. Propantheline bromide (Pro-Banthine) belongs to which drug group?
    a. tranquilizers
    b. anticholinergic
    c. suppression of gastric acid
    d. antacids

29. You assess D.Z. for side effects of Pro-Banthine which include all of the following EXCEPT:
    a. bradycardia.
    b. urinary retention.
    c. constipation.
    d. decreased secretions.

30. For best results, you know that Pro-Banthine should be taken:
    a.   with meals.
    b.   before meals.
    c.   two hours after meals.
    d.   with two glasses of fluid.

31. D.Z. is also receiving an antacid. The best time to administer the antacid is:
    a.   with belladonna.
    b.   two hours before meals.
    c.   two hours after meals.
    d.   with meals.

Situation: J.M., a senior in college, complains of pain in the stomach after eating. He reports that pain is intensified at exam time. The health care provider recommends an antacid. The next four questions relate to this situation.

32. J.M. is taking cimetidine (Tagamet). Side effects include all of the following EXCEPT:
    a.   headache.
    b.   gynecomastia.
    c.   nausea.
    d.   loss of libido.

33. Cimetidine may cause an increase in which of the following laboratory tests?
    a.   platelets
    b.   BUN
    c.   WBC
    d.   blood sugar

34. As you review J.M.'s current drug therapy for his many conditions, you are aware of cimetidine's enhancement of all of the following drugs EXCEPT:
    a.   oral anticoagulants.
    b.   laxatives.
    c.   phenytoin (Dilantin).
    d.   propranolol (Inderal).

35. The enhancement of these drug effects is due to cimetidine:
    a.   inhibiting hepatic metabolism.
    b.   inhibiting renal excretion.
    c.   prolonging the half-life.
    d.   displacing protein binding sites.

36. A new synthetic prostaglandin analog used for the prevention and treatment of peptic ulcer is:
    a.   Pepcid.
    b.   Zantac.
    c.   Indocin.
    d.   Cytotec.

37. Which of the following drugs inhibits gastric acid secretions to a greater extent than histamine antagonists?
    a.   Prilosec
    b.   Pepcid
    c.   Pro-Banthine
    d.   Quarzan

38. Which of the following drugs are proton pump inhibitors?
    a.   esomeprazole (Nexium)
    b.   pantoprazole (Protonix)
    c.   rabeprazole (Aciphex)
    d.   all of the above

Give the rationale for the nursing interventions related to antacids.

Nursing Interventions	Rationale
39. Assess renal function.	39.
40. Monitor urinary pH, calcium and phosphate levels, and electrolytes.	40.
41. Avoid administering antacids with other oral drugs.	41.
42. Shake suspension well before administering.	42.
43. Instruct the client to report pain, coughing, and vomiting of blood.	43.
44. Instruct the client not to take the drug with meals.	44.
45. Instruct the client to notify the health care provider if constipation or diarrhea occurs.	45.
46. Advise the client to check antacid labels for sodium content.	46.
47. Instruct the client in use of relaxation techniques.	47.

Drug Chart: Complete the drug chart for omeprazole (Prilosec):

Proton Pump Inhibitor

Drug Name Omeprazole (Prilosec) **Pregnancy Category:**	**Dosage:**	Assessment and Planning	Nursing Process
Contraindications:	**Drug-Lab-Food Interactions:**		

Pharmacokinetics:
Absorption:
 	
Distribution: PB:
 	
Metabolism: t½:
 	
Excretion:
	Pharmacodynamics:
	PO: Onset:
	
	          Peak:
	
	          Duration:
		Interventions	

Therapeutic Effects/Uses: **Mode of Action:**		Evaluation	
Side Effects:	**Adverse Reactions:** **Life-Threatening:**		

Critical Thinking Exercises

S.S., 63 years old, has a high-stress job as county judge. He complains of abdominal distress after eating. He is currently taking aluminum hydroxide (Amphojel) 600 mg q4h while awake.

1. Is the dose within the therapeutic range? What are the nursing responsibilities, if any?

2. What is the mode of action of aluminum hydroxide? Compare its action with that of ranitidine and sucralfate.

3. Describe drug-drug and drug-lab interactions.

4. What is a common side effect of aluminum hydroxide?

5. What is the major contraindication for use of aluminum hydroxide? Indications for cautious use?

6. What dietary recommendations would you make to S.S.?

7. Describe important health teaching to include with S.S.

45 Drugs for Disorders of the Eye and Ear

Study Questions

Complete the following (word search) for questions 1–15. Circle your responses.

```
A  A  F  O  R  E  I  G  N  B  O  D  Y  L  B
M  C  N  O  S  M  O  T  I  C  S  S  S  I  L
A  G  O  U  M  N  U  A  M  N  R  C  I  W  O
V  L  Q  N  R  D  K  N  S  A  I  L  N  S  O
N  A  P  H  J  I  C  U  E  G  U  V  C  N  D
O  U  T  M  Y  U  A  T  E  Y  F  A  R  E  S
I  C  T  G  W  Q  N  L  O  X  D  J  E  R  U
T  O  F  K  W  K  P  C  S  P  Z  G  A  D  G
A  M  K  L  E  O  B  U  T  H  M  V  S  L  A
R  A  P  P  L  C  I  I  Y  I  B  E  E  I  R
D  H  P  C  X  B  B  U  Z  Y  V  S  J  H  D
Y  O  Y  W  P  E  N  J  I  T  M  I  I  C  Y
H  C  M  G  E  S  A  E  R  C  E  D  T  A  S
E  M  Y  D  R  I  A  T  I  C  S  R  A  I  C
D  C  E  R  A  L  U  C  O  A  R  T  N  I  S
```

1. Topical anesthetics are used during an eye exam and prior to removal of a _____ _____ from the eye.

2. Lubricants are used to moisten contact lenses and/or to replace
   _____.

3. Miotics are used to lower _____ pressure.

4. Carbonic anhydrase inhibitors were developed as _____.
   They are effective in treating _____
   _____.

5. Osmotic drugs are used to (**decrease/increase**) the amount of aqueous humor. (Circle correct answer)

6. Mannitol is contraindicated for clients with the condition of _____
   or _____.

7. Diabetic clients taking Glyrol require monitoring of _____.

8. The drug group used to paralyze the muscles of accommodation is _____.

9. BufOpto atropine is frequently used for refraction in _____.

10. Instruct clients with glaucoma to avoid atropine-like drugs because they (**decrease/increase**) intraocular pressure. (Circle correct answer)

11. Antiinfectives are used to treat infections of the eye, including inflammation of the membrane covering the eyeball and lining the eyelid known as _____.

12. Drugs that interfere with production of carbonic acid leading to decreased aqueous humor formation and decreased intraocular pressure belong to the group

    _____.

13. Beta adrenergic blockers used to treat open-angle glaucoma may (**increase/decrease**) the effect of systemic beta blockers. (Circle correct answer)

14. The group of eye medications contraindicated in persons allergic to sulfonamides is

    _____.

15. The volume of vitreous humor is reduced by the _____ group of drugs.

16. The group of drugs that dilates pupils is

    _____.

17. Describe at least four client teaching suggestions for clients with disorders of the eye:

    _____,

    _____,

    _____, and

    _____.

18. A side effect of the antiinfectives is _____ of nonsusceptible organisms.

19. Carbonic anhydrase inhibitors (CAIs) (**are/are not**) first-line drugs in the treatment of open angle glaucoma. (Circle correct answer)

20. Renal calculi formation is a side effect of the drug group _____.

21. For optimal results from irrigation of the ear, direct visualization of the _____

    _____ is required.

22. Solutions commonly used to irrigate the ear are _____,

    _____, and

    _____.

23. Preparations that are helpful in loosening wax from the ear canal belong to the group

    _____.

24. Combination products, in general, (**are/are not**) preferred over single-action drugs. (Circle correct answer)

25. Herbal remedies that alter coagulation (**are/are not**) generally stopped prior to ophthalmic surgery. (Circle correct answer)

Select the appropriate response:

Situation: E.Q. is receiving Isopto-Eserine eye drops for treatment of glaucoma. The next four questions refer to this situation.

26. You would assess E.Q. for possible side effects including all of the following EXCEPT:
    a. headache.
    b. nausea.
    c. brow pain.
    d. decreased vision.

27. Nursing care for E.Q. would include all of the following EXCEPT:
    a. monitoring for postural hypotension.
    b. assessing for increased bronchial secretions.
    c. increasing fluid intake.
    d. maintaining oral hygiene.

28. Health teaching for this medication includes all of the following EXCEPT:
    a. first dose to be administered by health care provider.
    b. follow-up with tonometry readings.
    c. increase caloric intake.
    d. importance of regular medical supervision.

29. Administration of eyedrops requires all of the following EXCEPT:
    a. client to be in supine position.
    b. gentle pressure on nasolacrimal canal.
    c. prevention of dropper contamination.
    d. instruct client to report eye pain immediately.

Situation: C.G., seven years old, is receiving Bactrim (trimethoprim/sulfamethoxazole) for an inner-ear infection. The next three questions refer to this situation.

30. Nursing care for C.G. includes all of the following EXCEPT:

    a.   obtaining culture and sensitivity.

    b.   assessing for hematuria and oliguria.

    c.   restricting fluids.

    d.   monitoring intake and output.

31. Your health teaching plan for C.G. includes all of the following EXCEPT:

    a.   if feeling better, stop medication after seven days.

    b.   encourage client to eat yogurt to maintain intestinal flora.

    c.   avoid getting water in ears.

    d.   take medication for full 10 days.

32. When administering eardrops to C.G., the nurse should perform all of the following EXCEPT:

    a.   pulling down and back on auricle.

    b.   pulling up and back on auricle.

    c.   tilting head to unaffected side.

    d.   instilling medication at room temperature.

Critical Thinking Exercises

D.Z. is 82 years old and comes to the office for her regular glaucoma follow-up. She denies any problems but admits to having blurred vision. She reports self-administration of pilocarpine, 2 gtt q4h.

1.   Describe the mode of action of pilocarpine. Why is it used in the treatment of glaucoma?

2.   Is the dose that D.Z. reports taking within the therapeutic range? What are the related nursing responsibilities, if any?

3.   What is the most likely cause of D.Z.'s blurred vision?

4.   Systemic absorption of pilocarpine is contraindicated in what conditions?

5.   As part of your assessment, you ask D.Z. about any side effects of pilocarpine. What side effects would you include?

6. What client teaching would be appropriate for D.Z.?

7. What are the advantages and disadvantages of the Ocusert system? Do you think this would be appropriate for D.Z.? State your rationale.

46 Drugs for Dermatologic Disorders

Study Questions

Match the description with the correct term:

Term	Description
____ 1. macule	a. round, palpable lesion, < 1 cm in diameter
____ 2. vesicle	
____ 3. plaques	b. hard, rough, raised lesion; flat on top
____ 4. papule	c. flat lesion with varying colors
	d. raised lesion filled with fluid and < 1 cm in diameter

Complete the following:

5. Moderate-type acne is commonly treated with
   _____
   and _____.

6. Oral _____ and
   topical _____
   may be prescribed for severe-type acne.

7. Megadoses of vitamin A (**are/are not**) a valid therapy for treating acne. (Circle correct answer)

8. Maintenance doses of tetracycline in the treatment of acne are (**lower than/higher than/ the same as**) initial therapy. (Circle correct answer)

9. Psoriasis affects _____ to _____% of the US population and usually appears before age
   _____.

10. Psoriatic scales are loosened with
    _____.

11. Drugs used to treat psoriasis include
    _____ _____
    products and _____.

12. Drug-induced dermatitis may vary from a rash to life-threatening skin eruptions such as
    _____ syndrome
    (large blisters in the oral mucosa, pharynx, eyes, and viscera).

13. A hypersensitive reaction to a drug is caused by _____ _____.

14. Contact dermatitis is caused by
    _____ or
    _____ irritation.

15. A moderately severe sunburn is an example of a _____-degree burn.

16. Antibacterials frequently applied to burned skin areas are _____,
    _____,
    _____,
    and _____.

17. The drug indicated for treatment of venereal warts (and not as effective against the common wart) is _____.

18. Keratolytic agents are used in the treatment of
    _____.

19. Label the structures of the skin as follows:
    a.
    b.
    c.
    d.
    e.
    f.
    g.
    h.

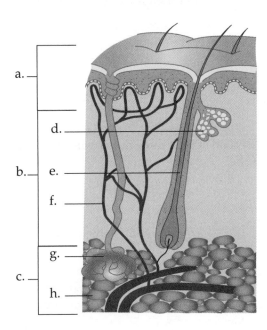

Select the appropriate response:

Situation: J.T., 18 years old, is receiving treatment for acne vulgaris. The next four questions refer to this situation.

20. The usual dose of tetracycline for this condition is:
    a. 250–500 mg bid.
    b. 500–1000 mg bid.
    c. 500 mg qd.
    d. 1 g qd.

21. A major side effect of tetracycline is:
    a. urinary retention.
    b. photosensitivity.
    c. hypersensitivity.
    d. hepatotoxicity.

22. Health teaching for J.T. about tetracycline includes all of the following about drug interactions EXCEPT:
    a. tetracycline increases the effects of oral anticoagulants.
    b. tetracycline decreases the effects of oral contraceptives.
    c. tetracycline increases the effects of oral contraceptives.
    d. antacids decrease absorption.

23. Areas for general health teaching with J.T. include all of the following EXCEPT:
    a. not to use harsh skin cleansers.
    b. to report adverse effects.
    c. eat diet high in fiber.
    d. alert health care provider if pregnant or possibly pregnant.

24. To control severe psoriasis, the anticancer drug _____ may be prescribed.
    a. benzoyl
    b. tretinoin
    c. etrectinate
    d. methotrexate

25. Contact dermatitis may be treated with all of the following drugs EXCEPT:
    a. Burow's solution.
    b. calamine.
    c. Percocet.
    d. Benadryl.

26. Antipruritics used in the treatment of contact dermatitis include all of the following EXCEPT:
    a. Peri-Colace.
    b. Periactin.
    c. Decadron.
    d. Aristocort.

27. The amount and rate of absorption of topical glucocorticoids depend on all of the following EXCEPT:
    a. percent of drug concentration.
    b. fluid intake.
    c. drug composition.
    d. skin area involved.

28. Drugs known to cause alopecia include all of the following EXCEPT:

   a.   antineoplastic agents.

   b.   sulfonamides.

   c.   selected NSAIDs.

   d.   oral contraceptives.

29. The FDA-approved drug for the treatment of baldness is:

   a.   Tretonoin.

   b.   Methoxsalen.

   c.   Etrectinate.

   d.   Minoxidil.

30. Finasteride (Propecia) is used to treat male pattern baldness. In higher doses, this drug is used to treat which of the following?

   a.   benign prostatic hypertrophy

   b.   gastroesophageal reflux

   c.   migraine headache

   d.   impotence

Critical Thinking Exercises

C.S., 2 years old, has a third-degree burn over her right chest and shoulder and second-degree burns on her hands caused when she hit the handle of a pot filled with boiling water. Mafenide acetate is ordered to be applied to chest, shoulder, and hands, $\frac{1}{16}$-inch layer, bid.

1. What are the depths and characteristics of second- and third-degree burns?

2. Is the dose within the therapeutic range for C.S.?

3. Describe the mode of action of mafenide acetate. What other drug is used for the prevention and treatment of sepsis in second- and third-degree burns?

4. Identify important nursing assessments for C.S.

5. Explain at least three nursing interventions for C.S.

6. What possible side effects of mafenide acetate would you discuss with C.S.'s family?

7. What health teaching is important to include with C.S.'s family?

47 Endocrine Pharmacology: Pituitary, Thyroid, Parathyroids, and Adrenals

Study Questions

With these definitions, locate and circle the term in the word search below.

a. Growth hormone hypersecretion after puberty

b. Anterior pituitary gland

c. Initials for adrenocorticotropic hormone

d. Initials for antidiuretic hormone

e. Severe hypothyroidism in children

f. Ductless glands that produce hormones

g. Growth hormone hypersecretion during childhood

h. Cortisol hormone secreted from the adrenal cortex

i. Pituitary gland

j. Aldosterone hormone secreted from the adrenal cortex

k. Severe hypothyroidism in adults

l. Posterior pituitary gland

m. Toxic hyperthyroidism because of hyperfunction of the thyroid gland

n. T_4 hormone secreted by the thyroid gland

o. T_3 hormone secreted by the thyroid gland

```
T F M L E I B G H M X Y I B P N L D E T S A X
B T R I I O D O T H Y R O N I N E N M E C Q L
S H Y P O P H Y S I S B E A C L S S L G D O A
V Y R U I M T S D L A N G J E L I F L I P M P
H R T A C T H I K N I G R B T T A F O T Y R U
F O I D B S A U O X X A A C N D E C J L K D I
I T Z H G F U I O H J L L A M O I P L I B A K
R O O B E X S R S U T B G I D T E T O N E B Y
J X I B N S Y E Y A M I N P R A V J H Q O D G
Y I P M E H T O B J G I D O O L K M O L A S N
A C R E T I N I S M S W C M V D I U Q E R Y M
W O G N A T M J K T Y O O T A L U G E R U H I
B S P D L I Y R E G L U C O C O R T I C O I D
P I Y O V R I A K A C R O M E G A L Y E M N F
A S O C Y L P U R A E B H T E S S C P O L Q C
L K K R E I E E E R S O N A L T E L N E F S O
R E J I U G N E U R O H Y P O P H Y S I S V L
J H I N N I C E Y A M K N P E A V J H Q O D E
S T C E M Y X E D E M A T A C L S F L G T O R
P A D E N O H Y P O P H Y S I S S L F E M N W
```

Complete the following:

1. The pituitary gland is divided into two major lobes, the _____ and _____.

2. The growth hormone of the anterior pituitary gland (adenohypophysis) acts on all body tissues, especially the _____ and _____.

3. A child with a growth hormone (GH) deficiency may develop _____, and another child with an oversecretion of GH may develop _____.

4. Prolonged GH therapy can antagonize insulin secretion, thus causing the condition _____.

5. The tropic hormone from the anterior pituitary gland that stimulates the release of glucocorticoids and mineralocorticoids is _____.

6. The thyroid-stimulating hormone (TSH) drug Thytropar is the diagnostic drug to differentiate between _____ and _____ hypothyroidism.

7. The drug used in the treatment of diabetes insipidus is _____.

8. List four nursing interventions associated with drugs for disorders of the pituitary gland:

    a.

    b.

    c.

    d.

9. The two thyroid hormones secreted by the thyroid gland are _____and _____.

10. Thyroid crisis (storm) may proceed to _____ and _____.

11. A serious adverse effect of antithyroid drugs is _____.

12. The parathyroid gland regulates the _____ (electrolyte) levels in the blood.

13. Parathyroid hormone is useful in treating _____ and the synthetic calcitonin drug is used to treat _____.

14. Tetany symptoms as a result of severe hypocalcemia include _____, _____, and _____.

Match the description from Column II with the applicable term in Column I:

Column I		Column II	
____ 15. hyperglycemia	a.	adrenal hyposecretion
____ 16. buffalo hump	b.	adrenal hypersecretion
____ 17. hypoglycemia		
____ 18. seizures		
____ 19. fatigue		
____ 20. impaired clotting		
____ 21. cataract formation		
____ 22. hypotension		
____ 23. hypervolemia		
____ 24. peptic ulcer		

Complete the following:

25. The glucocorticoid drugs are administered orally, parenterally, and topically. The _____ route is not recommended for administration of glucocorticoids.

26. Drugs for adrenocortical insufficiency contain both glucocorticoids and mineralocorticoids; however, for use as an antiinflammatory and immunosuppressive drug, the (**glucocorticoids/mineralocorticoids**) are generally prescribed. (Circle correct answer)

27. As the result of severe head trauma or allergic reaction, the glucocorticoid used to treat a severe inflammatory response is

_____.

28. When a glucocorticoid is to be discontinued, the drug dose should be (**stopped immediately/tapered over several days**). (Circle correct answer)

State rationale: _____
_____
_____.

29. An increase in aldosterone (a mineralocorticoid) leads to _____ and

_____.

30. Fludrocortisone (Florinef) is an oral form of mineralocorticoid. It can cause a negative nitrogen balance; therefore, it is recommended that a diet high in

_____ be included.

Select the appropriate response:

Situation: E.A., 49 years old, is under treatment for hypothyroidism. E.A. is taking levothyroxine (Synthroid) 100 µg/day. The next seven questions refer to this situation.

31. The usual maintenance dose of Synthroid is:
    a. 25–50 µg/d.
    b. 50–200 µg/d.
    c. 200–300 µg/d.
    d. 300–500 µg/d.

32. Clients report feeling the effect of levothyroxine (Synthroid) within:
    a. 3–4 days.
    b. 4–7 days.
    c. 1–3 weeks.
    d. 3–5 weeks.

33. You assess E.A. for symptoms of hyperthyroidism. Which one of the following is NOT a symptom of hyperthyroidism?
    a. tachycardia
    b. tinnitus
    c. chest pain
    d. excess sweating

34. All of the following drugs are known to interact with Synthroid EXCEPT:
    a. anticoagulants.
    b. oral antidiabetics (hypoglycemics).
    c. digitalis.
    d. acetaminophen.

35. You suggest that E.A. avoid foods that can inhibit thyroid secretion, including all of the following EXCEPT:
    a. strawberries.
    b. cabbage.
    c. radishes.
    d. string beans.

36. The best time of the day to take Synthroid is:
    a. before breakfast.
    b. with breakfast.
    c. after breakfast.
    d. with lunch.

37. E.A.'s health teaching plan would include all of the following EXCEPT:
    a. take medication at same time each day.
    b. wear medic-alert information device.
    c. increase food and fluid intake.
    d. avoid over-the-counter (OTC) drugs.

Situation: L.T., 56 years old, is taking prednisone for an exacerbation of arthritic knee pain. The next eight questions refer to this situation.

38. The usual dose of prednisone is:
    a. 0.5–6 mg/d.
    b. 5–60 mg/d.
    c. 60–100 mg/d.
    d. 100–125 mg/d.

39. While L.T. is taking this medication, close monitoring of which of the following is required?
    a. sodium
    b. potassium
    c. hemoglobin
    d. hematocrit

40. You assess L.T. for the side effects of pred-
    nisone, which may include all of the following
    EXCEPT:
    a.   increased blood sugar.
    b.   edema.
    c.   hypertension.
    d.   rash.

41. The best time to take this drug is:
    a.   before meals.
    b.   with meals.
    c.   one hour after meals.
    d.   at bedtime.

42. Which one of the following drugs does NOT
    alter the action of prednisone?
    a.   NSAIDs, including aspirin
    b.   potassium-wasting diuretics
    c.   acetaminophen
    d.   oral anticoagulants

43. You advise L.T. to avoid a potassium loss by
    eating all of the following foods EXCEPT:
    a.   nuts.
    b.   vegetables.
    c.   fruits and dried fruits.
    d.   milk products.

44. Specific nursing interventions for L.T. include
    all of the following EXCEPT:
    a.   monitor vital signs.
    b.   monitor the signs and symptoms of
         hypokalemia.
    c.   obtain complete medication history.
    d.   follow physical therapy regimen.

45. Which one of the following would NOT be
    included in the health teaching plan for L.T.?
    a.   take glucocorticoids only as ordered
    b.   wear medic-alert device or carry card
    c.   force fluids
    d.   do not abruptly stop medication

*Give the rationale for the nursing interventions
related to glucocorticoid drug administration.*

Nursing Interventions	Rationale
46. Monitor vital signs.	46.
47. Montior weight after taking a cortisone preparation for more than 10 days.	47.
48. Monitor laboratory values, especially electrolytes and blood glucose.	48.
49. Instruct the client to take the cortisone preparation at mealtime or with food.	49.
50. Advise the client to eat foods rich in potassium.	50.
51. Instruct the client not to abruptly discontinue the cortisone preparation. Drug dose is normally tapered.	51.
52. Report changes in muscle strength and signs of osteoporosis.	52.
53. Teach client to report signs and symptoms of drug overdose.	53.

54. When an herbal laxative such as cascara or senna and herbal diuretics such as celery seed or juniper are taken with a corticosteroid, what imbalance may occur?

    a. hypervolemia

    b. hyperkalemia

    c. hypokalemia

    d. hypernatremia

55. Ginseng taken with a corticosteroid may cause:

    a. CNS depression.

    b. CNS stimulation and insomnia.

    c. serum potassiuan excess.

    d. counteraction of the effects of the corticosteroid.

56. A drug that is used to diagnose adrenal gland dysfunction is:

    a. metyrapone (Metopirone).

    b. mitotane (Lysodren).

    c. ketoconazole (Nizoral).

    d. prednisolone.

Critical Thinking Exercises

M.N., age 52, is taking prednisone 10 mg, tid, for an acute neurologic problem. She also has a cardiac problem and is taking digoxin 0.25 mg daily, and hydrochlorothiazide 25 mg daily. Her serum potassium level is 3.2 mEq/L.

1. Is M.N.'s prednisone dosage within normal range?

2. From which drug groups are digoxin and hydrochlorothiazide?

3. What electrolyte imbalance(s) may occur with the use of prednisone and hydrochlorothiazide?

4. How could M.N.'s electrolyte imbalance be avoided?

5. What effect could hypokalemia have on digoxin? Explain.

6. With continuous use of prednisone, what systemic side effects may occur?

7. What are the similarities and differences among prednisone, prednisolone, and dexamethasone?

8. When discontinuing prednisone, why is it recommended that the doses be tapered?

9. What should the nurse include in the teaching plan for M.N.?

48   Antidiabetic Drugs

Study Questions

Define the following:

1. Diabetes mellitus

2. Insulin

3. Hypoglycemic reaction

4. Type 1 diabetes

5. Type 2 diabetes

6. Ketoacidosis

7. Lipodystrophy

8. Polydipsia

9. Polyphagia

10. Polyuria

Complete the following:

11. Diabetes mellitus is characterized by the three Ps: _____, _____, and _____.

12. Drugs that may cause an increased blood sugar and hyperglycemia in the prediabetic are _____, _____, and _____.

13. The beta cells of the pancreas normally secrete _____ units of insulin per day.

14. The two groups of antidiabetic agents are _____ and _____.

15. Insulin injection sites are rotated to prevent _____.

16. The only type of insulin that may be administered intravenously (IV) is _____.

17. Insulin requirements may vary. Usually (**less/more**) insulin is needed with increased exercise and (**less/more**) insulin is needed with infections and high fever. (Circle correct answers)

18. Combination insulins are commercially premixed; e.g., Humulin 70/30. Some clients who need insulin (**would/would not**) benefit from commercially combined insulins. (Circle correct answer)

19. The insulin most closely related to human insulin is (**pork insulin/ beef insulin**) (Circle correct answer)

20. List six signs and symptoms of hypoglycemic (insulin) reaction:

    a.

    b.

    c.

    d.

    e.

    f.

21. List six signs and symptoms of diabetic ketoacidosis (hyperglycemia):

    a.

    b.

    c.

    d.

    e.

    f.

22. In maturity-onset, or type 2, diabetes, the oral antidiabetic (hypoglycemic) drug group that stimulates beta cells to secrete more insulin is _____. For juvenile-onset, or type 1, diabetes, oral hypoglycemics (**are/ are not**) prescribed. (Circle correct answer)

Match the terms with their definitions.

Terms		Definitions
____ 23. NPH insulin	a.	oral hypoglycemic drug group
____ 24. lipoatrophy		
____ 25. sulfonylureas	b.	hyperglycemic hormone that stimulates glyco-genolysis
____ 26. glucagon		
____ 27. Lispro insulin		
	c.	intermediate-acting insulin
	d.	long-acting insulin
	e.	tissue atrophy
	f.	rapid-acting insulin

Select the appropriate response:

28. Site and depth of insulin injection affect absorption. Insulin absorption is greater when given in:

    a. ventrogluteal and abdominal areas.

    b. deltoid and abdominal areas.

    c. deltoid and rectus femoralis.

    d. dorsogluteal and ventrogluteal.

29. Lipoatrophy is a complication that occurs when insulin is injected repeatedly in one site. The physiologic effect that occurs is:

    a. a depression under the skin surface.

    b. a raised lump or knot on the skin surface.

    c. rash at a raised area on the skin surface.

    d. bruising under the skin.

Situation: R.K., 47 years old, takes insulin daily at 0700: 6 units of U100 regular, and 14 units of U100 NPH. R.K.'s daily insulin dosage is regulated by using the sliding-scale (insulin coverage) method. He uses a glucometer at 1100, 1600, and bedtime (2100) to check his blood sugar. The next seven questions refer to this situation.

30. Insulin must be stored:

    a. in the refrigerator.

    b. in a cool place.

    c. wrapped in aluminum.

    d. in the light.

31. Prior to use, the nurse/client must prepare the insulin by:

    a. shaking the bottle well.

    b. allowing air to escape from the bottle.

    c. rolling the bottle in hand.

    d. adding diluent to the bottle.

32. You are going to give R.K. his 0700 insulin. You prepare:

    a. two separate injections.

    b. one injection; draw up regular insulin first.

    c. one injection; draw up NPH insulin first.

    d. one injection; draw up both simultaneously and mix well.

33. In administering R.K.'s insulin, you use the following syringe:

    a.   2 ml (cc) syringe.

    b.   5 ml syringe.

    c.   U40 insulin syringe.

    d.   U100 insulin syringe.

34. R.K. needs to develop a "site rotation pattern" for insulin injections. The American Diabetic Association suggests all of the following EXCEPT:

    a.   choose an injection site for a week.

    b.   inject insulin each day at the injection site at 1 ½ inches apart.

    c.   change the injection area of the body every day.

    d.   with two daily injection times, use the right side in the morning and the left side in the evening.

35. You review with R.K. that regular insulin peaks in _____ hours.

    a.   ½ to 1

    b.   2–6

    c.   6–8

    d.   8–10

36. NPH insulin peaks in _____ hours.

    a.   1–2

    b.   2–6

    c.   6–12

    d.   12–15

37. At what time is R.K. most likely to have a hypoglycemic reaction?

    a.   1300 and 1900

    b.   1200 and 2000

    c.   1000 and 2200

    d.   0900 and 1500

38. Lantus is a new long-acting insulin. Which one of the following statements regarding Lantus is NOT correct?

    a.   It is given in the evening and has a 24-hour duration of action.

    b.   Some clients complain of pain at the injection site.

    c.   It is safe because hypoglycemia cannot occur.

    d.   It is available in a 3 ml cartridge insulin pen.

39. Insulin resistance can be a problem for some clients taking insulin. There are various causes for insulin resistance such as:

    a.   antibody development in clients taking animal insulin over time.

    b.   clients taking increased units of Humulin insulin over time.

    c.   clients who are allergic to dust, mold, cat dander, and other allergens.

    d.   clients with diabetes who are malnourished.

40. A method to determine if the client has insulin resistance is:

    a.   chemistry laboratory tests.

    b.   urinalysis to check for glucose.

    c.   skin test with different insulin preparations.

    d.   history of other allergies.

41. Insulin pump, though expensive, has become popular in the management of insulin. This method of insulin delivery:

    a.   is more effective for use by the type 2 diabetic client.

    b.   is effective in lessening long-term diabetic complications.

    c.   can be used with modified insulins (NPH) as well as regular insulin.

    d.   can be used with the needle inserted at the same site for weeks.

*Give the rationale for the nursing interventions
related to insulin administration.*

| Nursing Interventions | Rationale |

Nursing Interventions   **Rationale**

42. Monitor blood glucose levels. 42.

43. Instruct the client to report signs and symp- 43.
toms of "insulin shock" (hypoglycemic
reaction).

44. Inform the client to have available orange 44.
juice or sugar-containing drink if a hypoglycemic reaction occurs.

45. Instruct the client to check the blood sugar 45.
daily.

46. Instruct the client to adhere to the prescribed 46.
diet.

47. Instruct family members on how to administer 47.
glucagon by injection for a hypoglycemic
reaction.

48. Advise the client to obtain a medical alert card 48.
or tag.

Situation: A.B., a 55-year-old obese female, has type
2 diabetes mellitus. She is receiving the oral hypoglycemic (antidiabetic) drug acetohexamide
(Dymelor) daily in the morning. The next seven
questions refer to this situation.

49. The oral hypoglycemic action is to:
    a. increase the number of insulin cell
       receptors.
    b. increase the number of insulin-produc-
       ing cells.
    c. replace receptor sites.
    d. replace insulin.

50. Recommended guidelines for use of oral
    antidiabetics or hypoglycemics include all of
    the following EXCEPT:
    a. onset at age 40 or older.
    b. diagnosis of diabetes mellitus for < 10
       years.
    c. fasting blood sugar less than 200 mg/dl.
    d. normal renal and hepatic function.

51. A.B. asks if Dymelor is oral insulin. The best
    response would be:
    a. "Yes, it is the same as injected insulin,
       except it is taken orally."
    b. "Yes, it is similar; however, hypoglyce-
       mic reactions (insulin shock) do not
       occur with Dymelor."
    c. "No, it is not the same as insulin, and
       Dymelor can be taken even when the
       blood sugar remains greater than 250
       mg/dl."
    d. "No, it is not the same as insulin.
       Dymelor can be used only when there is
       some beta cell function."

52. Acetohexamide (Dymelor) is a _____
    hypoglycemic drug. Its duration of action is
    _____ than tolbutamide (Orinase).
    a. short-acting; shorter
    b. intermediate-acting; longer
    c. intermediate-acting; shorter
    d. long-acting; longer

53. Which of the following will NOT cause a drug interaction with acetohexamide?
    a. aspirin
    b. anticoagulants
    c. antacids
    d. anticonvulsants

54. Contraindications for the use of oral antidiabetic (hypoglycemic) drugs include the following EXCEPT:
    a. pregnancy.
    b. breastfeeding.
    c. severe infection.
    d. type 2 diabetes.

55. Health teaching related to acetohexamide includes avoidance of alcohol due to:
    a. poor nutritional state.
    b. decreased mental alertness.
    c. inability to drive.
    d. increases half-life of acetohexamide.

56. List four health teaching points to be included for clients taking insulin:

    a.

    b.

    c.

    d.

57. List four health teaching points to be included for clients taking oral antidiabetic (hypoglycemic) drugs:

    a.

    b.

    c.

    d.

58. The effects of second-generation sulfonylureas include all of the following EXCEPT that:
    a. they have a less hypoglycemic potency than first-generation sulfonylureas.
    b. effective doses are less than the first-generation sulfonylureas.
    c. they have less displacement from protein-binding sites by other highly protein-bound drugs.
    d. they increase tissue response and decrease glucose production by the liver.

59. New antidiabetic drugs are the nonsulfonylureas. These drugs are used to control serum glucose levels following a meal. They act by:
    a. raising the serum glucose following a meal.
    b. increasing the absorption of glucose from the small intestine.
    c. causing a hypoglycemic reaction.
    d. decreasing hepatic production of glucose from stored glycogen.

60. Correct the incorrect responses in question 59.

    _____
    _____
    _____

61. An example of a nonsulfonylurea is acarbose (Precose), an alpha-glucosidase inhibitor, that acts by:
    a. increasing insulin production; thus, it can cause a hypoglycemic reaction.
    b. inhibiting digestive enzyme in the small intestine, which releases glucose from the complex carbohydrate in the diet (less sugar is available).
    c. stimulating the beta cells to produce insulin.
    d. increasing glucose metabolism.

62. The newest class of nonsulfonylureas is thiazolidinedione group. This group of oral antidiabetics does not promote insulin release, but:
    a. promotes absorption of glucose from the large intestine.
    b. increases the uptake of glucose in the liver and small intestine.
    c. increases insulin sensitivity for improving blood glucose control.
    d. decreases glucose utilization.

63. The first thiazolidinedione, troglitazone (Rezulin), was removed from the market in 2000. The reason for this drug's withdrawal by FDA is that it caused:
    a. kidney failure.
    b. severe liver dysfunction.
    c. blood dyscrasia.
    d. peptic ulcer.

64. Clients taking thiazolidinedione drugs such as pioglitazone (Actos) and rosiglitazone (Avandia) should have which laboratory test(s) monitored?
    a. BUN
    b. hemoglobin and hematocrit
    c. cardiac enzyme
    d. liver enzyme

65. Herb-drug interaction needs to be assessed by clients taking herbs and antidiabetic agents. Ginseng and garlic taken with insulin or oral antidiabetic drugs:
    a. can decrease the effect of insulin and antidiabetic drugs, thus causing a hyperglycemic effect.
    b. can lower the blood glucose level, thus causing a hypoglycemic effect.
    c. may decrease insulin requirements.
    d. can be taken with insulin without any effect but can cause a hypoglycemic reaction with oral antidiabetic drugs.

Drug Chart: Complete the drug chart for glimepiride (Amaryl):

Second-Generation Sulfonylurea

Drug Name Glimepiride (Amaryl) Pregnancy Category:	Dosage:	Assessment and Planning	
Contraindications:	Drug-Lab-Food Interactions:		
Pharmacokinetics: *Absorption:* *Distribution:* PB: *Metabolism:* t½: *Excretion:*	Pharmacodynamics: *PO:* Onset: Peak: Duration:	Interventions	Nursing Process
Therapeutic Effects/Uses: Mode of Action:			
Side Effects:	Adverse Reactions: Life-Threatening:	Evaluation	

Critical Thinking Exercises

N.V., age 39, was diagnosed with diabetes mellitus 15 years ago. Symptoms of diabetes occurred three weeks after he had hepatitis. N.V. takes 42 units of NPH and 8 units of regular insulin daily (see drug labels).

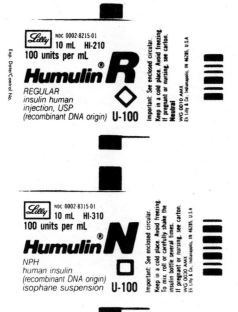

1. Why do you think N.V. is taking Humulin regular and Humulin NPH insulins rather than the same type of insulin from pork and beef?

2. Indicate on the insulin syringe the amount of regular and NPH insulin that is to be given.

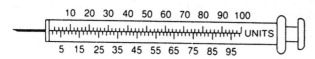

3. Could N.V. take sulfonylurea or nonsulfonylurea instead of insulin? Explain.

4. What instruction should you give N.V. concerning insulin injection sites?

5. N.V. weighs 72 kg. As a diabetic, is N.V. within the "average" insulin dosage?

6. When is it likely that N.V. might have an hypoglycemic (insulin) reaction?

7. What are the signs and symptoms of hypoglycemic reaction of which N.V. should be aware?

8. What client teaching strategies should the nurse include for N.V.?

9. What effect can occur when mixing two insulins together, such as NPH and regular insulins, and Lente and regular insulins?

10. What teaching points should you give N.V. and significant others about reversing the onset of a hypoglycemic reaction?

49 50 Drugs Associated With the Female Reproductive Cycle I and II

Study Questions

Define the following:

1. Labor augmentation

2. Labor induction

3. Oxytocic

4. Progesterone

5. Surfactant

6. Tocolytic therapy

Complete the following:

7. Therapeutically prescribed drugs such as antibiotics (**are/are not**) ordered in lower doses during pregnancy. (Circle correct answer)

8. Maternal physiological changes during pregnancy that affect drug dosing include:

_____,

_____,

_____,

_____, and

_____.

9. Highly protein-bound drugs (**do/do not**) readily cross the placenta. (Circle correct answer)

10. The placenta (**does/does not**) act as a protective barrier to keep substances from going from the maternal circulation into the fetal circulation. (Circle correct answer)

11. Drug excretion is (**slower/faster**) in the fetus than in the mother. (Circle correct answer)

12. The mechanism by which drugs cross the placenta is similar to the way drugs infiltrate _____ tissue.

13. Important factors that determine the teratogenicity of any drug ingested during pregnancy include _____,

_____, and

_____.

14. Surfactant is composed of the two phospholipids _____ and

_____.

15. The L/S ratio is a predictor of

_____.

16. a. Administration of the glucocorticoid _____ (name), preferably _____ hours (but less than _____ days) prior to delivery in the _____ week of gestation or before, may promote fetal lung maturity.

b. The goal in administering glucocorticoids during this time is

_____

_____

_____.

237

17. Surfactant replacement therapy in the new-born with Survanta or Exosurf Pediatric is administered in one of two modes: _____ and _____.

18. In addition to the delivery of an uncompromised infant, the two primary treatment goals in pregnancy-induced hypertension (PIH) are prevention of _____ and _____.

19. The first and second most common complaints of pregnancy associated with client requests for medication are _____ and _____.

20. The nonanemic pregnant woman is generally instructed to increase iron intake from a recommended _____ mg nonpregnant daily allowance to _____ mg, while anemic clients generally receive _____ mg of elemental iron. These supplements generally continue following delivery for _____ weeks. Clients who exhibit a validated iron-deficiency anemia generally respond to iron supplementation therapy within _____ weeks as evidenced by increased _____ (blood test) values.

21. Vitamin and mineral megadoses during pregnancy (will/will not) improve health. (Circle correct answer)

22. Cultural variations exist in regard to the use of prenatal vitamins. One country in which some individuals are known to view vitamins as a hot food to avoid in pregnancy is _____ .

23. When a pregnant woman is taking methadone, she should not detoxify prior to _____ weeks gestation due to increased risk of _____.

24. When narcotic-agonists are administered during labor, birth should be anticipated to occur within _____ hours, or after _____ hours following administration, to prevent _____.

25. When pain medication is administered to the laboring client using the IV route, the medication should be given at the (beginning/end) of the contraction. (Circle correct answer)

Argue in support of giving the medication at the time period selected.
_____
_____
_____

Match the letter(s) of the substances in Column II with the associated adverse effect(s) in Column I.

Adverse Effects		Substance
_____ 26. increased risk of spontaneous abortion	a.	alcohol
	b.	caffeine
_____ 27. smaller head circumference without catch-up	c.	cocaine
	d.	heroin
	e.	methadone
_____ 28. hypertonicity, tremulousness in baby	f.	barbiturates
	g.	tobacco/nicotine
_____ 29. abruptio placenta and premature delivery	h.	tranquilizer
_____ 30. degenerative placental lesions		
_____ 31. decreased intervillous blood flow		
_____ 32. inadequate maternal calorie and protein intake		
_____ 33. ataxia, syncope, vertigo		
_____ 34. rapidly crosses placenta and causes CNS depression in the fetus		

Select the appropriate response:

35. During pregnancy, the amount of iron neces-
    sary is _____ that of the prepregnant state.
    a. the same as
    b. twice
    c. triple
    d. one-half

36. Side effects of iron include all of the following
    EXCEPT:
    a. nausea.
    b. constipation.
    c. epigastric pain.
    d. jaundice.

37. You advise the client that all of the following
    foods are rich in iron EXCEPT:
    a. lettuce.
    b. liver.
    c. spinach.
    d. cereal.

38. The pregnancy RDA for folic acid is:
    a. 100–400 µg.
    b. 400–800 µg.
    c. 800–1000 µg.
    d. 1000–1200 µg.

39. Folic acid deficiency in pregnancy may result
    in any of the following EXCEPT:
    a. placenta previa.
    b. spontaneous abortion.
    c. neural tube defects.
    d. small for gestational age (SGA) infant.

40. List four nonpharmacological measures to
    decrease nausea and vomiting during early
    pregnancy:
    a.

    b.

    c.

    d.

41. List four nonpharmacological measures
    preferred for the management of heartburn:

    a.

    b.

    c.

    d.

42. Antacids may cause drug interactions with all
    of the following EXCEPT:
    a. digitalis.
    b. anticonvulsants.
    c. tetracyclines.
    d. iron.

43. To enhance both drugs' effectiveness, iron and
    antacids should be administered:
    a. at the same time.
    b. two hours apart.
    c. the antacid first.
    d. the iron first.

44. The drug most commonly selected and
    ingested by clients during pregnancy is:
    a. ferrous sulfate.
    b. Tigan.
    c. Mylanta.
    d. acetaminophen.

45. Use of aspirin late in pregnancy is related to
    all of the following EXCEPT:
    a. increased maternal blood loss at delivery.
    b. low birth weight infant.
    c. increased risk of anemia.
    d. decreased hemostasis in newborn.

Situation: W.C. is receiving a beta-sympathomimetic drug to stop her preterm labor. The next four questions refer to this situation.

46. Nursing interventions for W.C. include all of the following EXCEPT:

    a. monitoring maternal and fetal vital signs every 15 minutes when receiving IV dose.

    b. monitoring daily weight.

    c. being alert to hypoglycemia and hypokalemia in newborn delivered within five hours of discontinuing the drug.

    d. restricting all fluids.

47. The health care provider should be notified of any of the following findings EXCEPT:

    a. auscultated dysrhythmias.

    b. respirations greater than 30/minute.

    c. systolic blood pressure greater than 100.

    d. fetal baseline heart rate greater than 180 bpm.

48. Health teaching for W.C. includes all of the following EXCEPT:

    a. palpitations are uncommon.

    b. notify health care provider of frequent contractions while on drug.

    c. consult health care provider before taking any other medications.

    d. take medications as directed.

49. You instruct W.C. that if she misses a dose of the tocolytic medication, she should:

    a. call the health care provider.

    b. take the missed dose if less than one hour overdue.

    c. double the next scheduled dose.

    d. take no action about the missed dose.

50. A client receiving magnesium sulfate for PIH requires all of the following nursing interventions EXCEPT:

    a. continuous fetal monitoring and documentation every 15 minutes.

    b. airway suction equipment readily available.

    c. antidote calcium gluconate at bedside.

    d. monitoring vital signs every 4 hours.

51. While caring for a client on magnesium sulfate, you notify the health care provider of any of the following EXCEPT:

    a. absence of patellar reflexes.

    b. respiration greater than 15/minute.

    c. absent bowel sounds.

    d. change in affect.

52. Magnesium toxicity is manifested by which of the following?

    a. rapid decrease in blood pressure and respiratory paralysis

    b. rapid increase in blood pressure and respiratory paralysis

    c. sudden fever and somnolence

    d. muscle pain and excessive weight gain

53. The client being treated during labor with magnesium sulfate asks how long she will need this drug. Your best response is that the drug will probably be discontinued:

    a. at the time of delivery.

    b. 1–4 hours after delivery.

    c. 24 hours after delivery.

    d. 48–72 hours after delivery.

54. List four teaching goals for clients with PIH:

    a.

    b.

    c.

    d.

55. Systemic drug groups used during labor include all of the following EXCEPT:

    a. NSAIDs.

    b. narcotic agonists.

    c. ataractics.

    d. mixed narcotic agonists-antagonists.

56. If the client is abusing narcotics, a drug commonly used during labor is:

    a. Nembutal.

    b. Atarax.

    c. Stadol.

    d. Demerol.

Situation: S.R., a primipara, is 3 cm dilated and requesting medication for pain. The next eight questions refer to pain control in labor.

57. You are aware that many factors influence the choice of pain control. The MOST important factor is:
    a. intensity of contractions.
    b. amount of time likely until delivery.
    c. frequency of contractions.
    d. client requests.

58. You know that with the use of barbiturates in labor:
    a. delivery time is unpredictable.
    b. narcotic antagonists will not counteract respiratory depression.
    c. narcotics offer more complete relief.
    d. active labor is the most appropriate time for their use.

59. Client teaching for S.R. about an analgesic includes all of the following EXCEPT:
    a. expected effects on labor.
    b. expected effects on newborn.
    c. expected time delivery will occur.
    d. restrictions placed on her mobility.

60. Regional anesthesia planned for S.R.'s delivery may result in:
    a. increase in urge to push.
    b. elimination of all pain and pressure.
    c. increased intensity of contractions.
    d. inhibition of urge to push.

61. Nursing interventions for a client receiving regional anesthesia include the following EXCEPT:
    a. monitoring for increased blood pressure.
    b. positioning client on left side.
    c. assuring appropriate prehydration.
    d. having atropine readily available.

62. Which of these statements about the client who receives continuous lumbar epidural block anesthesia in repeated doses is accurate?
    a. Prior to 8 cm dilation, there is a risk of arresting the first stage of labor.
    b. The method is suitable for vaginal delivery, but not for a C/S delivery because the density of the block cannot be manipulated.
    c. Following injection, the client needs to be placed flat immediately to assure dispersion of the local anesthetic toward the diaphragm.
    d. Each time the injection procedure occurs, documentation must be complete.

63. In relation to uterine contractions, spinal anesthesia should be administered:
    a. before.
    b. during.
    c. immediately after.
    d. 1–2 minutes after.

64. An example of a local anesthetic metabolized by pseudocholinesterase is:
    a. chloroprocaine (Nesacaine).
    b. mepivacaine (Carbocaine).
    c. lidocaine (Xylocaine).
    d. bupivacaine (Marcaine).

65. You assess a client receiving local anesthetic for side effects including all of the following EXCEPT:
    a. palpitations.
    b. "metallic taste" in mouth.
    c. nausea.
    d. hypertension.

Situation: Your client J.M. is having an IV oxytocin induction at 41+ weeks gestation. The next four questions refer to this situation.

66. You collect all of the following baseline data on J.M. EXCEPT:
    a. pulse and blood pressure.
    b. deep tendon reflexes.
    c. uterine activity.
    d. fetal heart rate.

67. You observe J.M. and her fetus for side effects and adverse reactions to oxytocin, including which of the following?
    a. tetanic uterine contractions
    b. fetal tachycardia
    c. generalized muscular weakness
    d. urinary retention

68. As a precaution, you have the antidote drug _____ readily available.
    a. prednisone
    b. Narcan
    c. calcium gluconate
    d. magnesium sulfate

69. In addition, you monitor J.M. for signs of uterine rupture, including any of the following EXCEPT:
    a. hypertension.
    b. sudden increased pain.
    c. hemorrhage.
    d. loss of fetal heart rate.

70. A delivered client who bled heavily is receiving ergonovine maleate (Ergotrate). Checking her orders, you notice the statement, "Watch carefully for signs of ergot toxicity (ergotism)." You recall that ergotism includes all of the following signs EXCEPT:
    a. pain in arms, legs, and lower back.
    b. muscular weakness.
    c. hallucinations.
    d. hypertension.

71. Discuss the possible complication(s) of administering methylergonovine maleate (Methergine) during labor and/or prior to the delivery of the placenta. _____
    _____
    _____
    _____

Critical Thinking Exercises

S.B., 38 years old, mother of a five- and seven-year-old, currently 28 weeks pregnant and recently separated from her husband of 15 years, frantically calls the OB triage unit from the department store in the local mall where she works. She states that she has been unable to get through to her doctor's office due to busy signals and interruptions by her customers. She states that she is "terrified I might be going into labor." She stutters that she had a "baby born early" five years ago. She desperately says, "This just can't be happening again, I have no benefits yet in this job. My husband has been out of work due to his company downsizing; he has no benefits either. Plus he is keeping company with another lady in the meantime, which is why we are apart. Please, please tell me what to do now." She further conveys, "I'm having contractions about every eight minutes and I feel like there is some kind of pressure inside my lower belly. My children are in school and daycare and will be home three hours from now."

1. If you were the nurse in the OB triage unit who received this call from S.B., what data supplied in her brief telephone history support a diagnosis of PTL?

2. What additional data would you collect during evaluation at the triage unit to support the accuracy of the preliminary PTL diagnosis?

3. What risk factors are present that increase the likelihood of the PTL diagnosis for S.B.?

4. Considering that (1) you are talking with S.B. on the phone while she is at work; (2) your preliminary data analysis supports that S.B. is indeed at risk for PTL; and (3) S.B. has not been able to reach her personal health care provider; how would you counsel S.B.? (Note: Consider the biopsychosocial implications for the children and employer while constructing your plan of action.)

5. S.B.'s PTL contractions are not relieved following the conservative measures you suggested. Her doctor agrees that S.B. should be directed to the OB triage unit for further evaluation. The decision is made following interview, fetal monitoring, and cervical examination that S.B. is a suitable candidate for tocolytic therapy. Indicate four findings that, had they been present, would have contraindicated tocolytic therapy for S.B.:

6. You share with S.B. that the goal in tocolytic therapy is to **(increase/decrease)** (Circle correct answer) the level of _____ in order to _____ labor, to create time for maturation _____ within the _____ environment.

7. The treatment plan for S.B. calls for the use of SQ terbutaline. Considering that the goal of the tocolytic therapy is to depress or quiet the myometrial contractions, (1) what information would you need to record on the fetal monitoring strip and/or document on the agency-specified flow sheet; (2) what information could you gain from the monitor strip in tracking the effectiveness of the tocolytic therapy; and (3) what findings would you determine important to convey specifically to the health care provider in addition to documenting it?

8. Criteria for determining that SQ tocolytic therapy is successful for S.B. are:

   Contractions decrease to _____ apart

   Cervical dilatation and/or effacement
   _____

9. Assume the decision is made for S.B. to continue on oral terbutaline after discharge. The purpose of this oral therapy is to

   _____

   _____.

10. The high-risk unit nurse has worked with S.B. to address identified knowledge deficits, emphasizing the importance of medication compliance. S.B. states that she knows she must take her oral terbutaline on a schedule but questions, "If I go back to the store to work, it is hard to get free to go to the bathroom and to the breakroom for fluids; it is also difficult to get my purse, as we aren't allowed to keep purses at the counter where I work."

   (a) Discuss some strategies for how S.B. could handle her medication needs while at work.

   (b) If S.B. realizes that she missed taking a dose within the past hour and calls for advice, you correctly tell her to:

   _____
   _____
   _____
   _____

51 Drugs Associated with the Postpartum and the Newborn

Study Questions

Define the following:

1. Lactation

2. Prolactin

3. Puerperium

4. Rh immune globulin D

5. Rh sensitization

6. Titer

Complete the following:

7. Two drugs commonly used for the relief of perineal pain due to episiotomy/laceration are _____ and
_____.

8. Three common drugs for the relief of hemorrhoids are _____,
_____, and _____.

9. High levels of _____
are necessary to initiate the onset of lactation.

10. Explain the purpose/action of a stool softener ordered for a postpartum client:

_____
_____
_____

11. You have an order to administer Bisacodyl USP at lunch so the client can swallow it with her milk. Determine your response to the question and support your answer below.

Administer as ordered

_____ (check if correct)

Question the order

_____ (check if correct)

Why _____
_____
_____

12. A postpartum client with a repaired fourth-degree laceration has benzocaine topical spray. She asks if she can also use a heat lamp on her perineum for additional comfort.

What would you tell her?

_____

Support your answer.

_____
_____
_____

13. What is the correct procedure for application of an ointment (e.g., Anusol) to hemorrhoids in a postpartum client?

_____

_____

What is the rationale for the method you described?

_____

_____

_____

What would possibly occur if you managed this client as if she were a nonmaternity client?

_____

_____

_____

14. The lubricant laxative _____ should not be given with meals or immediately after.

15. Erythromycin ophthalmic ointment is prescribed as prophylactic treatment for gonococcal _____ due to *Neisseria gonorrhea* which, if left untreated, can cause _____ in the newborn.

16. Describe three approaches the nurse may use to evaluate the effectiveness of products used to relieve discomfort during the postpartum period:

   a.

   b.

   c.

   Support your selection of one of the three previously described approaches as the most important to acknowledge.

   _____

   _____

17. One form of administering "iced witch hazel compresses" is pouring witch hazel over ice and placing a packet of 4 x 4 absorbent pads into the solution prior to placing one at a time against the perineal tissue. Given that a newly delivered postpartum client has an alteration in skin integrity due to her episiotomy with risk for infection, how could the nurse instruct the mother to apply the compresses against her perineum and keep both skin and compress as clean as possible?

   _____

   _____

   _____

   _____

18. A postoperative cesarean birth mother states she "has not passed gas" since delivery. While assessing this client, the nurse observes the abdomen is distended. As a part of the assessment, the nurse should evaluate for the presence of _____ sounds. To do this assessment correctly, the nurse places a stethoscope _____ (where). In addition, this client may be ordered to receive _____ (medication name) to help relieve her distention. Describe the process by which this medication must be ingested _____, followed by _____ oz. water. If the client remains distended, uncomfortable, and does not pass gas, what additional type of medication will likely be employed?

   _____

Select the appropriate response:

19. Relief of "afterbirth pains" may be a concern for the multiparous postpartum client. As the nurse, you appropriately assess for all of the following EXCEPT:

   a. bowel function with codeine sulfate.

   b. gastrointestinal irritation with acetaminophen.

   c. respiratory status with meperidine.

   d. respiratory status with morphine sulfate.

20. Estrogenic substances once used to suppress lactation are less popular today due to:

   a. increased incidence of phlebitis.

   b. nephrotoxic effects of drugs.

   c. high costs of drugs.

   d. potential cardiogenic effects.

21. Today, lactation suppression therapy is most commonly:

    a. Deladumone.

    b. nonpharmacologic.

    c. Parlodel.

    d. Tace.

22. Which of the following nonpharmacologic measures is NOT recommended for lactation suppression?

    a. binder x 5 days postdelivery

    b. ice x 15 minutes prior to feeding

    c. q2–3h feedings of 15 minutes or more

    d. restricted fluids x 3 days postdelivery

23. Prior to administration of Rh immune globulin D, an appropriate nursing intervention is to:

    a. monitor blood pressure.

    b. check for signed informed consent.

    c. administer an analgesic.

    d. confirm that patient is Rh+.

24. The best time(s) to administer the standard dose of Rh immune globulin D is:

    a. at 28 weeks gestation.

    b. before amniocentesis and at 38 weeks gestation.

    c. at 28 weeks gestation and again within 72 hours after delivery.

    d. after chorionic villus sampling and at 38 weeks gestation.

25. A microdose of Rh immune globulin D is indicated after:

    a. amniocentesis.

    b. abortion of <12 weeks.

    c. abortion of >16 weeks.

    d. chorionic villus sampling.

26. Rubella can be a devastating infection to the fetus depending on which of the following?

    a. gestational age at exposure

    b. sex of fetus

    c. severity of maternal infection

    d. all of the above

27. Which of the following is NOT a commonly reported side effect of the "-caine" drugs used in local or topical agents ordered for postpartum clients?

    a. stinging

    b. burning

    c. itching

    d. petechiae

28. Which of the following is NOT a commonly reported side effect of the hydrocortisone local or topical drugs used in products ordered with occlusive dressings for postpartum clients?

    a. burning

    b. alopecia

    c. folliculitis

    d. swelling

29. The newborn is given which of the following ophthalmic ointments immediately after birth?

    a. erythromycin

    b. bacitracin

    c. gentamicin

    d. penicillin

30. Correct instillation of the eye ointment used for newborn eye prophylaxis is:

    a. directly onto the cornea.

    b. into the inner canthus of the eye.

    c. into the lower conjunctival sac.

    d. under the upper eyelid.

31. Client teaching regarding drugs administered to the neonate immediately after birth includes:

    a. swelling of eyes usually disappears in the first 24–48 hours.

    b. it is a legal requirement.

    c. the injection is not painful for the baby.

    d. all of the above.

32. Which of the following statements about vitamin K administration to the newborn is NOT correct?

    a. The newborn did not receive adequate vitamin K transplacentally.

    b. The newborn is unable to synthesize due to limited intestinal flora.

    c. If the mother is on anticoagulants or anticonvulsants, a lower dose is needed.

    d. If the mother is on anticoagulants or anticonvulsants, a higher dose is needed.

Critical Thinking Exercises

M.F., a newly delivered postpartum client, is transported from the labor/delivery suite to the postpartum unit where you are a staff nurse. Another nurse fills in and receives the transfer report about M.F.; you overhear a comment that M.F. is Rh-negative and rubella-negative.

1. What information from M.F.'s past and current history must you consider to address the question of whether she will be a candidate for Rh immune globulin D?

2. If M.F. is a Rh immune globulin D candidate, what are two potential knowledge deficits M.F. might exhibit?

3. M.F. asks you what the Coombs test is and why her caregivers seem so interested in this particular test. You explain to M.F. that it is a test that screens for the presence of (**antigen/antibodies**) (Circle correct answer) to the Rh (**antigen/antibodies**) (Circle correct answer). The outcome is expressed as an (**antigen/antibody**) (Circle correct answer) titer.

You continue to explain that M.F. is referred to as sensitized or nonsensitized. You tell her that Rh immune globulin D candidates are (**sensitized/nonsensitized**) (Circle correct answer) Rh-negative clients. The goal is, through the use of Rh immune globulin D, to _____ her from becoming _____ by suppressing the active (**antigen/antibody**) (Circle correct answer) response by coating the (**antigen/antibody**) (Circle correct answer).

Match items in Column II with those in Column I.

Column I

Test

_____ 4. Direct Coombs Test

_____ 5. Indirect Coombs Test

Column II

Test Subject

a. mother

b. baby

Result

_____ 6. Negative indirect Coombs

_____ 7. Positive indirect Coombs

Interpretation

a. Antigen-antibody immunologic reaction has occurred (as shown by reaction of rabbit immune serum to antibodies coating the RBCs; an agglutination reaction; some quantity of antibodies is present)

b. Antigen-antibody immunologic reaction has not occurred (no antibodies are present)

Substance

_____ 8. antigen

_____ 9. antibody

Descriptor

a. Protein developed by the body in response to presence of a foreign body; found in plasma

b. Invader; usually a protein

Rh System

_____ 10. Rh+ individual

_____ 11. Rh– individual

*Relationship to the D Antigen**

a. Red cells contain D antigen

b. Red cells lack D antigen

*(most commonly implicated antigen in maternal-fetal iso-immunization)

12. M.F. needs to understand that if the baby she just delivered is Rh (**positive/negative**) (Circle one), she could, based on factors from her history and/or this pregnancy, labor, and delivery, develop anti-D (**antibodies/antigens**) (Circle one) as an outcome; therefore, her caregiver's goal is to ascertain that the D (**antibody/antigen**) (Circle one) is _____. Likewise, a laboratory report of the baby's blood type and sensitization status (based on detection of red blood cells coated with antibody) is reviewed. If M.F. and the baby both test (**positive/negative**) (Circle one) for sensitization, general practice is for M.F. to receive Rh immune globulin D within _____ hours postpartum to prevent iso-immunization which could present difficulties for a fetus in a subsequent pregnancy.

13. There are safety measures that the nurse must observe when he or she administers Rh immune globulin D to a client. Among these is agreement of lot numbers on the vial with cross-match lab slips; match between the ID band and the lab slip numbers; signed consent; return of vial and lab slips; and careful screening for known hypersensitivity reactions to immune globulins. Discuss the rationale for these safety measures.

14. M.F.'s history indicated she is rubella-negative. You check her chart and find that she is listed in one section of the chart as rubella-immune and in another section of the chart as rubella-susceptible. Describe appropriate nursing action to resolve the discrepancy.

16. Based on her history, what would you convey to M.F. as her postdischarge responsibility in regard to the rubella vaccine she received?

15. Assume that M.F. is to receive both Rh immune globulin D and rubella vaccine. What would you explain to M.F. about the interaction of the two drugs?

52 Drugs Related to Women's Health and Disorders

Study Questions

Define the following:

1. Estrogen replacement therapy (ERT)

2. Hormone replacement therapy (HRT)

3. Progestin

4. Oral contraceptives

Complete the following:

5. The two main types of oral contraceptives are:
   a. _____-_____
      combination products, "the pill."
   b. _____-_____
      products, the "mini pill."

6. List the serious side effects (ACHES) associated with oral contraceptives:
   A =
   C =
   H =
   E =
   S =

7. The newest combination product designed to give low doses of both hormones with minimal side effects is/are the

   _____.

8. The mini pill acts primarily by

   _____.

9. The nurse can accurately explain to a client that the Depo-Provera injection acts by
   _____ and
   _____ to make
   the uterine wall mucosa less hospitable for

   _____.

10. A 17-year-old G.P. postpartum client has decided to use long-acting injectable Depo-Provera as a birth control method because of the three-month interval and the fact that she often "forgot" to take her oral contraceptives. The nurse gives the first injection on October 10 and advises the client that she will need to schedule subsequent injections for January 10, April 10, July 10, and again on October 10. The nurse circles these dates on the small purple wallet reminder card supplied with the product. The client responds, "Thanks! This is great and easy to remember." Comment on the way the nurse chose to handle follow-up injection planning and documentation and expected standards of practice.

11. Long-lasting implantable contraceptives, such as Norplant, have recently become less favored by clients primarily due to reported side effects—most notably:

    a.   protracted gastrointestinal distress.

    b.   visible and mobile rods in upper arm.

    c.   infection at insertion site.

    d.   swollen tender breasts.

12. Match characteristics associated with the investigational drugs in Column II with the drugs in Column I. Some Column II characteristics may be used more than once.

Column I	Column II
____ 12.1 misoprostol	a. chemotherapeutic agent
____ 12.2 methotrexate	b. ulcer agent
	c. destabilizes uterine lining
	d. creates contractions that shed uterine lining in 24 hours
	e. given one week after the first drug

13. Which of the following modes of action is NOT correct for emergency contraception?

    a.   delays ovulation

    b.   interferes with hormones for implantation

    c.   causes an abortion

    d.   interferes with tubal transport of embryo

14. Which of the following statements about intrauterine devices is NOT correct?

    a.   Increased menstrual bleeding and cramps are side effects.

    b.   They are appropriate for all women.

    c.   ParaGard's active ingredient is copper.

    d.   Progestasert is reinserted annually.

15. Common symptoms associated with premenstrual syndrome (PMS) are:

    a.

    b.

    c.

    d.

    e.

    f.

16. List four points to be included in a client's health teaching plan for premenstrual syndrome:

    a.

    b.

    c.

    d.

17. The four most common physical changes associated with menopause are:

    a.

    b.

    c.

    d.

18. The most widely used treatment for the relief of menopause-associated changes is

    _____.

19. The goal of hormone replacement therapy (HRT) has some bearing upon the dosage. (**true/false**) (Circle correct answer)

20. Estrogen (**is/is not**) thought to cause breast cancer. (Circle correct answer)

Select the appropriate response:

21. The advantages of oral contraceptives include all of the following EXCEPT:
    a. relative safety.
    b. ease of use.
    c. low cost.
    d. high degree of effectiveness.

22. Which of the following does NOT contraindicate the use of oral contraceptives?
    a. breast cancer
    b. coronary artery disease
    c. pregnancy, confirmed or suspected
    d. emphysema

23. Considering common concerns of teenage girls, which of these oral contraceptive benefits would be most likely to motivate use?
    a. protection against breast disease
    b. dysmenorrhea relief
    c. reduction in iron-deficiency anemia
    d. decreased risk of endometrial cancer

24. Considering concerns common to teenage girls in this society, which of these oral contraceptive-associated issues or side effects would be most likely to deter use?
    a. decreased tearing (dry eyes)
    b. risk of interaction with other drugs
    c. weight gain
    d. recommendation against smoking

25. Cautious use of oral contraceptives is recommended with all of the following EXCEPT:
    a. women over 35 who smoke; over 40 nonsmokers.
    b. diabetes.
    c. grand multiparity.
    d. epilepsy.

26. The major risk associated with the use of leuprolide acetate for the treatment of endometriosis is:
    a. depression.
    b. decreased libido.
    c. cardiac arrhythmias.
    d. potential loss of bone density.

27. Which of the following is correct regarding the administration of Lupron?
    a. Shake reconstituted product until clear; use 2 cc syringe.
    b. Reconstituted product is stable for 48 hours; use supplied syringe.
    c. Reconstituted solution is "milky"; use supplied syringe.
    d. Store product in refrigerator; use 2 cc syringe.

28. When teaching a client about the correct use of nafarelin acetate (Synarel nasal solution), include all EXCEPT which of the following?
    a. Precise guidelines must be followed.
    b. Medication is expensive; need to plan for six months' expenses to avoid interruptions in therapy.
    c. Clear nasal passage and administer spray in one nostril only.
    d. Avoid use of nasal decongestant sprays.

29. Which of the following is NOT a contraindication to hormone replacement therapy (HRT)?
    a. impaired renal function
    b. history of thromboembolic disorder
    c. impaired liver function
    d. uncontrolled hypertension

Situation: N.M. has been taking Tri-Levlen for contraception. The next seven questions refer to this client situation.

30. N.M. reports a variety of side effects. The side effect NOT due primarily to an excess in estrogen is:
    a. acne.
    b. nausea.
    c. fluid retention.
    d. breast tenderness.

31. N.M. reports the most troubling side effects to be weight gain and depression. You know that these are usually associated with:
    a. estrogen deficiency.
    b. excess of progestin.
    c. progestin deficiency.
    d. excess of estrogen.

32. As you listen to N.M.'s current drug history, you are alert to drugs that interact with oral contraceptives and are NOT concerned with her reported use of:
    a. phenytoin.
    b. caffeine.
    c. vitamins.
    d. theophyllines.

33. Which of the following laboratory values would NOT be expected to change for N.M.?
    a. thyroid and liver function
    b. blood glucose
    c. triglycerides
    d. BUN

34. N.M. calls and reports missing one pill. Your best response is to advise her to:
    a. take no special action; resume pills next morning.
    b. discard missed tablet, take next tablet on schedule and use secondary form of contraception until menses.
    c. discard current pill pack and start a new package of pills.
    d. do a pregnancy test; report the results.

35. The family planning nurse would be correct to tell N.M. to stop taking her oral contraceptive pills and notify her health-care provider if she experiences:
    a. increased vaginal discharge.
    b. severe headaches.
    c. lighter/shorter periods.
    d. menstrual cramping.

36. N.M. asks you to review the advantages and disadvantages of oral contraceptives. List four of each:

Advantages	**Disadvantages**
a.	a.
b.	b.
c.	c.
d.	d.

37. List four major points to include in health teaching plans for oral contraceptives:
    a.

    b.

    c.

    d.

Situation: M.B. is taking danazol (Danocrine) for the treatment of endometriosis. The next three questions refer to this client situation.

38. Which of the following is NOT true about this drug?
    a. It is a pituitary gonadotropin-inhibiting agent.
    b. Menses cease during therapy.
    c. Ovulation occurs during therapy.
    d. It has no estrogenic action.

39. Which of the following is NOT a side effect of Danocrine?
    a. weight gain
    b. rash
    c. decrease in breast size
    d. hot flashes

40. M.B. asks what are the chances of conception during a cycle? The most accurate response is:
    a. 4%.
    b. 6%.
    c. 8%.
    d. 10%.

Situation: E.H. is on hormone replacement therapy (HRT) for menopause. The next six questions relate to this client situation.

41. This therapy is treatment for all of the following EXCEPT:
    a. gastrointestinal disturbances.
    b. vasodilation.
    c. decreased risk of cardiovascular disease.
    d. prevention of osteoporosis.

42. Use of Progestin in HRT is to decrease:
    a. endometrial hyperplasia.
    b. risk of endometrial cancer.
    c. risk of breast cancer.
    d. risk of cervical cancer.

43. The most common dosing for natural estrogen is:
    a. 0.325 mg/d for days 1–25.
    b. 0.625 mg/d for days 1–25.
    c. 1.2 mg/d for days 1–25.
    d. 1.2 mg/d for days 1–15.

44. The most common dosing of progesterone (Provera) is:
    a. 5 mg for days 1–25.
    b. 10 mg/d for days 1–25.
    c. 10 mg/d for days 15–25.
    d. 15 mg/d for days 1–25.

45. Which of the following is NOT an advantage of the Estraderm transdermal system?
    a. less expensive than tablets
    b. applied 2 x /week for 3 weeks using rotation of sites
    c. drug absorbed directly into bloodstream
    d. results in less nausea and vomiting

46. List four factors to be included in your health teaching with clients using HRT:
    a.

    b.

    c.

    d.

Critical Thinking Exercises

During her GYN intake interview with the nursing case manager at her company's new health-care clinic, C.W., age 55, states, "I seem to be having more discomfort when I have intercourse. I don't lubricate when I want and need to; if Charlie hurries me, it is downright painful. This is probably my problem, but Charlie thinks that after a 35-year marriage, I just don't really want to have sex any more."

Sarah, the nurse, compiles a few more facts about C.W. for review and consideration. In addition to her dyspareunia, C.W. has urinary frequency and urgency, leukorrhea, itching, thinning vaginal epithelium with a glazed looking appearance and minimal elasticity upon speculum examination. C.W. is Caucasian, thin overall, and reports no periods for nearly two years. She has no history of vaginal infections; her hygiene is excellent.

1. The most likely physiologic explanation for C.W.'s current experiences during intercourse is _____. Given the fact that C.W. has had no periods for more than a year, Sarah knows that menopause (**has/has not**) (Circle correct answer) occurred. Sarah asks C.W. if she has considered exploring the use of hormone replacement therapy. C.W. responds that she has thought about it, listens to every news report that addresses the issue, but is afraid to take hormones unless she can perceive more benefits than potential liabilities for her personally. How might Sarah advise C.W.?

2. While conducting an assessment of C.W. for other physical changes associated with menopause, what other physical characteristics Sarah might discuss with C.W.?

3. C.W.'s physical characteristics put her at particular risk for _____.

    Why is this risk an especially important consideration for C.W.?

4. In advising C.W., Sarah knows that the two major reasons women often choose NOT to use estrogen replacement therapy or do not continue it include: _____ _____. As a result, significant preventive health-care benefits from the therapy _____.

5. Benefits of HRT that Sarah will want to discuss with C.W. include (in priority order):

    Give information to support the order in which you listed these.

6. As the discussion progresses, C.W. mentions that, "If the estrogen is so beneficial, it doesn't make sense why a person also has to take a medication with it that partially blocks these beneficial effects." Explain the reason the synthetic hormone progestin is added:

    What is the goal for selecting the dosage of progestin used?

7. C.W. asks how long she should plan to use HRT to prevent bone loss. Sarah should correctly answer:

    C.W. asks, "Do I need to swallow pills if I just want to get rid of these vaginal problems?" Sarah correctly responds:

8. Sarah reviews C.W.'s history for the presence of any factors that might contraindicate the use of estrogens. What factors should Sarah look for?

9. If C.W. elects to start HRT and returns complaining of premenstrual syndrome (PMS)-type complaints, what is the most likely cause? _____

    What should Sarah advise C.W. to do?

If C.W. is perimenopausal with irregular periods, what additional contraindication should be ruled out?

10. C.W. elects to try HRT. Several months go by and Sarah receives a call from C.W. stating that she isn't having bleeding between her periods but is having bleeding during the last week of her cycle that lasts a few days but doesn't quite resemble her former periods. She also says she is having an occasional hot flash during this period and she thought these would completely disappear on the therapy. Sarah correctly advises C.W. that:

53 Drugs Related to Reproductive Health I: Male Reproductive Health

Study Questions

Define the following:

1. Anabolic steroids

2. Androgens

3. Hirsutism

4. Spermatogenesis

5. Virilization

Complete the following:

6. The primary androgen _____ is synthesized in the testes and adrenal cortex.

7. The human sexual response cycle consists of five phases: desire, excitement, _____, _____, and _____.

8. The rate of testosterone production is controlled by a _____.

9. Synthetic androgens have (**shorter/longer**) half-lives. (Circle correct answer)

10. Levels of testosterone in elderly men are _____ of the peak value.

11. The intermittent approach to androgen therapy allows for _____ between courses of therapy.

12. Clients on androgen therapy with elevated serum calcium levels need 3–4 liters/day of liquid intake to prevent kidney stones. Signs of hypercalcemia include the following: nausea and vomiting, lethargy, _____, _____, and _____.

13. The synthesis or actions of androgens may be blocked by _____.

14. When luteinizing hormone (LH) and follicle stimulating hormone (FSH) are low, the drug _____ is injected intramuscularly. When reconstituted, the drug must be used _____.

15. Insufficient _____, _____, or _____ accounts for up to 5% of cases of delayed puberty.

16. The occurrence of testicular tumors peaks in early _____. Combinations of _____, _____, and _____ are used in their treatment.

17. The drug _____ is effective in stimulating libido in non-Parkinson's clients.

18. Viagra is contraindicated for men using _____ and in men with significant _____.

Select the appropriate response:

Situation : P.S. is a 17-year-old male receiving androgen therapy for hypogonadism. The next nine questions refer to this situation.

19. P.S. asks the nurse what androgen therapy does. The nurse's best response would be:
    a. "It ensures the ability to respond sexually."
    b. "It ensures adequate sperm production."
    c. "It promotes larger stature through protein deposition."
    d. "It stimulates the development of secondary sex characteristics."

20. P.S. observes that some of the football players at his school take hormones to help them bulk up. The nurse replies that:
    a. "This is safe as long as they use the proper dosage."
    b. "This can cause serious, often irreversible, health problems years later."
    c. "Most athletic organizations endorse this practice."
    d. "As long as they don't use other street drugs, this is probably safe."

21. You teach P.S. to observe for common side effects of the drug, which may include:
    a. abdominal pain and hives at injection site.
    b. dry mouth and dizziness.
    c. weight gain and blurred vision.
    d. generalized rash.

22. P.S. asks how often and for how long he must come for his testosterone enanthate injection. Therapy is expected to be given:
    a. daily for a month.
    b. biweekly for four months.
    c. biweekly for four years.
    d. weekly for a year.

23. Evidence that P.S. is receiving too much testosterone enanthate would include all EXCEPT:
    a. deepening of his voice.
    b. continuous erection.
    c. breast soreness.
    d. urinary urgency.

24. Before P.S. can be started on his androgen therapy regimen, the following contra-indications must be ruled out EXCEPT:
    a. nephrosis.
    b. hepatic insufficiency.
    c. diabetes.
    d. pituitary insufficiency.

25. In reviewing P.S.'s current medication, the nurse is aware that:
    a. androgens may decrease blood glucose in diabetics, so insulin dose may need adjustment.
    b. barbiturates potentiate androgens.
    c. there is no interaction with steroids.
    d. androgens decrease the effect of anticoagulants.

26. During one of his clinic visits, P.S. tells you his great-aunt said she took male hormones. He asks you why they would be given to a woman. An appropriate response would be:
    a. "Women are not treated with male hormones."
    b. "Women bodybuilders take androgens."
    c. "The doctor will explain this to you later."
    d. "Women with advanced breast cancer or severe menopausal symptoms may benefit from androgens."

27. On one of his clinic visits, P.S. tells you that his grandfather is taking antiandrogens. He asks you why these drugs are used. Indications include all EXCEPT:
    a. cancer of the prostate.
    b. male pattern baldness.
    c. virilization syndrome in women.
    d. precocious puberty in girls.

Critical Thinking Exercises

M.T., age 16, is the shortest male in his class. His parents bring him to the endocrine clinic because of their concern.

1.   Why would the treatment team explore family feelings about this before initiating treatment?

2.   What should the family be told about the effectiveness of androgen treatment for delayed growth?

3.   How is an androgen selected for therapy?

4.   Which body systems' functioning need to be monitored during therapy?

5.   How long can this therapy be expected to last?

54 Drugs Related to Reproductive Health II: Infertility and Sexually Transmitted Diseases

Study Questions

Define the following:

1. Pelvic inflammatory diesease

2. Basal body temperature

3. Ovulation

4. Infertility: primary, secondary

5. Sexually transmitted disease (STD)

6. Vertical transmission

Complete the following:

7. Sexually transmitted diseases, if not treated early, can result in _____, _____, and _____.

8. The infection of a fetus or neonate by the infected mother is _____ transmission.

9. The disease _____ is transmitted transplacentally.

10. The modes of transmission of STDs are _____, _____, or by sexual contact with oral-fecal exposure.

11. Infants' eyes are treated with erythromycin 0.5% to prevent _____.

12. The only STD for which a vaccine exists is _____.

13. A spirochete is the cause of the STD _____, and _____ is the drug of choice for its treatment.

14. The most effective risk-reducing behavior for avoidance of STDs is _____ or sexual contact with _____.

15. Recurrent candidiasis may be indicative of _____ or _____.

16. There is no cure for genital herpes. The drug _____ is used for a primary infection.

17. Infertility is diagnosed when the couple have engaged in frequent, unprotected coitus around the time of ovulation and not conceived in _____.

18. When infertile couples experience low levels of hormones, _____ is used to achieve physiologic levels.

19. In about _____ % of cases of infertility no cause can be found.

20. When endometriosis causes infertility it can be treated with _____ to _____.

21. Women with inadequate luteal phase progesterone output are treated with _____ intravaginally or intramuscularly.

22. Evaluation and intervention for infertility is both _____ and _____ draining for the couple.

23. Some women have been helped to conceive by taking guaifenesin (Robitussin) because it _____.

Select the appropriate response:

Situation: J.C., 19 years old, comes to the clinic complaining of dysuria and yellow-green discharge. Culture confirms *N. gonorrhea.* The next three questions refer to this situation.

24. The drug therapy of choice for J.C. is:
    a. ceftriaxone and doxycycline.
    b. ceftriaxone only.
    c. spectinomycin.
    d. probenecid.

25. Because she has presented with a sexually transmitted disease, which test should J.C. be counseled to consider?
    a. fasting blood sugar
    b. liver function
    c. HIV test
    d. fertility work-up

26. All recent sexual partners need to be informed of J.C.'s gonorrhea and until reculturing demonstrates cure, J.C. should:
    a. abstain or use condoms during sex.
    b. ask partners to take antibiotics.
    c. douche before intercourse.
    d. only engage in anal intercourse.

Situation: A.Z. has repeated gonorrhea and chlamydia as well as HPV, and is being followed at the infectious disease clinic. The next eight questions refer to this situation.

27. In teaching A.Z. about the transmission of STDs, the nurse observes that the most risky form of sexual contact because of tissue trauma is:
    a. genital-genital.
    b. genital-anal.
    c. oral-genital.
    d. mouth-to-mouth.

28. The nurse tells A.Z. that HIV is spread in all of the following ways EXCEPT:
    a. contact with contaminated blood.
    b. sexual contact.
    c. urine.
    d. breast milk.

29. The nurse tells A.Z. that she may want to be tested for HIV for all of the following reasons EXCEPT:
    a. STDs indicate risky behavior.
    b. repeated infections suggest immune compromise.
    c. early detection is the best hope for cure.
    d. treatment will prevent her passing it on.

30. A.Z. asks how long she must abstain from sex. The nurse responds:
    a. "Two months."
    b. "You may have sex using condoms."
    c. "Until the medication is finished."
    d. "Until your partner is treated."

31. A.Z. asks if gonorrhea and syphillis are the same. The nurse responds:
    a. "No, but if you have one, you should consider being tested for the other."
    b. "Yes, they are essentially the same."
    c. "No, syphilis cannot be cured."
    d. "No, gonorrhea has no serious effects."

32. A.Z. says she might be pregnant. What is the risk to her baby?

   a. If she is treated now and avoids sexual risk, there is no risk to her baby.

   b. Her baby will have an eye infection.

   c. Her baby will have a birth defect.

   d. She will need a cesarean delivery.

33. A.Z. wonders if her HPV will be cured. Which of the following is true?

   a. The lesion can be removed but the HPV cannot be cured.

   b. Cryotherapy will cure her.

   c. Medications can eliminate recurrences.

   d. HPV cannot be cured, but it is not highly contagious.

Situation: Jane and Joe have a fertility work-up. Jane has been started on clomiphene citrate. The next four questions relate to this situation.

34. The nurse explains to the clients that clomiphene citrate's action is to:

   a. stimulate ovulation.

   b. replace FSH.

   c. stimulate LH.

   d. normalize prolactin levels.

35. Jane and Joe ask you about the side effects of clomiphene citrate. Your best response is:

   a. decreased appetite.

   b. insomnia.

   c. breast discomfort.

   d. dehydration.

36. Contraindications for the use of clomiphene citrate include all of the following EXCEPT:

   a. pregnancy.

   b. fibroids.

   c. depression.

   d. diabetes mellitus.

37. General health teaching for a couple such as Jane and Joe includes all of the following EXCEPT:

   a. instructions on how to evaluate and record basal body temperature.

   b. increase fluid intake by one liter per day.

   c. frequency and timing of coitus.

   d. need to take medication at same time each day.

Critical Thinking Exercises

Tess and Tom, both age 32, are being evaluated for infertility.

1. Why is Tess's history of several episodes of gonorrhea while she was in college significant?

2. Because of that history, it is suggested that Tess consider HIV testing. How are HIV and gonorrhea interrelated?

3. It is determined that Tom's sperm count is within the range of normal, but Tess is not ovulating regularly. A course of clomiphene citrate is recommended. What side effects can Tess expect? What adverse effects might require that the regimen be interrupted?

4. How does a woman's basal temperature change throughout her ovulatory cycle, and when should she engage in coitus? How might this affect the clients' relationship?

5. What stresses might a couple experience during infertility therapy? What damage might be inflicted on their relationship if pregnancy is not achieved?

55 Adult and Pediatric Emergency Drugs

Study Questions

Define the following:

1. Anaphylactic shock

2. Angina pectoris

3. Asystole

4. Extravasation

5. Hypoxemia

6. Torsades de pointes

Select the appropriate response:

7. Sublingual nitroglycerin may be prescribed for chest pain. What is the most important vital sign to assess BEFORE giving this drug?
   a. temperature
   b. blood pressure
   c. heart rate
   d. respiratory rate

8. Following administration of intravenous morphine to treat chest pain associated with acute myocardial infarction, the most important aspect of client monitoring is:
   a. measurement of central venous pressure.
   b. strict intake and output records.
   c. assessment of respiratory status.
   d. documentation of neurologic function.

9. An emergency drug indicated for the treatment of symptomatic bradycardia is:
   a. lidocaine.
   b. atropine.
   c. naloxone.
   d. epinephrine.

10. When monitoring a client with an isoproterenol (Isuprel) infusion, the nurse must be alert to the development of these dangerous adverse effects, which may require slowing or discontinuing drug administration:
    a. tachycardia and cardiac ectopy (PVCs and ventricular tachycardia).
    b. bradycardia and hypotension.
    c. bradycardia and hypertension.
    d. respiratory depression and cardiac ectopy.

11. Verapamil is classified as a:
    a. calcium channel blocker.
    b. beta blocker.
    c. cardiac glycoside.
    d. nitrate.

12. Adenosine is indicated in the treatment of
    _____.

13. Lidocaine is commonly prescribed to treat ventricular dysrhythmias. List three signs and symptoms of lidocaine toxicity that must be recognized and reported to the primary health care provider:
    a.

    b.

    c.

14. A dangerous adverse effect of intravenous procainamide administration is the development of:

    a. respiratory depression.
    b. hypertension.
    c. hypotension.
    d. urinary retention.

15. Amiodarone IV is used to treat:

    a. atrial dysrhythmias.
    b. ventricular dysrhythmias.
    c. a and b.
    d. none of the above.

16. Which of the following statements regarding epinephrine is NOT true?

    a. Epinephrine is a catecholamine.
    b. Indications for epinephrine include asystole and ventricular fibrillation.
    c. The action of epinephrine is enhanced if it is infused through alkaline solutions such as sodium bicarbonate.
    d. Metabolic acidosis decreases the effectiveness of epinephrine.

17. The best indication for sodium bicarbonate is:

    a. metabolic alkalosis.
    b. metabolic acidosis.
    c. respiratory alkalosis.
    d. respiratory acidosis.

18. C.N. is admitted to the neurosurgical floor with a closed head injury. Mannitol is ordered to decrease intracranial pressure. Mannitol exerts its pharmacologic effects through:

    a. cerebral constriction.
    b. peripheral vasodilation.
    c. loop diuresis.
    d. osmotic diuresis.

19. Methylprednisolone (Solu-Medrol) is an adjunctive therapy in the treatment of acute spinal cord injury. The nurse must be aware that the loading dose of this drug must be given within _____ hours of the injury.

    a. 2
    b. 4
    c. 6
    d. 8

20. Naloxone reverses the effects of _____ drugs. Name at least three drugs in this category that may be reversed by naloxone:

    a.

    b.

    c.

21. Client and family teaching regarding administration of ipecac syrup should include all of the following points EXCEPT:

    a. water should be given after the ipecac to enhance its effectiveness.
    b. administration may be repeated as often as necessary until vomiting occurs.
    c. clients who are unconscious or semiconscious should not be given ipecac.
    d. clients who ingest petroleum products or corrosive agents should not receive ipecac.

22. The nurse should remember that activated charcoal must not be given with _____ because the adsorptive properties of charcoal are decreased.

23. Magnesium citrate is given to clients who have been poisoned to act as a(n):

    a. cathartic.
    b. emetic.
    c. osmotic diuretic.
    d. anticonvulsant.

24. Dopamine should NOT be administered to clients with hypotension due to:

    a. neurogenic shock.
    b. hypovolemic shock.
    c. septic shock.
    d. cardiogenic shock.

25. Dobutamine elevates blood pressure through:

    a. vasoconstriction.
    b. vasodilation.
    c. increasing cardiac output.
    d. positive alpha effects.

26. J.S. has a diagnosis of septic shock. A norepinephrine drip is infusing through a central intravenous line. The bag of norepinephrine is almost empty. The nurse makes it a priority to prepare a new bag because:

   a. hypertensive crisis can result if the infusion is interrupted.

   b. profound hypotension can occur if the infusion is abruptly discontinued.

   c. the client is at high risk for bradycardia and heart block.

   d. the organisms responsible for septic shock will proliferate.

27. S.A. is brought to the emergency department with complaints of severe respiratory distress, hives, and edema after being stung on the face by a bee. An accurate nursing assessment of the situation includes all of the following EXCEPT:

   a. hypotension and bronchospasm will progress rapidly if treatment is delayed.

   b. the client is suffering from anaphylactic shock.

   c. epinephrine and diphenhydramine are the drugs of choice as first-line agents.

   d. prompt treatment with drug therapy will prevent this syndrome from occurring again.

28. Dextrose 50% is most commonly prescribed:

   a. as a maintenance infusion to keep a vein open.

   b. to increase urine output.

   c. to treat hyperglycemia.

   d. to treat insulin shock.

29. To document that glucagon administration has been effective, the nurse should note:

   a. improvement in level of consciousness.

   b. elevation in respiratory rate.

   c. suppression of heart rate.

   d. reduction in blood pressure.

30. Nursing considerations when caring for the client with a nitroprusside infusion should include all of the following EXCEPT:

   a. the solution must be protected from light.

   b. thiocyanate levels should be monitored.

   c. a blue or brown color to the solution is typical.

   d. continuous blood pressure measurement is required.

31. The proper method of administering adenosine is:

   a. slow IV push.

   b. diluted in 50 cc of normal saline and infused via an electronic pump over 30 minutes.

   c. rapid IV push as a bolus.

   d. via a nebulizer.

32. Following administration of a total intravenous lidocaine dose of 3 mg/kg to an adult:

   a. a continuous infusion of lidocaine must be initiated to maintain a therapeutic serum level.

   b. a therapeutic serum level will be achieved and maintained.

   c. it is recognized that a lidocaine overdose has occurred.

   d. additional bolus doses must be administered to achieve a therapeutic serum level.

33. Vasopressin:

   a. is a vasoconstrictor.

   b. is an adjunct to epinephrine in the treatment of cardiac arrest.

   c. can induce myocardial ischemia in patients with coronary artery disease.

   d. all of the above.

34. To administer epinephrine .3 mg for subcutaneous injection, the nurse should select a:

   a. 1:10,000 solution of epinephrine.

   b. 1:100 solution of epinephrine.

   c. 1:1,000 solution of epinephrine.

   d. 1:1 solution of epinephrine.

35. To administer epinephrine 1 mg for intravenous injection, the nurse should select a:
    a. 1:10,000 solution of epinephrine.
    b. 1:100 solution of epinephrine.
    c. 1:1,000 solution of epinephrine.
    d. 1:1 solution of epinephrine.

36. The lowest adult dose of atropine for heart block or symptomatic bradycardia is .5 mg IV because at lower doses:
    a. vagal activity is completely blocked.
    b. paradoxical bradycardia can occur.
    c. miosis occurs.
    d. the patient is at high risk for tachycardia.

37. All of the following are commonly associated with atropine administration EXCEPT:
    a. dry mouth.
    b. urinary retention.
    c. mydriasis.
    d. miosis.

38. Flumazenil is used to reverse the effects of which of the following?
    a. narcotics
    b. antipsychotics
    c. benzodiazepines
    d. paralytic agents

39. Magnesium sulfate is indicated for which of the following?
    a. the treatment of Torsades de pointes
    b. treatment of hypomagnesemia
    c. a and b
    d. none of the above

40. Furosemide exerts its effects in pulmonary edema through which two mechanisms?
    a. venodilation and diuresis
    b. bronchodilation and antiinflammatory actions
    c. vasoconstriction and diuresis
    d. bronchodilation and diuresis

41. Oxygen therapy should never be withheld from clients experiencing medical emergencies such as chest pain, trauma, or other causes of hypoxemia, even if they have a history of COPD.
    a. True
    b. False

42. Albuterol is a _____ (class of drug) used to treat clients experiencing _____ and _____.

Critical Thinking Exercises

Case Study #1

T. M., an acutely ill 64-year-old male, is brought to the emergency department by his family to be treated for "the flu." His initial vital signs are as follows: blood pressure 70/40 mm Hg, heart rate 140, respiratory rate 32, and temperature 40.2° C po. After examination and diagnostic studies, T.M. is diagnosed with pneumonia and septic shock.

A triple lumen subclavian line is inserted for fluids, IV medications, and measurement of central venous pressure (CVP). His initial CVP reading is 3 cm of H_2O. A 2,000 ml normal saline fluid bolus is infused rapidly which elevates his CVP to 9 cm of H_2O. His BP increases to 86/60 and his heart rate decreases to 110 beats per minute. A dopamine infusion is initiated at 5 µg/kg/min and titrated to 8 µg/kg/min to achieve a systolic BP of >100 mm Hg. He is medicated with acetaminophen for fever. T.M. will be admitted to the ICU for placement of a pulmonary artery catheter and further aggressive management.

The following questions relate to the case study:

1. Why were IV fluids given to raise BP before initiating dopamine?

2. What are the beneficial pharmacologic effects of dopamine at the dose range in the case study?

3. How should dopamine be administered for precise dosing?

4. What are pertinent nursing considerations/assessments when monitoring a patient receiving a dopamine infusion?

5. What actions should be taken if a dopamine infusion should infiltrate and produce tissue extravasation?

6. T.M. had a heart rate of 140 on arrival in the case study. Is verapamil or adenosine indicated in this case to treat the client's tachycardia?

Case Study #2

C.S., a 56-year-old male, is admitted to coronary care step-down after a 3-day critical care unit stay for an inferior wall myocardial infarction. After dinner, C.S. summons nursing assistance for complaints of severe substernal chest pain with radiation into his left arm. He has an IV of D_5W infusing at KVO. He has O_2 on at 4 L by nasal cannula. C.S. has a PRN order for nitroglycerin (NTG) 0.4 mg SL for chest pain.

1. Should the NTG 0.4 mg SL be administered based on the case study?

2. What nursing assessment data should be collected prior to administering the NTG?

C.S. continues to complain of severe chest pain after three NTG, five minutes apart. The health care provider is notified. Morphine sulfate, 2 mg IVP is ordered, which may be repeated at five-minute intervals until chest pain is relieved or until 10 mg has been administered.

3. If respiratory depression occurs due to the morphine, what drug should be available to reverse the effects?

C.S. is transferred back to the critical care unit. Intravenous nitroglycerin is ordered to be started at 10 μg/kg/min and titrated to relieve chest pain while keeping systolic blood pressure >100 mm Hg.

4. What are pertinent nursing considerations when administering IV nitroglycerin?

5. What actions should the nurse take if systolic BP falls to 96 mm Hg?

6. What if the client's BP dropped precipitously to 75 mm Hg?

C.S.'s chest pain is relieved with the nitroglycerin infusion. He remains comfortable over the next three hours until his cardiac monitor alarms for a low heart rate of 38. C.S. is found to be diaphoretic with a BP of 60 mm Hg by palpation. The nurse turns off the nitroglycerin infusion.

7. What is the drug of choice for symptomatic bradycardia? What is the minimum and maximum adult dose?

8. How does this drug exert its effects?

ANSWER KEY

CHAPTER 1—
Drug Action: Pharmaceutic, Pharmacokinetic, and Pharmacodynamic Phases

Crossword Puzzle

Crossword answers: PHARMACEUTIC, HALFLIFE, PHARMACOGENETIC, PHARMACOKINETIC, TOXICITY, ANTAGONIST, PROTEINBINDING

12. suspension

13. intestine; enteric-coated pill disintegrates in alkaline environment

14. interferes with

15. absorption, distribution, metabolism, elimination

16. lipid-soluble; nonionized

17. poor circulation, pain, stress, hunger, fasting and pH of the drug

18. absorption; bioavailability is the percentage that reaches the systemic circulation

19. increase

20. Drug accumulation that leads to drug toxicity

21. (1) clinical factors [age, weight and others]; (2) administration [route, drug interaction]; (3) pharmacokinetics; and (4) pharmacodynamics [onset, peak, and duration of action]

22. e

23. d

24. b

25. a

26. f

27. c

28. a

29. c

30. b

31. d

32. b

33. a

34. c

35. b

36. c

37. b

38. a

39. a

40. d

41. d

42. b

43. c

44. a

45. d

46. b

47. b

48. c

49. a

50. c

Critical Thinking Exercise

1. bleeding under skin

2. protein-binding; with two highly protein-bound drugs, the drugs compete for sites, causing more free drug. With more warfarin release, bleeding could occur; increased half-life may contribute to drug accumulation, especially with long protein-binding and half-life.

3.   inform health care provider; request appropriate laboratory tests

4.   inform client of your actions; tell client drug doses may be adjusted/changed

5.   no; digoxin level is elevated; because of two highly protein-bound drugs: digoxin and warfarin. Digoxin is displaced from site, thus serum value increases.

6.   may cause drug accumulation and drug toxicity because of a decrease in urine output

7.   check vital signs; monitor urine output; report findings, and others

CHAPTER 2—
Nursing Process and Client Teaching

Questions 1–4: refer to text.

5.   a

6.   a

7.   b

8.   a

9.   c

10.   a

11.   d

12.   c

13.   c

14.   a

15.   d

16.   subjective

17.   objective

18.   variable; related to potential for injury, knowledge deficit, and/or altered thought process

19.   client-centered, clearly stated expected change, acceptable to both client and nurse, realistic and measurable, realistic deadline, shared with other health care providers.

20.   variable

21.   general, skill, diet, and side effects

22.   include return demonstration, provide written instructions, use of colorful charts, provide time for questions, review community resources

23.   forgetfulness, knowledge deficit, side effects, low self-esteem, depression, lack of trust in the healthcare system, language barriers, cost of medications, anxiety, and lack of motivation

24.   What factors help you to take the medications as you should? What factors prevent you from taking medications as you should? What should you do when you forget to take a medication?

25.   Promote the development of a quality care plan.

26.   b

27.   a

28.   c

29.   c

30.   d

31.   e

32.   b

33.   d

34.   e

35.   b

36.   d

CHAPTER 3—
Principles of Drug Administration

Questions 1–6: refer to text.

7.   right client, right drug, right dose, right time, right route, right assessment, right evaluation, right documentation, client's right to education, and right to refuse. Variable nursing implications.

8.   variable: age, body weight, toxicity, route, time of administration, emotional factors, preexisting disease states, drug–drug interactions, etc.

9.   standing

10.   STAT

11.   one time/single and PRN (as needed)

12.   recheck how you set up the problem to be solved and the arithmetic involved

13.   no calculations required, time-saver for the nurse, and the client is billed only for doses given

14.   short; plasma

15.   narcotics, analgesics, sedatives, antiemetics, and any with unexpected reactions

16. draw a single line through incorrect information and sign your initials

17. Notify charge nurse and/or health care provider. Do not give medication.

18. 1) when you first locate drug, 2) when you handle container to obtain actual medication, and 3) when you return container to shelf

19. eye level; at the low point of the curve

20. the curved line formed by liquids in a container

21. report your finding and have a correct identification band put on the client

22. document promptly; medication, dose, time, route, initials, special considerations (apical pulse with digoxin)

24. ventrogluteal

25. vastus lateralis

26. deltoid

27. gluteal

28. dorsogluteal

23.

Route	Needle Size	Angle of Insertion	Sites
ID	26–27 g	10–15°	Area where inflammatory reaction can be observed
SQ	23, 25–27 g	45–90°	abdomen, upper hips, upper back, lateral upper arms, lateral thighs
IM	18–23 g	90°	most common: ventrogluteal, dorsogluteal, deltoid, vastus lateralis
IV	20–21 g		most common: median cubital vein, basilic vein, cephalic vein, radial vein

```
S I L A R E T A L S U T S A V
O M D V Z T W G G K N E Y I E
B U D L E A M F L O H S C P N
I I R D O N O T U D X Q M U T
D O R S O G L U T E A L G H R
E F B D I O T L E D W A N B O
S B E I M C R L A F Z I Y K G
D C O P A J T I L Q O T R N L
R E F U S A L R E A S O N A U
D E N E P O E M I T E T A D T
S L A I T I N I F Y M W H J E
B N T U O X R N T R L D A P A
T D E M N T R W I G Q M H U L
```

29. do not
30. date and time vial opened; your initials
31. reason(s) for refusal
32. a
33. a
34. b
35. a
36. b
37. a
38. oral
39. enteric coated and timed release
40. an empty stomach
41. decrease
42. applicator or gloves
43. placement of the tube
44. refer to Table 3–9 in text
45. five minutes
46. unaffected
47. down
48. should not
49. help the client manage medications during hospital stay and prepare him or her to keep as comfortable as possible at home
50. anticipate developmental needs, be creative

CHAPTER 4—
Medication and Calculations

Section 4A

1. metric; gram; liter; meter
2. one space; right
3. one space; left
4. gram; fluid ounce; fluid dram; and minim (also quart, pint)
5. in the home setting
6. cup; glass; spoonful (tablespoon, teaspoon)
7. g
8. mg
9. L, l
10. ml
11. kg
12. mcg, μg
13. ng
14. M
15. gr
16. fl oz
17. fl dr
18. qt
19. pt
20. m
21. c
22. T
23. t
24. gtt
25. a. 1000 mg; b. 1000 ml; c. 1000 mcg (μg)
26. 3000 milligrams
27. 1500 milliliters
28. 100 milligrams

29. 2.5 liters or 2 ½ liters
30. 0.25 liters
31. 0.5 gram
32. 4 pints
33. 32 fluid ounces
34. 48 fluid ounces
35. 2 pints
36. 16 fluid dram
37. 1 medium-sized glass = 8 ounces; 1 coffee cup = 6 ounces; 1 ounce = 2 tablespoons; 1 tablespoon = 3 teaspoons; 1 drop = 1 minim
38. convert gram to milligrams; drug label is in milligrams
39. 1000 mg; 15 gr
40. 0.5 g; 7 ½ gr
41. 100 mg; 1 ½ gr
42. 60 or 64 mg
43. 1/150 gr
44. 1 liter; 1 quart
45. 8 fl oz; 1 medium-sized glass
46. 1 ounce; 2 tablespoons; 6 teaspoons
47. 1 teaspoon
48. 15 (16) minim; 15 (16) drops
49. 1 ½ ounces; 9 teaspoons
50. 150 ml; 10 tablespoons

Section 4B

1. drug label
2. 1 g
3. 15 gr
4. ½ or ss
5. 250 mg

6. 5 gr
7. $\frac{1}{200}$ gr
8. 75 ml; 5 T
9. ½ ounce; 1 T; 3 t
10. 12 t
11. 2 ml
12. 2 t
13. Principen
14. ampicillin
15. 250 mg per 5 ml
16. oral suspension
17. Milligrams. Convert to the unit on the drug label.
18. a. Yes. Convert grams to milligrams. Move the decimal point three spaces to the right.

$$0.2 \text{ g} = 0.200 \text{ mg}$$

   b. $\dfrac{D}{H} \times V = \dfrac{200 \text{ mg}}{100 \text{ mg}} \times 1 \text{ cap} =$

   2 capsules of Norvir

   $$H : V :: D : X$$
   $$100 \text{ mg} : 1 \text{ cap} :: 200 \text{ mg} : X \text{ cap}$$

   $100 X = 200$
   $X = 2$ capsules of Norvir

19. a. No. Conversion is NOT needed. The units in the drug order and on the drug label are the same.

   b. $\dfrac{D}{H} \times V = \dfrac{25 \text{ mg}}{12.5 \text{ mg}} \times 5 \text{ ml} =$

   $\dfrac{10.}{12.5 \overline{)125.0}} = 10 \text{ ml}$ of Benadryl

   $$H : V :: D : X$$
   $$12.5 \text{ mg} : 5 \text{ ml} :: 25 \text{ mg} : X \text{ ml}$$

   $12.5 X = 125$
   $X = \dfrac{125}{12.5} = 10$ ml of Benadryl

20. a. Yes, conversion is needed. Convert grams to milligrams. Move the

decimal point three spaces to the right.

$$0.25 \text{ g} = 0.250 \text{ mg}$$

b. $\dfrac{D}{H} \times V = \dfrac{\overset{2}{\cancel{250} \text{ mg}}}{\underset{1}{\cancel{125} \text{ mg}}} \times 5 \text{ ml} =$

10 ml of Biaxin

$$
\begin{array}{ccccccc}
H & : & V & :: & D & : & X \\
125 \text{ mg} & : & 5 \text{ ml} & :: & 250 \text{ mg} & : & X \text{ ml}
\end{array}
$$

$$
\begin{aligned}
125 X &= 1250 \\
X &= 10 \text{ ml of Biaxin}
\end{aligned}
$$

21. a. No, conversion is NOT needed. The unit in the drug order and on the drug label are the same.

 b. $\dfrac{D}{H} \times V = \dfrac{100 \text{ mg}}{50 \text{ mg}} \times 1 \text{ ml} =$

 $\dfrac{100}{50} = 2 \text{ ml of Vistaril}$

$$
\begin{array}{ccccccc}
H & : & V & :: & D & : & X \\
50 \text{ mg} & : & 1 \text{ ml} & :: & 100 \text{ mg} & : & X \text{ ml}
\end{array}
$$

$$
\begin{aligned}
50 X &= 100 \\
X &= 2 \text{ ml}
\end{aligned}
$$

22. a. Yes. Convert milligrams to grams. The drug label is in grams.

 $$500 \text{ mg} = 500 \text{ g } (0.5 \text{ g})$$

 According to the drug label, the drug solution after reconstitution is 3 ml = 1 g.

 b. $\dfrac{D}{H} \times V = \dfrac{0.5 \text{ g}}{1 \text{ g}} \times 3 \text{ ml} =$

 $\dfrac{1.5}{1} = 1.5 \text{ ml of Kefzol}$

$$
\begin{array}{ccccccc}
H & : & V & :: & D & : & X \\
1 \text{ g} & : & 3 \text{ ml} & :: & 0.5 \text{ g} & : & X \text{ ml}
\end{array}
$$

 $1 X = 1.5 \text{ ml of Kefzol}$

23. a.

 $\text{tab} = \dfrac{1 \text{ tab}}{25 \text{ mg}} \times \dfrac{\overset{2}{\cancel{50} \text{ mg}}}{1} = 2 \text{ tablets}$

 b. Select the 25 mg drug label. If the 100 mg drug label was

selected, then the client should receive ½ tablet.

24.

 $\text{tab} = \dfrac{1 \text{ tab}}{50 \text{ mg}} \times \dfrac{\overset{20}{\cancel{1000} \text{ mg}}}{1 \text{ g}} \times \dfrac{0.1 \text{ g}}{1}$

 $= 2 \text{ tablets}$

 Give 2 tablets (50 mg tablets) daily.

25. cubic centimeter
26. gram
27. drops
28. liter
29. microgram
30. milliequivalent
31. milliliter
32. milligram
33. kilogram
34. fluid ounce
35. one-half
36. tablespoon
37. teaspoon
38. suppository
39. greater than
40. less than
41. telephone order
42. right ear
43. left ear
44. both ears
45. right eye
46. left eye
47. both eyes
48. intramuscular
49. intravenous
50. keep vein open
51. sublingual
52. subcutaneous

53. by mouth, orally
54. before meals
55. after meals
56. with
57. without
58. nothing by mouth
59. whenever necessary
60. hour of sleep
61. every day
62. every 8 hours
63. twice a day
64. three times a day
65. qid is four times a day, usually during the day (8 AM, 12 PM, 4 PM, 8 PM).

 q6h is every 6 hours (four times in 24 hours) such as 6 AM, 12 PM, 6 PM, 12 AM.

66. cc and ml are used interchangeably. For liquids, the preferred symbol is ml (milliliter).

Section 4C

1. 2 tablets of Cogentin 0.5 mg

 $\dfrac{D}{H} \times V = \dfrac{1 \text{ mg}}{0.5 \text{ mg}} \times 1 \text{ tab} =$

 $0.5 \overline{)1.0}^{\,2.0} = 2 \text{ tablets}$

$$
\begin{array}{ccccccc}
H & : & V & :: & D & : & X \\
0.5 \text{ mg} & : & 1 \text{ tab} & :: & 1 \text{ mg} & : & X \text{ tab}
\end{array}
$$

 $$
\begin{aligned}
0.5 X &= 1 = \dfrac{1}{0.5} \\
X &= 2 \text{ tablets}
\end{aligned}
$$

2. 2 tablets of codeine 30 mg.

 If codeine 15 mg bottle is used, give 4 tablets.

 To give codeine 60 mg, it would be more desirable to give fewer tablets.

3. 1 ½ tablets of propranolol 10 mg. It would be difficult to obtain ¾ of a tablet from propranolol 20 mg.

$$\frac{D}{H} \times V = \frac{15\,mg}{10\,mg} \times 1\,tab =$$

1 tab

$$\begin{array}{ccccccc} H & : & V & :: & D & : & X \\ 10\,mg & : & 1\,tab & :: & 15\,mg & : & X\,tab \end{array}$$

$$10\,X = 15$$
$$X = \frac{15}{10} = 1\tfrac{1}{2}\,tab$$

4. ½ tablet of V-Cillin K 500 mg.

$$\frac{D}{H} \times V = \frac{\overset{1}{\cancel{250}}\,mg}{\underset{2}{\cancel{500}}\,mg} \times 1\,tab =$$

½ tab

$$\begin{array}{ccccccc} H & : & V & :: & D & : & X \\ 500\,mg & : & 1\,tab & :: & 250\,mg & : & X\,tab \end{array}$$

$$500\,X = 250$$
$$X = \frac{250}{500} = \tfrac{1}{2}\,tab$$

5. 3 tablets of cimetidine 200 mg.

6. ½ tablet of verapamil 120 mg.

Verapamil 120 mg tablet

$$\frac{D}{H} \times V = \frac{\overset{1}{\cancel{60}}\,mg}{\underset{2}{\cancel{120}}\,mg} \times 1\,tab =$$

½ tab

Verapamil 80 mg tablet

$$\begin{array}{ccccccc} H & : & V & :: & D & : & X \\ 80\,mg & : & 1\,tab & :: & 60\,mg & : & X\,tab \end{array}$$

$$80\,X = 60$$
$$X = \frac{60}{80} = \tfrac{3}{4}\,tab$$

Difficult to divide a tablet into ¾.

7. 2 tablets of Artane sequels (sustained release [SR] capsule)
   The drug order is for SR capsule/tablet.

8. 3 tablets of Desyrel 50 mg tablet.
   1 ½ tablet of Desyrel 100 mg.

9. Select Coumadin 5 mg container. 1 ½ tablet of Coumadin 5 mg.

$$\frac{D}{H} \times V = \frac{7.5\,mg}{5\,mg} \times 1\,tab =$$

$$5\,)\overline{7.5} \quad\begin{array}{l}1.5\\ \end{array} = 1\tfrac{1}{2}\,tablet$$

$$\begin{array}{ccccccc} H & : & V & :: & D & : & X \\ 5\,mg & : & 1\,tab & :: & 7.5\,mg & : & X\,tab \end{array}$$

$$5\,X = 7.5$$
$$X = \frac{7.5}{5} = 1\tfrac{1}{2}\,tablet$$

10. D. The serum lithium level of 1.8 mEq/L is NOT within the normal range. The drug should be withheld and the health care provider notified.

11. Select Nitrostat 0.3 mg. Conversion table indicates gr $\frac{1}{200}$ is equal to 0.3 mg. Also, the drug label indicates 0.3 mg (gr $\frac{1}{200}$).

12. a. 4 tablets per dose.
    b. 8 tablets per day.

13. 2 bottles of Zithromax 15 ml bottle. The 22.5 ml bottle would not be sufficient for 5 days of Zithromax therapy.
    First day: 10 ml/d; days 2–5: 5 ml/d (total 30 ml)

14. Label reads trihexyphenidyl 2 mg = 1 teaspoon or 5 ml.
    2 ½ ml of Artane 2 mg/ 5 ml.

$$\frac{D}{H} \times V = \frac{1\,mg}{2\,mg} \times 5\,ml =$$

$$\frac{5}{2} = 2\tfrac{1}{2}\,ml$$

$$\begin{array}{ccccccc} H & : & V & :: & D & : & X \\ 2\,mg & : & 5\,ml & :: & 1\,mg & : & X\,ml \end{array}$$

$$2\,X = 5$$
$$X = 2\tfrac{1}{2}\,ml$$

15. First day: 2 tablets of Vibra-Tabs; days 2–7: 1 tablet per day.

16. 2 tablets of Lanoxin (digoxin) 0.125 mg.

The two tablets are equivalent to the digoxin dose; the 0.25 mg tablets are not available.

OR

Drug is the same but drug strength is half so 2 tablets are needed.

$$\frac{D}{H} \times V = \frac{0.25\,mg}{0.125\,mg} \times 1\,tab =$$

$$0.125\,)\overline{0.250} \quad = 2\,tablets$$

$$\begin{array}{ccccccc} H & : & V & :: & D & : & X \\ .125\,mg & : & 1\,tab & :: & 0.25\,mg & : & X\,tab \end{array}$$

$$0.125\,X = 0.25$$
$$X = 2\,tablets$$

17. 8 ml of Augmentin.

$$\frac{D}{H} \times V = \frac{400\,mg}{250\,mg} \times 5\,ml =$$

$$\frac{2000}{250} = 8\,ml$$

$$\begin{array}{ccccccc} H & : & V & :: & D & : & X \\ 250\,mg & : & 5\,ml & :: & 400\,mg & : & X\,ml \end{array}$$

$$250\,X = 2000$$
$$X = 8\,ml$$

18. 10 ml of cefadroxil (Duricef) 500 mg/5 ml.
    Convert grams to milligrams by moving the decimal point three spaces to the right.
    1 g = 1.000 mg.

$$\frac{D}{H} \times V = \frac{1000\,mg}{500\,mg} \times 5\,ml =$$

$$\frac{5000}{500} = 10\,ml$$

$$\begin{array}{ccccccc} H & : & V & :: & D & : & X \\ 500\,mg & : & 5\,ml & :: & 1000\,mg & : & X\,ml \end{array}$$

$$500\,X = 5000$$
$$X = 10\,ml$$

19. Select 5 mg tablets. Give 2 tablets.

20. Select 25–250 mg strength. Give ½ tablet.

21.

$$ml = \frac{5\,ml}{\underset{5}{\cancel{25}}\,mg} \times \frac{\overset{4}{\cancel{20}}\,mg}{1} = \frac{20}{5}$$

$$= 4\,ml\,per\,day$$

22.

$$ml = \frac{5\,ml}{250\,mg} \times \frac{\overset{4}{\cancel{1000}}\,mg}{1\,g} \times \frac{\cancel{0.5}\,g}{1}$$
$$ \quad \frac{}{1}$$
$$= 10\,ml\ per\ dose$$

Section 4D

1. intradermal, subcutaneous, and intramuscular. Also intravenous.

2. subcutaneous and intravenous. Only regular insulin can be administered intravenously.

3. self-sealing rubber top; reusable if properly stored.

4. date to discard; dosage equivalence of solution; nurse's initials.

5. solutions less than 1 ml and heparin dosages. Also pediatric dosages. Is NOT.

6. units

7. a

8. c

9. b

10. b

11. c

12. d

13. Select the 5,000 U vial. The drug order is for 3,000 U of heparin. If 10,000 U is selected, give 0.3 ml.

$$\frac{D}{H} \times V = \frac{3000\,U}{5000\,U} \times 0.6\,ml =$$

$$\frac{3}{5} = \frac{0.6}{5\,)\,3.0} = 0.6\,ml\ of\ heparin$$

H	:	V	::	D	:	X
5000 U	:	1 ml	::	3000 U	:	X ml

$$5000\,X = 3000$$
$$X = 0.6\,ml\ of\ heparin$$

14. Convert grains to milligrams. The dose on the cartridge is in milligrams. gr ss = gr ½ = 30 mg (see Table 2–4).

$$\frac{D}{H} \times V = \frac{\overset{1}{\cancel{30}}\,mg}{\underset{2}{\cancel{60}}\,mg} \times 1\,ml =$$

0.5 ml or ½ ml of codeine

H	:	V	::	D	:	X
60 mg	:	1 ml	::	30 mg	:	X ml

$$60\,X = 30 = \frac{30}{60} =$$
$$X = 0.5\,ml\ or\ \tfrac{1}{2}\ ml\ of\ codeine$$

15. Convert grains to milligrams. The dose on the drug label is in milligrams. gr ⅙ = 10 mg (see Tables 2–4 or 3–1).

$$\frac{D}{H} \times V = \frac{10\,mg}{15\,mg} \times 1\,ml =$$

$$\frac{.667}{3\,)\,2.0} = \begin{array}{l}0.66\,ml\ or\ 0.7\\ of\ morphine\end{array}$$

H	:	V	::	D	:	X
15 mg	:	1 ml	::	10 mg	:	X ml

$$15\,X = 10$$
$$X = \tfrac{2}{3}\ or\ .66\,ml$$
$$= 0.7\,ml\ of\ morphine$$

16. Withdraw 36 U of Humulin L (Lente) insulin. Each line on the insulin syringe is 2 U.

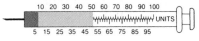

17. First withdraw 8 U of regular insulin and then 44 U of NPH insulin. TOTAL: 52 U of insulin.

18. Digoxin 0.25 mg = 1 ml.

$$\frac{D}{H} \times V = \frac{0.25\,mg}{0.5\,mg} \times 2\,ml =$$

$$\frac{\cancel{0.5}}{\cancel{0.5}} = 1\,ml\ of\ digoxin$$

H	:	V	::	D	:	X
0.5 mg	:	2 ml	::	0.25 mg	:	X ml

$$0.5\,X = 0.5$$
$$X = 1\,ml\ of\ digoxin$$

19. Select cyanocobalamin 1000 µg. The drug order is for 400 µg and the 100 µg cartridge would not contain enough medication.

$$\frac{D}{H} \times V = \frac{400\,µg}{1000\,µg} \times 1\,ml =$$

0.4 ml of vitamin B₁₂

H	:	V	::	D	:	X
1000 U	:	1 ml	::	400 µg	:	X ml

$$1000\,X = 400$$
$$X = 0.4\ ml\ of\ vitamin\ B_{12}$$

20. Clindamycin 300 mg = 2 ml.

$$\frac{D}{H} \times V = \frac{\overset{1}{\cancel{300}}\,mg}{\underset{3}{\cancel{900}}\,mg} \times 6\,ml = \frac{\overset{2}{\cancel{6}}}{\underset{}{3}} =$$

2 ml of Clindamycin

H	:	V	::	D	:	X
900 mg	:	6 ml	::	300 mg	:	X ml

$$900\,X = 1800$$
$$X = 2\,ml\ of\ Clindamycin$$

21. Discard 0.4 ml of meperidine 100 mg.
    Administer 0.6 ml of meperidine 100 mg and 1.25 ml of atropine SO₄.
    TOTAL VOLUME: 1.85 ml.

Meperidine

$$\frac{D}{H} \times V = \frac{\cancel{60}\,mg}{\cancel{100}\,mg} \times 1\,ml =$$

0.6 ml of meperidine

Atropine

H	:	V	::	D	:	X
0.4 mg	:	1 ml	::	0.5 mg	:	X ml

$$0.4\,X = 0.5 = \frac{0.5}{0.4} = \begin{array}{l}1.25\,ml\ of\\ atropine\end{array}$$

22. Narcan 0.8 mg = 2 ml

$$\frac{D}{H} \times V = \frac{0.8\,mg}{0.4\,mg} \times 1\,ml =$$

2 ml of Narcan

H	:	V	::	D	:	X
0.4 mg	:	1 ml	::	0.8 mg	:	X ml

$$0.4\,X = 0.8$$
$$X = 2\,ml\ of\ Narcan$$

23. Hydroxyzine (Vistaril) 35 mg = 0.7 ml.

24. Convert milligrams to grams, indicated on the drug label. Move the decimal point three spaces to the **left**.

    500 mg = 0.500 g or 0.5 g

    Drug label states to add 5.7 ml of sterile water to yield 6 ml of drug solution (oxacillin 1 g = 6 ml).

    $$\frac{D}{H} \times V = \frac{0.5\,g}{1\,g} \times 6\,ml =$$

    $$\frac{3}{1} = 3\,ml\ of\ oxacillin$$

    $$\begin{array}{ccccc} H & : & V & :: & D & : & X \\ 1\,g & : & 6\,ml & :: & 0.5\,g & : & X\,ml \end{array}$$

    (1) X = 3
        X = 3 ml of oxacillin

25. Drug label states to add 2.7 ml of diluent to yield a total of 3 ml of drug solution or 1.5 ml = 250 mg of oxacillin (oxacillin 500 mg = 3 ml)

    $$\frac{D}{H} \times V = \frac{300\,mg}{500\,mg} \times 3\,ml =$$

    $$\frac{900}{500} = 1.8\,ml\ of\ oxacillin$$

    $$\begin{array}{ccccc} H & : & V & :: & D & : & X \\ 500\,mg & : & 3\,ml & :: & 300\,mg & : & X\,ml \end{array}$$

    $$500\,X = 900$$
    $$X = \frac{900}{500} = 1.8\ ml\ of\ oxacillin$$

26. Drug label states to add 1.8 ml of diluent to yield a total of 2 ml of drug solution or 1 ml = 250 mg of nafcillin. (nafcillin [Nafcil] 500 mg = 2 ml)

    Since the drug label states that 250 mg = 1 ml after the drug has been reconstituted, calculation of this problem is not necessary. Nafcillin 250 mg = 1 ml.

    However, if you wish to work the problem:

    $$\frac{D}{H} \times V = \frac{250\,mg}{500\,mg} \times 2\,ml =$$

    $$\frac{1}{1} = 1\,ml\ of\ nafcillin$$

    $$\begin{array}{ccccc} H & : & V & :: & D & : & X \\ 500\,mg & : & 2\,ml & :: & 250\,mg & : & X\,ml \end{array}$$

    (1) X = 1 ml of nafcillin

27. Trimethobenzamide (Tigan) 100 mg = 1 ml.

28. 0.8 ml of Thorazine.

    $$\frac{D}{H} \times V = \frac{20\,mg}{25\,mg} \times 1\,ml = \frac{4}{5} = 0.8\,ml$$

29. Add 2 ml of diluent to yield 2.6 ml of drug solution. Change 400 mg to grams (400 = 0.4 g)

    $$\frac{D}{H} \times V = \frac{0.4\,g}{1\,g} \times 2.6\,ml = 1\,ml$$

    1 ml of ticarcillin.

30. a. 750 mg of cefonicid is equivalent to 0.75 g.

    b. Drug label indicates that 2.5 ml of diluent should be added to the drug powder, which yields 3.1 ml of drug solution.

    c. $\frac{D}{H} \times V = \frac{0.75\,g}{1\,g} \times 3.1\,ml =$

    2.32 ml or 2.3 ml of cefonicid solution.

31.

    a. $ml = \frac{2.4\,ml}{1\,g} \times \frac{1\,g}{\overset{4}{\cancel{1000}}\,mg} \times \frac{\overset{3}{\cancel{750}}\,mg}{1}$

    $= \frac{7.2}{4} = 1.8\ ml\ per\ dose\ of\ Cefotan.$

    b. The remaining 0.6 ml of drug solution in the vial can be saved for 24 hours or 96 hours if refrigerated.

32.

    $ml = \frac{2.6\,ml}{1.5\,g} \times \frac{1\,g}{1} = \frac{2.6}{1.5}$

    $= 1.73\ or\ 1.7\ ml\ per\ dose\ of\ Unasyn.$

Section 4E

1. drop factor; amount of fluid to be administered; and time period

2. macrodrip set: 10–20 gtt/ml; microdrip set: 60 gtt/ml

3. microdrip set

4. keep vein open; 250 ml IV bag

5. Prior to administration

6. D_5W

7. NS or 0.9% NaCl

8. $D_5/\frac{1}{2}$ NS or 5% D/0.45% NaCl

9. D_5/LR or 5% D/LR

10. small; short

11. calibrated cylinder with tubing; intermittent IV administration

12. volumetric regulator

13. uniform serum concentration of drug for avoiding drug "peaks and valleys"

Continuous Intravenous Administration

14. 27 to 28 gtt/minute.
    Method 2: a. 1000 ml ÷ 6 hours = 167 ml/hr

    b. $\frac{167\,ml}{60\,minutes/hr} \times \overset{1}{\cancel{10}}\,gtt/ml = \frac{167}{6} = \underset{6}{}$

    27–28 gtt/minute

15. Inject KCl and MVI into the bag **before** administering IV fluids. Regulate IV flow rate to 31–32 gtt/minute.
    Drug Calculation: Order: KCl 10 mEq in 1 liter of IV fluids.
    Available: KCl 20 mEq/10 ml

$$\frac{D}{H} \times V = \frac{10\ mEq}{20\ mEq} \times 10\ ml =$$

$$\frac{10}{2} = 5\ ml\ of\ KCl$$

$$
\begin{array}{cccccc}
H & : & V & :: & D & : & X \\
20\ mEq: & & 10\ ml & :: & 10\ mEq: & & X\ ml
\end{array}
$$

$$
\begin{array}{rcl}
20\ X & = & 100 \\
X & = & 5\ ml\ of\ KCl
\end{array}
$$

IV flow rate:

Method 3: $\dfrac{1000\ ml \times \overset{1}{\cancel{15}}\ gtt/ml}{8\ hours \times \underset{4}{\cancel{60}}\ minutes} = \dfrac{1000}{32} =$

31–32 gtt/min

16. Use the microdrip set. Regulate IV flow rate at 83 gtt/minute.

a. 1000 ml ÷ 12 hours = 83 ml/hr

b. $\dfrac{83\ ml \times \overset{1}{\cancel{60}}\ gtt/ml}{\underset{1}{\cancel{60}}\ min/hr} =$

83 gtt/min

17. a. 1000 ml

b. 2500 ml

c. 100 ml/hr (actual amount is 104 ml/hr)

d. macrodrip set, 10 gtt/ml

e. 16–17 gtt/minute

IV flow rate:

$\dfrac{100\ ml \times \overset{1}{\cancel{10}}\ gtt/ml}{\underset{6}{\cancel{60}}\ minutes/hr} = \dfrac{100}{6} =$

16–17 gtt/min

18. a. 500 ml of IV fluid is left.

b. Recalculated to run at 27–28 gtt/minute.

IV flow rate recalculated:

a. 500 ml ÷ 3 hrs left = 167 ml/hr

b. $\dfrac{167\ ml \times \overset{1}{\cancel{10}}\ gtt/ml}{\underset{6}{\cancel{60}}\ minutes/hr} = \dfrac{167}{6} =$

27–28 gtt/min

Intermittent Intravenous Administration

19. Drug calculation:

$$\frac{D}{H} \times V = \frac{200}{300} \times 2\ ml = \frac{400}{300} =$$

1.3 ml of cimetidine (Tagamet)

IV flow calculation:

$$\frac{Amount\ of\ solution \times gtt/ml}{Minutes\ to\ administer} = gtt/minute$$

$\dfrac{50\ ml \times \overset{3}{\cancel{60}}\ gtt/ml}{\underset{1}{\cancel{20}}\ minutes} = 150\ gtt/minute$

Answer: a. 1.3 ml of cimetidine; b. 150 gtt/minute

20. a. Add 10 ml of sterile water to cefamandole.

b. Total drug solution equals: 1 g = 10 ml.

Drug calculation: Convert milligrams to grams (gram is on the drug label). Move the decimal point three spaces to the **left**.

500 mg = .500 g = 0.5 g

$$
\begin{array}{cccccc}
H & : & V & :: & D & : & X \\
1\ g: & & 10\ ml & :: & 0.5\ g & : & X\ ml
\end{array}
$$

(1) X = 5 ml of cefamandole

IV flow calculation:

$\dfrac{55\ ml \times \overset{2}{\cancel{60}}\ ml}{\underset{1}{\cancel{30}}\ minutes} = 110\ gtt/minute$

5 ml drug + 50 ml diluent = 55 ml

Answer: 5 ml of cefamandole, 110 gtts/minute

21. a. Add 6.6 ml of diluent to nafcillin.

b. Total drug solution equals 2g = 8 ml
Drug calculation: Convert milligrams to grams (gram is on the drug label). Move the decimal point three spaces to the **left**.

1000 mg = 1.000 g = 1 g

$$\frac{D}{H} \times V = \frac{1\ g}{2\ g} \times 8\ ml = \frac{8}{2} =$$

4 ml of nafcillin

IV flow calculation:

$\dfrac{100\ ml \times 15\ gtt/ml}{40\ minutes} = \dfrac{1500}{40} =$

37–38 gtt/minute

Answer: 4 ml of nafcillin, 37–38 gtts/minute

22. Drug calculation: Convert milligrams to grams. Move the decimal point three spaces to the **left**.

250 mg = .250 g = 0.25 g

$$
\begin{array}{cccccc}
H & : & V & :: & D & : & X \\
1\ g: & & 3\ ml & :: & 0.25\ g & : & X\ ml
\end{array}
$$

(1) X = 0.75 ml of kanamycin (Kantrex)

IV flow calculation:

$\dfrac{100\ ml \times 15\ gtt/ml}{45\ minutes} = \dfrac{1500}{45} =$

33–34 gtt/minute

Answer: 0.75 ml of kanamycin, 33–34 gtt/minute

23. a. Add 4 ml of sterile water to ticarcillin (Ticar).

b. Total drug solution equals 1 g = 4 ml

Drug calculation: Convert milligrams to grams. Move the decimal point three spaces to the **left**.

$$750 \text{ mg} = .750 \text{ g} = 0.75 \text{ g}$$

$$\frac{D}{H} \times V = \frac{0.75 \text{ g}}{1 \text{ g}} \times 4 \text{ ml} =$$

3 ml of ticarcillin

IV flow calculation:

$$\frac{75 \text{ ml} \times \overset{2}{\cancel{60}} \text{ gtt/ml}}{\underset{1}{\cancel{30}} \text{ minutes}} = 150 \text{ gtt/minute}$$

Answer: 3 ml of ticarcillin, 150 gtt/minute

24. Drug calculation:

$$\begin{array}{ccccc} \text{H} & : \text{V} & :: & \text{D} & : \text{X} \\ 160/800 \text{ mg} & : 10 \text{ ml} & :: & 80/400 \text{ mg} & : \text{X ml} \end{array}$$

$$160/800 \text{X} = 10 \times 80/400$$

$$160/800 \text{X} = 800/4000 = \frac{\overset{5}{\cancel{800/4000}}}{\underset{1}{\cancel{160/800}}}$$

$$= 5 \text{ ml of Septra}$$

Volumetric pump regulator:

Amount of solution ÷ $\dfrac{\text{minutes to administer}}{60 \text{ minutes/hr}}$ =

$$125 \text{ ml} \div \frac{90 \text{ minutes}}{60 \text{ minutes}} =$$

$$125 \text{ ml} \div 5 \text{ ml (drug)} \div \frac{90 \text{ min}}{60 \text{ min}}$$

(invert the divisor and multiply)

$$130 \text{ ml} \times \frac{\overset{2}{\cancel{60}} \text{ min}}{\underset{3}{\cancel{90}} \text{ min}} = \frac{260}{3} = 87 \text{ ml/hr}$$

Answer: 5 ml of Septra; 87 ml/hr

25. Drug calculation: 75 mg of Vibramycin = 7.5 ml

$$\frac{D}{H} \times V = \frac{75 \text{ mg}}{100 \text{ mg}} \times 10 \text{ ml} =$$

$$\frac{750}{100} = 7.5 \text{ ml of Vibramycin}$$

Volumetric pump regulator:

$$107.5 \text{ ml} \div \frac{60 \text{ min}}{60 \text{ min}} =$$

$$107.5 \text{ ml} \times \frac{\overset{1}{\cancel{60}} \text{ min}}{\underset{1}{\cancel{60}} \text{ min}} = 107.5 \text{ ml/hr or } 108 \text{ ml/h}$$

26. Drug calculation: Change 400 mg to grams (400 = 0.4 g)

$$\frac{D}{H} \times V = \frac{0.4 \text{ g}}{1 \text{ g}} \times 4 \text{ ml} =$$

1.6 ml of amikacin

400 mg of amikacin = 1.6 ml

Volumetric pump regulator:

$$125 \text{ ml} \div \frac{\overset{1}{\cancel{60}} \text{ minutes (1 hr)}}{\underset{1}{\cancel{60}} \text{ minutes}} =$$

125 ml/hr (60 minutes)

27.

$$\frac{D}{H} \times V = \frac{75 \text{ mg}}{100 \text{ mg}} \times 5 \text{ ml} = \frac{375}{100} =$$

3.75 ml of minocycline

75 mg of minocycline = 3.75 ml

Volumetric pump regulator:

$$500 \text{ ml} \div \frac{120 \text{ minutes}}{60 \text{ minutes}} = 500 \times \frac{\overset{1}{\cancel{60}}}{\underset{2}{\cancel{120}}} =$$

$$\frac{500}{2} = 250 \text{ ml/hr}$$

28. Selection of the amount of diluent is 3.4 ml = 4.0 ml

Change 500 mg to 0.5 g or 2 g to 2000 mg

$$\frac{D}{H} \times V = \frac{0.5 \text{ g}}{2 \text{ g}} \times 4 \text{ ml} =$$

1 ml of cefepime twice a day

$$\frac{50 \text{ ml} \times \overset{2}{\cancel{60}} \text{ gtt}}{\underset{1}{\cancel{30}} \text{ minutes}} = 100 \text{ gtt/min of Maxipime}$$

---

29. Drug calculation:

$$\text{ml} = \frac{10 \text{ ml}}{\underset{2}{\cancel{3} \text{ g}}} \times \frac{\overset{1}{\cancel{1.5} \text{ g}}}{1} = \frac{10}{2}$$

$$= 5 \text{ ml of Unasyn.}$$
Conversion factor is not needed.

IV flow calculation:

$$\frac{105 \text{ ml} \times \overset{2}{\cancel{60}} \text{ gtt/ml}}{\underset{1}{\cancel{30}} \text{ minutes}} = 210 \text{ gtt/minute}$$

30. Drug calculation:

$$\text{ml} = \frac{10 \text{ ml}}{\cancel{1} \text{ g}} \times \frac{\cancel{1} \text{ g}}{\underset{2}{\cancel{1000}} \text{ mg}} \times \frac{\cancel{500} \text{ mg}}{1}$$

$$= 5 \text{ ml of Mefoxin.}$$

Volumetric pump regulator:

105 ml with drug solution + $\dfrac{45 \text{ minutes}}{60 \text{ minutes}}$

= (invert the divisor)
(Drug will be infused entirely in 45 minutes)

$$\frac{105 \text{ ml} \times \overset{4}{\cancel{60}} \text{ min}}{\underset{3}{\cancel{45}} \text{ minutes}} = \frac{420}{3} = 140 \text{ ml/hr}$$

Section 4F

1. 2 ½ ml of V-Cillin K 400,000 U/5 ml per dose.
   Drug order is in units; use units that are on the drug label.
   Dose is within safe parameters.
   25,000 U × 21 kg = 525,000 U
   90,000 U × 21 kg = 1,890,000 U

$$\frac{D}{H} \times V = \frac{\overset{}{\cancel{200,000}} \text{ U}}{\cancel{400,000} \text{ U}} \times 5 \text{ ml} =$$

$$\frac{10}{4} = 2 \frac{1}{2} \text{ ml}$$

$$\begin{array}{ccccc} \text{H} & : \text{V} & :: & \text{D} & : \text{X} \\ 400,000 \text{ U} & : 5 \text{ ml} & :: & 200,000 \text{ U} & : \text{X ml} \end{array}$$

$$400,000 \text{X} = 500$$
$$\text{X} = 2 \frac{1}{2} \text{ ml}$$

2. Child's weight: 75 pounds = 34.1 kg

   10 mg × 34.1 kg = 341 mg/d

15 mg × 34.1 kg = 511.5 mg/d

Child to receive 400 mg/d. Dose is within safe parameters.

Child should receive 4 ml of Ceftin per dose.

3. NO, drug order per day is NOT within the safe parameters.

50 mg × 5 kg = 250 mg per day.

Order: 75 mg × 4 doses (q6h) = 300 mg per day.

Notify the health care provider.

4. 7.8 ml or 8 ml of acetaminophen 160 mg/ 5 ml.

$$\frac{D}{H} \times V = \frac{250 \text{ mg}}{160 \text{ mg}} \times 5 \text{ ml} =$$

$$\frac{1250}{160} = 7.8 \text{ or } 8 \text{ ml}$$

$$H \quad : \quad V \quad :: \quad D \quad : \quad X$$
$$160 \text{ mg} : \quad 5 \text{ ml} \quad :: \quad 250 \text{ mg} : \quad X \text{ ml}$$
$$160 X = 1250$$
$$X = 8 \text{ ml}$$

5. 4 ml of cloxacillin (Tegopen) 125 mg/5 ml per dose.

Dose is within safe parameters.

50 mg × 8 kg = 400 mg per day

100 mg × 8 kg = 800 mg per day

100 mg × 4 doses (q6h) = 400 mg per day

$$\frac{D}{H} \times V = \frac{100 \text{ mg}}{125 \text{ mg}} \times 5 \text{ ml} =$$

$$\frac{500}{125} = 4 \text{ ml}$$

$$H \quad : \quad V \quad :: \quad D \quad : \quad X$$
$$125 \text{ mg} : \quad 5 \text{ ml} \quad :: \quad 100 \text{ mg} : \quad X \text{ ml}$$
$$125 X = 500$$
$$X = \frac{500}{125} = 4 \text{ ml}$$

6. 4 ml of erythromycin 200 mg/5 ml, q6h.

Dose is NOT within the drug parameters. The child is receiving less than the recommended dosage.

160 mg × 4 (q6h) = 640 mg per day. Check with the health care provider.

30 mg × 25 kg = 750 mg per day

50 mg × 25 kg = 1250 mg per day

7. 3 ml of cefaclor (Ceclor) 125 mg/5 ml per dose

OR

1.5 ml of cefaclor (Ceclor) 250 mg/5 ml per dose.

It may be easier to measure 3 ml than 1 ½ ml.

Convert 22 pounds to kg (22 ÷ 2.2 = 10 kg)

20 mg × 10 kg = 200 mg per day

40 mg × 10 kg = 400 mg per day

Order 75 mg × 3 (q8h) = 225 mg per day

Drug dose is within safe parameters.

Ceclor 125 mg/5 ml

$$\frac{D}{H} \times V = \frac{75 \text{ mg}}{125 \text{ mg}} \times 5 \text{ ml} =$$

$$\frac{375}{125} = 3 \text{ ml}$$

Dimensional analysis:

$$\text{ml} = \frac{5 \text{ ml}}{\underset{5}{\cancel{125}} \text{ mg}} \times \frac{\overset{3}{\cancel{75}} \text{ mg}}{1} = \frac{15}{5} = 3 \text{ ml}$$

Ceclor 250 mg/5 ml

$$H \quad : \quad V \quad :: \quad D \quad : \quad X$$
$$250 \text{ mg} : \quad 5 \text{ ml} \quad :: \quad 75 \text{ mg} : \quad X \text{ ml}$$
$$250 X = 375$$
$$X = 1.5 \text{ or } 1 ½ \text{ ml}$$

8. a. Child weighs 11.8 kg or 12 kg

b. Yes, it is within the dose parameter: 11.8 kg × 40 mg = 472 mg/d

Child to receive 150 mg × 3 doses = 450 mg/d

c. 6 ml of Augmentin per dose.

Basic formula:

$$\frac{D}{H} \times V = \frac{150 \text{ mg} \times 5 \text{ ml}}{125 \text{ mg}} = 6 \text{ ml/dose}$$

Dimensional analysis:

$$\text{ml} = \frac{5 \text{ ml}}{\underset{5}{\cancel{75}} \text{ mg}} \times \frac{\overset{6}{\cancel{150}} \text{ mg}}{1} = \frac{30}{5} = 6 \text{ ml/dose}$$

d. 450 mg/d; 18 ml/d total.

9. Child's body surface area (BSA) is 0.98 m². Safe dosage range: 60 mg × 0.98 m² = 58.8 or 59 mg

250 × 0.98 m² = 245 mg (59 mg to 245 mg of Cytoxan)

10. Child's body surface area (BSA) is 0.87 m².

250 mg × 0.87 m² = 218 mg per day AND

218 ÷ 2 divided doses = 109 mg per dose

$$\frac{D}{H} \times V = \frac{109 \text{ mg}}{30 \text{ mg}} \times 5 \text{ ml} =$$

$$\frac{545}{30} = 18 \text{ ml}$$

$$H \quad : \quad V \quad :: \quad D \quad : \quad X$$
$$30 \text{ mg} : \quad 5 \text{ ml} \quad :: \quad 109 \text{ mg} : \quad X \text{ ml}$$
$$30 X = 545$$
$$X = 18 \text{ ml}$$

18 ml of Dilantin 30 mg/5 ml twice a day.

11. Child weighs 12 kg (26 ÷ 2.2 = 11.8 or 12 kg).

Drug parameters: 25 mg × 12 kg = 300 mg per day

50 mg × 12 kg = 600 mg per day

Drug order is 100 mg × 4 doses (q6h) = 400 mg per day

Child's drug dose is within **safe** parameters. Drug label states to add 1.2 ml of diluent to equal ampicillin (Polycillin-N) 125 mg = 1.2 ml or 1 ml.

$$\frac{D}{H} \times V = \frac{100\,mg}{125\,mg} \times 1.2\,ml = \frac{120}{125}$$

$$125\overline{)120}^{\,.96} = 0.96 \text{ or } 1 \text{ ml of ampicillin}$$

$$\begin{array}{ccccccc} H & : & V & :: & D & : & X \\ 125\,mg & : & 1\,ml & :: & 120\,mg & : & X\,ml \end{array}$$

$$125\,X = 120$$
$$X = 0.96 \text{ or } 1 \text{ ml of ampicillin}$$

12. Child weighs 18 kg (40 ÷ 2.2 = 18.18 or 18 kg).
    Drug parameters: 3 mg × 18 kg = 54 mg
    5 mg × 18 kg = 90 mg per day
    Drug order is 25 mg. Drug dose is less than the drug parameters. Check with the health care provider. Drug dose order may be changed. Since the drug dose is NOT greater than the drug parameters, drug dose would be considered **safe**.
    Pentobarbital (Nembutal) 25 mg = 0.5 ml or ½ ml.

13. Child weighs 10 kg.
    Drug parameters: 15 mg × 10 kg = 150 mg in 2 divided doses.
    Drug order is 50 mg × 2 doses (q12h) = 100 mg
    Drug dose is **safe**.
    Drug label: Kantrex 75 mg/2 ml.

$$\frac{D}{H} \times V = \frac{50\,mg}{75\,mg} \times 2\,ml =$$

$$\frac{100}{75} = 1.3 \text{ ml of Kantrex}$$

$$\begin{array}{ccccccc} H & : & V & :: & D & : & X \\ 75\,mg & : & 2\,ml & :: & 50\,mg & : & X\,ml \end{array}$$

$$75\,X = 100$$
$$X = 1.3 \text{ ml of Kantrex}$$

Kanamycin (Kantrex) 50 mg = 1.3 ml.

Dimensional analysis:

$$ml = \frac{2\,ml}{\underset{3}{75\,mg}} \times \frac{\overset{2}{50\,mg}}{1} = \frac{4}{3} = 1.3 \text{ ml/dose}$$

14. Drug dose is safe. (45 mg to 67.5 mg per dose)
    5 mg × 9 kg = 45 mg q8h
    7.5 mg × 9 kg = 67.5 mg q12h

$$\frac{D}{H} \times V = \frac{50\,mg}{100\,mg} \times 2\,ml =$$

$$\frac{100}{100} = 1 \text{ ml of amikacin}$$

15. 48 pounds ÷ 2.2 = 21.8 kg or 22 kg
    Drug dose is safe. (550 mg to 1100 mg).
    Add 2 ml of diluent to yield 2 ml of drug solution (250 mg = 2 ml)
    Cefazolin sodium 125 mg = 1 ml.

16. 3 mg × 22 kg = 66 mg/d.
    5 mg × 22 kg = 110 mg/d.
    Child to receive 25 mg × 3 doses = 75 mg/d.
    Drug dose is safe.

$$\frac{25\,mg}{80\,mg} \times 2\,ml = \frac{50}{80} =$$

0.63 ml or 0.6 ml per dose

Dimensional analysis:

$$ml = \frac{2\,ml}{80\,mg} \times \frac{25\,mg}{1} = \frac{50}{}$$
$$= 0.63 \text{ ml/dose}$$

CHAPTER 5—
The Drug Approval Process (U.S. and Canadian), Resources, and Ethical Considerations

Questions 1–4: refer to text.

5. the *International Pharmacopeia*

6. *United States Pharmacopeia/National Formulary* (USP/NF)

7. to assure safety

8. Food, Drug, and Cosmetic Act of 1938

9. Durham-Humphrey

10. to tighten controls over drug safety by requiring that adverse reactions and contraindications be included in the literature.

11. Nurse Practice Act

12. a. provision of drug education and research into prevention and treatment of drug dependence
    b. strengthen enforcement authority
    c. establish treatment and rehabilitation facilities
    d. designate categories for controlled substances according to abuse liability

13. five

14. have

15. more

16. I

17. V

18. locked location

19. Canadian Food and Drug Act; Narcotics Control Act

20. similar

21. three

22. III

23. Pharmacy Acts

24. c

25. c

26. a

27. b

28. c

29. cheaper; same active ingredients

30. some variation in action or response; have not had extensive testing

31. not to present

32. D and X

33. misfeasance (negligence)

34. *American Hospital Formulary. Physician's Desk Reference* (PDR)

35. 3; home

36. iron, flavored acetaminophen, chocolate-covered laxatives, and flavored liquid medicines

37. Drug Regulation

38. Code of Ethics; variable

39. client

CHAPTER 6—
Transcultrual Considerations

Questions 1–4: refer to text.

5. African-American and Hispanic

6. Navajo

7. Amish

8. people of Chinese descent

9. African-American, Hispanic, and Polynesian (not covered in chapter 6.)

10. Jewish

11. European-American

12. European-American

13. Kashrut

14. Deitsch

15. d (values)

16. D (heredity)

17. B (religion)

18. B (length of time away from the country of origin)

19. A (are less responsive to beta-blockers than are European-Americans)

20. C (includes corn as a staple)

21. C (high rates of Hemophilia B

22. D (bloating)

23. A (leafy green vegetables)

24. D (culture)

25. A (maintenance of eye contact)

26. B (determine the amount of clay she eats)

27. D (encourage him to drink the tea, but be sure to continue taking his oral hypoglycemic medication)

Critical Thinking Exercise

1. Nurse did not give any attention to the father.

This may be perceived as a lack of respect among traditional Asians.

2. Cupping. The practice is not harmful.

3. Out of respect for the nurse who is in a hierarchical position.

4. 30-50 mg/kg per day.

5. Three times the prescribed dosage. A tablespoon is 15 milliliters. A teaspoon is 5 milliliters.

6. Yes.

7. Use an eye dropper and demonstrate its use or provide the correct size spoon.

8. Chinese language only has the present tense. Until people become fluent in a second language, they may use this speech pattern.

9. An older or same-aged person as the parents as well as an interpreter who speaks the same dialect. If the interpreter comes form the same socioeconomic background, rapport may be improved.

10. Demonstrate the procedure using an eye dropper or appropriate sized spoon.

CHAPTER 7—
Drug Interactions, Over-the-Counter Drugs and Drug Abuse

Questions 1–5: refer to text.

6. c

7. d

8. a

9. b

10. e

11. a

12. b, e

13. a, d

14. f

15. f

16. c

17. a

18. b

19. d

20. c

21. a

22. d

23. serum

24. increases; decreases

25. urine

26. use of sunscreen; avoiding excessive sunlight

27. enzyme inducer; increased

28. controlled substances

29. compulsive; craving; seeking

30. nausea and convulsions

31. psychological dependence; does not

32. overwork; chronic fatigue; physical illness; marital problems; insomnia; or pending retirement

33. professional help

34. information, referral, consultation, support groups, reentry and monitoring services

35. supportive

36. Durham-Humphrey

37. Kefauver-Harris

38. 3

39. phenylpropranolamine; heart; diabetes mellitus; thyroid

40. may

41. before

42. safe and effective

43. II

44. is not

45. increases

46. should

47. Handbook of Non-Prescription Drugs; Facts and Comparison

48. variable: symptoms may be masked; delay in professional diagnosis and treatment; OTC products may interact with other meds; need to consult health care provider before starting OTC products

CHAPTER 8—
Herbal Therapy and Nursing Implications

Word search:

```
O  M  D  V  Z  T  W  A  E  T
F  R  E  S  H  H  E  R  B  C
J  I  R  D  O  S  L  I  O  A
D  S  B  I  D  Y  C  U  T  R
E  J  B  D  I  R  T  L  E  T
T  I  N  C  T  U  R  E  A  X
D  A  O  P  A  P  T  R  E  E
R  P  F  U  S  A  L  R  E  A
D  E  N  Y  P  S  E  U  I  W
S  X  A  K  T  I  L  I  F  Y
```

1. f

2. d

3. c

4. a

5. h

6. b

7. e

8. g

9. j

10. i

11. syrup

12. tea

13. tincture

14. extract

15. oils

16. fresh herb

17. c

18. a

19. b

20. b

21. b

22. a

23. c

24. d

25. c

26. b

27. b

28. d

29. g

30. h

31. j

32. a

33. f

34. b

35. c

36. e

37. i

38. variable: do not use herbs if pregnant or nursing; not for children; seek care from HCP for severe or persistent symptoms; read labels and know expected information required on labels; check expiration date. Consult HCP about other meds and OTC products before starting herbal preparations

Critical Thinking Exercise

a. Suggest that J.C. discuss his questions and potential benefits and risks of taking specific herbal preparations with his health care provider before taking any preparations.

b. Echinacea is recommended to boost the immune system on a short-term basis, less than 8 weeks. Need to discuss individual concerns with health care provider first. Caution is required when taking herbs with antidepressant and sedative-hypnotic effects together. What other meds, herbs, and conditions does person have?

c. FDA-proposed controls on dietary supplements containing ephedra (ma Huang) not to exceed 25 mg ephedrine/d for <7 days and contraindicated in persons with diabetes mellitus, glaucoma, and hypertension. Use of this herb has diminished with reports of adverse events such as palpitations and stroke.

CHAPTER 9—
Pediatric Pharmacology

Questions 1–2: refer to text.

3. difficult to get pediatric sample; parents reluctant to take risks; potentially invasive nature of studies; smaller market share for meds

4. absorption, distribution, metabolism, excretion

5. may hinder drug absorption

6. may require higher dose of water-soluble meds due to greater volume of fluid for distribution

7. less

8. toxicity

9. readily/quickly

10. may have higher requirement for medication; increased amount and/or increased frequency

11. renal tubular function decreased; assess for hydration/dehydration

12. onset, peak, and duration of effect of medication; mechanism of action; very important in insulin therapy

13. a. weight of child

    b. body surface area

14. a. to administer the med

    b. evaulate effectiveness

    c. provide comfort after med is administered

15. a. minimum restraint; comforting

    b. simple explanation, firm approach, enlist imagination

    c. allow some choice

    d. involvement in administration process and information

    e. contract regarding plan of care, privacy

16. have child assist in placing EMLA on skin

and covering it with transparent dressing

17. so child does not fear "leakage" from the area

18. honesty, attention to vocabulary, forceful restraint not used, praise child after successful administration of med, never threaten or shame child into taking a med, teaching, developmental differences, and so forth

CHAPTER 10—
Geriatric Pharmacology

1. drug metabolism that occurs in the liver and contributes to the clearance of drugs

2. taking drugs according to the prescribed drug regimen

3. not taking the prescribed drugs as indicated

4. taking many (multiple) drugs together

5. increases

6. decreases

7. decreases

8. decreases

9. increases

10. creatinine clearance; 80-130

11. weight, adipose tissues, laboratory results, and present health problems

12. flurazepam (Dalmane)

13. calcium blockers and ACE inhibitors or AII inhibitors

14. digitalis toxicity; decline in kidney function

15. 30-50%

16. d

17. c

18. d

19. c

20. b

21. d

22. b

23. d

24. c

25. b

26. a

27. b

28. variable

Critical Thinking Exercises

1. BUN, creatinine, creatinine clearance, serum protein, urinalysis

2. warm bath prior to sleep, avoid caffeine products; coffee, cola, chocolates prior to bedtime, soft music, routine bedtime patterns, seek HCP help

3. keep written record of each drug taken, keep drugs in daily or weekly pill box container, other suggestions

4. see Nursing Process

CHAPTER 11—
Medication Administration in Community Settings

Word search:

```
T  F  M  L  E  I  B  G  H  M  X  Y  I  B  P  N  L  D  E  T  S  A
B  W  U  O  G  Z  H  K  L  Y  C  D  V  R  T  L  E  N  L  E  C  Q
S  T  C  E  F  F  E  E  D  I  S  L  T  A  C  L  S  F  L  G  T  O
V  A  R  U  I  M  T  S  D  L  A  E  G  J  E  L  B  F  L  I  P  M
H  E  T  B  V  P  X  I  K  N  R  G  R  B  T  S  A  F  E  T  Y  R
F  M  I  K  B  S  A  U  O  Y  T  A  A  C  X  D  E  M  J  L  K  D
I  G  C  J  G  F  U  I  M  H  J  L  L  R  M  O  Y  P  L  I  B  A
R  E  O  B  E  X  S  C  S  U  T  B  H  I  D  I  E  T  O  N  E  B
J  H  I  B  N  S  C  E  Y  A  M  K  N  P  E  A  V  J  H  Q  O  D
Y  T  P  M  E  E  T  O  B  J  E  I  D  F  O  L  K  M  O  L  A  S
A  S  D  F  R  E  T  N  U  M  S  W  I  M  V  D  I  U  Q  E  R  Y
N  Y  O  E  A  T  M  J  K  T  Y  R  O  T  A  L  U  G  E  R  U  H
B  R  P  W  L  I  Y  R  R  A  F  G  N  H  T  E  L  L  I  A  C  U
P  E  Y  B  V  R  I  A  K  L  J  C  H  I  L  D  S  A  F  E  M  N
A  G  O  C  U  L  T  U  R  A  L  B  H  T  E  S  S  C  P  O  L  Q
L  K  K  R  E  I  E  P  E  R  S  O  N  A  L  B  E  L  I  E  F  S
R  E  J  N  O  R  I  G  I  N  A  L  I  T  B  O  P  E  M  Y  E  V
T  Q  I  N  P  R  T  R  A  D  I  T  I  O  N  A  L  V  U  A  S  F
```

1. professional, legal, regulatory

2. avoid

3. general, diet, self-administration, side effects, and cultural considerations

4. safety

5. original labeled; child safe

6. personal beliefs

7. traditional; folk

8. d

9. a

10. d

11. b

12. c

13. drug, dose, frequency, route, health care provider signature

14. health care provider, pharmacist

15. report to health care provider

16. unused

17. self-administers

18. self-management

19. escalating health care costs and insurance

20. licensed nurses

Critical Thinking Exercise

Meds given only with parent's written permission; prescription drugs wirrten authorization of HCP; individual pharmacy labeled bottle for specific student; administration documented: name, med, dosage, time, and person giving; meds stored in locked, clean cabinet

CHAPTER 12—
The Role of the Nurse in Drug Research

Questions 1–4: refer to text.

5. autonomous

6. beneficence

7. justice

8. risk to benefit

9. 1 in 10,000

10. in vitro

11. in vivo

12. toxicity screening

13. II

14. long-term
15. d
16. a
17. g
18. b
19. c
20. f
21. e
22. i
23. j
24. h
25. k
26. c
27. b
28. b
29. Client/family advocate; liaison between health care provider and re-search nurse
30. variable
31. variable

CHAPTER 13—
Vitamin and Mineral Replacement

Questions 1–4: refer to text.
5. d
6. d
7. d
8. c
9. a
10. b
11. b
12. a
13. a
14. a

15. a
16. a
17. b
18. b
19. a
20. d
21. c
22. e
23. a
24. b
25. d
26. k
27. e
28. folic
29. iron
30. hemoglobin
31. egg yolks, dried beans, and fruit
32. slow
33. hemorrhage
34. discolor teeth enamel
35. c
36. b
37. d
38. a
39. d
40. administer with food to increase absorption; store in light-resistant con-tainer
41. d
42. a
43. c
44. variable: not to leave iron tablets within child's reach; telephone poison control center for over-doses; not to overdose;

avoid megadoses of iron during first trimester; take iron with food if gastrointestinal upset occurs

CHAPTER 14—
Fluid and Electrolyte Replacement

1. Serum calcium excess
2. Serum potassium excess
3. Serum sodium excess
4. Serum calcium deficit (loss)
5. Serum potassium deffcit (loss)
6. Serum sodium deficit (loss)
7. Concentration of body fluids
8. Effects of fluid on cellular volume
9. 275–295 mOsm/kg
10. Double the serum so-dium level *or*

2 × serum sodium level +

$$\frac{BUN}{3} + \frac{Glucose}{18}$$

11. iso-osmolar
12. hypertonic
13. crystalloids, colloids, blood products, and lipids
14. nerve impulses; skeletal, cardiac, and smooth muscles
15. cells
16. kidneys
17. minimum four ounces or ½ glass of fluids. Pre-

ferred: with meals or eight ounces of fluid

18. normal saline solution (0.9% sodium chloride); 3% saline solution

19. gastrointestinal tract

20. intracellular; extracellular

21. more

22. increase

23. twitching of mouth; tingling and numbness of fingers; carpopedal spasm; laryngeal spasm; spasmodic contractions

24. laxatives; antacids

25. c

26. a

27. d

28. e

29. potassium: 3.5–5.3 mEq/L

30. sodium: 135–145 mEq/L

31. calcium: 9–11 mg/dl; 4.5–5.5 mEq/L

32. magnesium: 1.5–2.5 mEq/L

33. b

34. a

35. d

36. d

37. c

38. a

39. Potassium is extremely irritating to the gastric mucosa. It may cause bleeding or gastric ulcer if taken undiluted.

40. Potassium should *never* be given as a bolus or IV push. Inverting the IV bag with potassium ensures that the potassium is diluted. If the bag is NOT inverted several times, potassium can accumulate at the neck of the IV bag; thus, a large portion of the potassium is given directly into the vein; cardiac dysrhythmias or arrest could result.

41. Potassium can cause tissue necrosis if it infiltrates into the fatty (subcutaneous) tissues.

42. 80% to 90% of potassium is excreted in the urine. With renal insufficiency, potassium can accumulate, causing hyperkalemia. Urine output should be at least 25 ml/h and 600 ml/24 h.

43. Serum potassium level should be 3.5 to 5.3 mEq/L. Hypokalemia occurs if the serum potassium level is <3.5 mEq/L; hyperkalemia occurs if it is >5.3 mEq/L.

44. If hypokalemia occurs, the T wave is flat or inverted and the ST segment is depressed. With hyperkalemia, the T wave is narrow and peaked and the QRS complex is spread.

45. Foods rich in potassium include citrus fruit juices, fruits, vegetables, nuts, and meats. Serum potassium level should be monitored while the client is taking potassium-wasting diuretics and cortisone. If serum level is low, potassium supplements should be taken.

46. Signs of hypokalemia include nausea, vomiting, cardiac dysrhythmias, abdominal distention, soft-flabby muscles. Signs of hyperkalemia include nausea, abdominal cramps, oliguria, tachycardia and later bradycardia, weakness, and numbness or tingling in the extremities.

47. Hypokalemia enhances the action of digitalis preparation. Signs of digitalis toxicity include nausea, vomiting, anorexia, bradycardia (pulse <60 mph), cardiac dysrhythmias, and visual disturbances. Serum potassium level should be checked while the client is receiving digoxin and a potassium-wasting diuretic or cortisone.

48. b

49. c

50. a

51. c

52. a

53. b

54. b

55. c

56. d

57. d

58. c

59. a

60. c

61. b

62. a

63. b

64. d

65. b

Critical Thinking Exercise

1. Crystalloids do not interfere with type and cross-match of the blood. They will raise the blood pressure rapidly; however, the blood pressure will remain elevated longer with colloids than with crystalloids.

2. Whole blood is useful when replacing a large volume of blood. If a client has cardiac problems, packed red blood cells are recommended (less fluid volume, thus less fluid overload).

3. A.F. is showing signs of shock due to loss of fluid volume and red blood cells to carry oxygen. The use of IV fluids should raise the blood pressure.

4. When client has shock-like symptoms, blood circulation is decreased, especially to the kidneys. Renal shutdown may occur if the decrease is severe.
   Less body fluids are circulated through the kidneys and less urine output occurs.

5. Body fluid volume has increased.

6. Sodium should be part of the daily intravenous order. Giving only dextrose in water over 24 hours or more may cause fluid imbalance, such as intracellular fluid volume excess (water intoxication).

7. Dextrose in water and lactated Ringer's solution is isotonic. Dextrose in ½ normal saline solution is hypertonic.

8. If the client receives only hypertonic solutions, dehydration could result. Fluid is pulled from the cells to the vascular space and then excreted.

9. A.F.'s serum potassium level is low. A healthy client with a normal potassium level should receive 40 mEq of potassium daily. A.F. should receive a higher dosage of potassium since he has a potassium deficit. It would take 100–200 mEq of potassium intravenously to raise the serum potassium level by 1 mEq/L.

10. Nursing assessment: the type of intravenous fluids A.F. is receiving; checking vital signs; determining if blood loss is still occurring, and so forth.

CHAPTER 15—
Nutritional Support

Questions 1–4: refer to text.

5. a. gastrostomy
   b. jejunostomy
   c. nasoduodenal/ nasojejunal
   d. nasogastric

6. enteral; parenteral

7. improving blood flow to major organs; enhancing wound healing; decreasing infection; shortening hospital stay; improving organ function

8. oral; gastric; small intestine.

9. carbohydrates; protein; fat

10. infuse enteral feeding over 8 to 16 hours per day

11. aspiration, diarrhea, or dehydration

12. hyperalimentation or intravenous hyperalimentation

13. GI tract obstruction or incapacitation, or uncontrolled vomiting

14. TPN solution is infused too rapidly, insufficient insulin coverage, or prediabetic client

15. abruptly stopping TPN therapy or too much insulin

16. d

17. b

18. b

19. a

20. c

21. c

22. d

23. b

24. b

25. d

Critical Thinking Exercise

1. The advantage of continuous and cyclic methods of enteral feeding for a severely ill client is that large amounts of highly concentrated (increased osmolality) solution is entered slowly into the GI tract, thus is more tolerable for absorption. Disadvantages of bolus and with some intermittent methods are that the enteral feeding is highly concentrated and when rapidly administered, diarrhea could occur. With continuous enteral feedings, the client is never free from the feeding, and other reasons.

2. T.A. would not receive adequate nutrition with IV solutions of crystalloids.

3. T.A. is to receive enteral feedings by the intermittent method.

    The enteral feedings may be given by drip or pump infusion for 30 to 60 minutes every three to six hours.

4. Share the family's concerns with the health care provider. Make appropriate referrals.

5. Elevate the head of the bed or place the client in the Fowler's position. Do not administer feedings while the client is lying flat. Check for residual feeding before administering a feeding.

6. Dilute the enteral feedings for several days until diarrhea stops. Dilute the medication. Check for GI bacteria.

7.

$$\frac{D \text{ (desired \%)}}{H \text{ (on hand vol.)}} \times V \text{ (desired)} = \text{total volume}$$

$$\frac{70}{100} \times 300 \text{ ml} = \frac{21000}{100} =$$

210 ml of Ensure Plus

Total amount − Amount of EF = amount of water

300 ml − 210 ml = 90 ml

Mix 210 ml of Ensure Plus and 90 ml of water for a total of 300 ml of solution.

CHAPTER 16—
Central Nervous System Stimulants

Questions 1–5: refer to text.

6. analeptics

7. psychological

8. normal waking

9. attention deficit hyperactivity disorder (ADHD)

10. are not

11. decongestants and caffeine, barbiturates/ decongestants, and antihypertensives

12. stimulation; toxicity or dysfunction

13. xanthine

14. apnea or respiratory distress

15. 500

16. do

17. d

18. d

19. b

20. a

21. d

22. b

23. a

24. c

25. d

26. b

27. d

28. a

29. narcolepsy, ADHD, obesity, and reversal of respiratory distress

30. variable: monitor heart rate and blood pressure and report significant changes, assess for side effects, administer 6–8 hours before sleep, taper the dose when discontinuing the drug, avoid administering CNS stimulants to nursing mothers.

31. Take drugs before meals; avoid alcohol and caffeine-containing foods; report weight loss; avoid hazardous equipment in the presence of tremors, nervousness, or tachycardia; and seek counseling

Critical Thinking Exercise

1. before meals to increase absorption

2. schedule children before lunch; have adequate space for number of children

3. fewer side effects

4. height, weight, and growth

5. CBC, differential WBC, and platelets

6. sugarless gum to relieve dry mouth; consult

health care provider before taking OTC drugs that may contain caffeine. High caffeine plasma levels could be fatal. Need for three nutritional meals in presence of anorexia.

7. Opportunity to discuss feelings and ask questions; need for appropriate counseling (not drugs alone!); long-term use may lead to drug abuse; diet; side effects and what to report to health care provider.

CHAPTER 17—
Central Nervous System Depressants: Sedative-Hypnotics and Anesthetics

Questions 1–5: refer to text.

6. sedative-hypnotics, general and local anesthetics, analgesics, narcotic analgesics, anticonvulsants, antipsychotics, and antidepressants

7. rapid eye movement (REM); and nonrapid eye movement (NREM)

8. sedation

9. hypnotic

10. arise at a specific hour; no naps; avoid caffeine drinks and large quantities of fluids six hours before bedtime; avoid heavy meals or exercise before bedtime; take a warm bath and/or listen to soft music at bedtime; avoid loud noises; drink warm milk

11. may

12. ultra short

13. central nervous, pain, consciousness

14. ether

15. surgical; analgesia, excitement or delirium, medullary paralysis

16. spinal

17. respiratory distress or failure

18. saddle block

19. are

20. long

21. short

22. zolpidem tartrate (Ambien)

23. Flumazenil (Romazecin)

24. esters and amides

25. d

26. f

27. e

28. a

29. b

30. c

31. variable: instruct the client about nonpharmacologic measures to induce/promote sleep; avoid alcohol, antidepressants, antipsychotic and narcotic drugs; not to drive or operate machinery; to report adverse effects, etc.

32. d

33. a

34. a

35. a

36. c

37. b

38. b

39. c

40. d

41. d

Critical Thinking Exercise

1. Take a detailed history of insomnia; vital signs, assess renal function

2. Promotes natural sleep; no hangover or undesirable effect

3. Drug dependence; drug tolerance

4. Yes; short-acting and decreased side effects

5. 15–30 minutes and 3–6 hours

6. Prepare for bed and then take med (short-acting); incorporate nonpharmacologic measures to promote sleep; not for long-term use; dose should be tapered to avoid withdrawal symptoms

CHAPTER 18—
Nonnarcotic and Narcotic Analgesics

Questions 1–4: refer to text.

5. c

6. a

7. d

8. e

9. b

10. analgesics

11. propionic acid

12. viral

13. prostaglandins

14. food, mealtime, glass of fluid

15. hepatonecrosis

16. is not

17. variable: keep out of reach of children, avoid alcohol and highly protein-bound drugs, take ibuprofen and aspirin with food, no aspirin for viral infections

18. central nervous system; peripheral nervous system

19. respiration and coughing

20. antitussive and antidiarrheal

21. head injury and respiratory depression

22. variable: avoid alcohol, increase fluid intake, report dizziness and difficulty breathing

23. b

24. d

25. d

26. a

27. d

28. MAOIs

29. side effect; health care provider

30. variable: anorexia, nausea, vomiting, constipation, drowsiness, dizziness, sedation, urinary retention, rash, blurred vision, bradycardia, flushing, euphoria, pruritus

31. b

32. d

33. c

34. narcotic abuse

35. IV

36. b

37. b

38. d

39. d

40. c

41. d

42. a

Critical Thinking Exercise

1. 0.67 ml; intravenously

2. yes

3. inject over five minutes

4. side effect of morphine sulfate

5. no; orthostatic hypotension is side effect

6. increases AST and ALT

7. not to take any CNS depressants and alcohol; use nonpharmacologic measures to relieve pain and reduce stress

CHAPTER 19—
Anticonvulsants

Questions 1–5: refer to text.

6. one

7. electroencephalogram

8. idiopathic

9. generalized; partial

10. preventing; do not

11. are not

12. hydantoins, long-acting barbiturates, succinimides, oxazolidones, benzodiazepines, carbamazepine, and valproate

13. phenytoin

14. carbamazepine

15. OTC

16. intramuscular

17. d

18. a

19. d

20. c

21. b

22. a

23. a

24. b

25. b

26. c

27. d

28. c

29. c

30. a

31. variable: not to drive or operate hazardous machinery when drug therapy is started; report nystagmus, slurred speech, rash; advise health care provider if pregnant or contemplating pregnancy; wear medic alert ID; not to abruptly stop drug, etc.

32. a

33. d

34. c

35. d

36. a

37. b

38. variable: monitor serum drug levels, maintain protective environment, monitor nutrition, assess contraception in women

39. resources, current information, support groups, sharing information, sharing knowledge of community resources

Critical Thinking Exercise

1. age; rate of metabolism and possible associated conditions

2. therapeutic serum or plasma level

3. below: seizures not controlled; within: seizures controlled; above: toxicity may occur

4. shorter half-life, thus decreased chance of cumulative drug effects

5. highly protein-bound

6. 15-50 µg/ml

7. nothing related to level if the seizures are controlled with no side effects.

8. variable: need to assess current knowledge base regarding anticonvulsants and seizures; understanding of need for regular follow-up and potential consequences of lack of follow-up; proceed accordingly

CHAPTER 20—
Antipsychotics and Anxiolytics

1. Facial grimacing, involuntary upward eye movement

2. Restless, difficulty standing still, paces the floor, rocking back and forth

3. Known as antianxiety drugs or sedative-hypnotics

4. Any drug the modifies psychotic behavior, an antipsychotic effect

5. Difficulty in processing information and coming to a conclusion, delusions, hallacinations, catatonia, aggressive or violent behavior

6. A chronic psychotic disorder, hallucination, delusion to the loss of function and motivation

7. Sucking and smacking movements of the lips, chewing motion, protrusion and rolling of tongue

8. b

9. d

10. b

11. d

12. b

13. c

14. a

15. b

16. b

17. a

18. d

19. c

20. a

21. c

22. b

23. b

24. d

25. thought process, behavior; dopamine

26. anxiety or depression

27. phenothiazines, thioxanthenes, butyrophenes, dibenzoxazepines

28. extrapyramidal

29. drowsiness

30. pruritus, photosensitivity

31. decrease

32. c

33. a

34. a

35. b

36. b

37. c

38. c

39. c

40. d

41. b

42. b

43. d

44. c

45. are not

46. tolerance

47. sedative-hypnotics

48. dyspnea, heart palpitations, dizziness, trembling

49. relaxation techniques, psychotherapy, support groups

50. buspirone (Buspar)

51. antihistamines

52. variable: dry mouth (offer throat lozenges); orthostatic hypotension (monitor vital signs); constipation (offer additional fluids); dizziness (teach need to rise slowly); urinary incontinence (offer emotional support)

Critical Thinking Exercise

1. B.B. is displaying negative symptoms of schizophrenia. Mesoridazine is more effective for treating positive symptoms of schizophrenia, whereas clozapine is effective for both positive and negative symptoms.

2. Agranulocytosis is a life-threatening side effect of clozapine. B.B.'s white blood cell count should be monitored at specified times.

3. The target daily dose is 300-450 mg per day. His prescribed daily dose is within low normal range. His daily dose may need to be increased; max: 900 mg/d.

4. The clozapine should be taken at the prescribed times. Any problem with dosage schedule should be discussed with the health care provider. Use of pill container may be of help to avoid missed doses.

5. Alcohol and CNS depressants with clozapine cause a depressant effect; antihypertensive drugs with clozapine may enhance a hypotensive state; and others.

6. Assess the effects of clozapine and lab results (WBCs). Instruct client to take clozapine as ordered; avoid drugs that may cause drug interaction; avoid orthostatic hypotension, and others.

CHAPTER 21—
Antidepressants and Mood Stabilizers

1. Bipolar (affective disorders)

2. SSRIs

3. MAOIs

4. Manic

5. Antidepressants

6. Reactive (depression)

7. Tricyclics

```
P  M  T  R  O  V  S  K  L  N  Q  M  B  C  E  I  B
J  A  N  T  I  D  E  P  R  E  S  S  A  N  T  S  W
P  O  X  R  J  T  W  Z  N  A  C  U  Y  K  H  F  L
K  I  W  I  Q  P  U  A  R  I  H  O  E  Y  I  R  W
Q  S  E  C  J  U  T  A  l  E  M  V  O  D  N  Z  S
R  X  C  Y  I  P  L  N  E  N  I  U  B  M  Z  A  I
T  W  R  C  I  O  J  P  X  T  Z  B  V  R  O  P  M
P  H  D  L  P  Y  M  N  C  R  S  B  I  E  W  F  H
R  O  U  I  I  N  M  A  N  I  C  A  P  C  Q  J  W
V  T  B  C  I  S  E  M  N  X  Z  P  O  T  A  W  E
F  R  P  S  S  R  I  S  I  W  T  J  O  B  M  I  A
```

8. tricyclic, monoamine oxidase (MAO) inhibitors, and second generation: SSRIs

9. two to four weeks

10. at night

11. imipramine hydrochloride

12. atypical antidepressants

13. major depressive disorders; anxiety disorders (obsessive-compulsive, panic, phobias)

14. MAOIs

15. should not

16. tranylcypromine (Parnate), isocarboxazid (Marplan), phenelzine (Nardil)

17. b

18. c

19. a

20. d

21. b

22. c

23. c

24. a

25. b

26. c

27. a

28. d

29. a

30. a

31. b

32. d

33. c

34. b

35. b

36. c

37. b

38. c

39. a

Critical Thinking Exercise

1. history of depression and coping behaviors, vital signs, liver and renal function tests, drug history

2. high end of recommended dosage; should be divided dose with most administered in the morning. Avoid nighttime administration.

3. three

4. primary

5. variable: grief support group, peer counseling programs, etc.

6. variable: take medicine as prescribed, avoid alcohol, take med with food, do not abruptly stop taking med, do not operate machinery until dosage is stabilized, etc.

CHAPTER 22—
Autonomic Nervous System Agents

Questions 1–6: refer to text.

```
G I T F M L E I B G H M X Y I B P N L D O T S A
W L B W U O G Z H K L Y C D V R T L E N P E C Q
A R S T C E S Y M P A T H E T I C L S F P G T O
J E V A R U I M T S D L S E G J E L B F O I P M
O U H E T B V P X I K L A T E L E K S F S T Y R
P Q F M I K B S A U O Y M A A C X D E M I L K D
A C E T Y L C H O L I N E L L I G O Y P T I B A
M T E N I R H P E N I P E R O N R I E V E N E B
K W J H I B N S C E Y A M K I V I S C E R A L D
Y H Y T P S I M I L A R E T D O O L K M O L A S
B L A S D F R E T N U M A W I L V D I U Q E R Y
R I N Y O E A T M J K L Y R O U A L U P E Y U H
S C B R P W L I Y R U A F G G N I S S E R P E D
C P T E Y B V R I M K L J C H T L D S O F W M N
E O A G O D U L I U R A L B H A E S S C P O L Q
O N L K K R E T E O E R S T N R L B P L I S F S
V T R E J N S G T D C R E D I Y I O B A L Y E V
```

7. visceral
8. involuntary
9. skeletal
10. the same
11. stimulating or depressing
12. norepinephrine
13. acetylcholine
14. similar

15. sympathetic
16. opposite
17. similar
18. d
19. b
20. a
21. c
22. d

23. Similar: sympathetic stimulants and parasympathetic depressants; and sympathetic depressants and parasympathetic stimulants.

NOTE: **X across the chart indicates similarities.**

Answer to chart:

Sympathetic Stimulants

sympathomimetics, adrenergics, adrenergic agonist

Action

increase blood pressure, increase pulse rate, relax bronchioles, dilate pupils of the eyes, uterine relaxation

Parasympathetic Stimulants

parasympathomimetics, cholinergics, cholinergic agonist, cholinesterase inhibitors

Action

decrease blood pressure, decrease pulse rate, constrict bronchioles, constrict pupils of the eyes, increase bladder contraction

Sympathetic Depressants

sympatholytics, adrenergic blockers, adrenergic antagonists

Action

decrease blood pressure, decrease pulse rate, constrict bronchioles

Parasympathetic Depressants

parasympatholytics, anticholinergics, cholinergic antagonists, antispasmodics

Action

increase pulse rate, decrease mucus secretions, decrease gastrointestinal motility, dilate the pupils of the eyes, increase urinary retention

CHAPTER 23—
Adrenergics and Adrenergic Blockers

Questions 1–5: refer to text.

6. smooth

7. alpha$_1$, alpha$_2$, beta$_1$, and beta$_2$

8. adrenergic

9. sitting up

10. do

11. sympatholytics

12. Regitine

13. Minipress

14. beta blockers

15. hypertension

16. asthma and hypotension

17. The two drugs could counteract each other (as antagonists), thus negating a therapeutic action.

18. d

19. c, a

20. a

21. a

22. b

23. d

24. c

25. d

26. b

27. b

28. a

29. d

30. b

31. d

32. d

33. c

34. b

35. c

36. b

37. c

38. b

39. d

40. variable: monitor vital signs; report drug side effects such as tachycardia, palpitations, tremors, dizziness, and increased blood pressure; check urinary output and assess for bladder distention; offer food when giving adrenergic drugs orally, etc.

41. variable: monitor vital signs; report complaints of dizziness and nasal congestion; assess lungs for congestion and for edema in legs and feet; insulin or oral hypoglycemic agent may need adjustment, etc.

Critical Thinking Exercise

1. beta$_1$ and beta$_2$

2. Daily doses are safe. The client is receiving less than most suggested drug doses; however, the client's pulse rate and blood pressure are not elevated.

3. Yes. By blocking beta$_2$, the bronchial tubes constrict.

4. Propranolol decreases heart rate; therefore, K.S.'s pulse rate should be closely monitored, especially since his pulse rate is low average.

5. Client teaching: check pulse rate, rise slowly to a standing position to avoid orthostatic hypotension, which causes

dizziness and light-headedness; decreased libido may occur; mood changes may occur.

6. It would be unlikely that K.S. would develop rebound tachycardia or hypertension. He is on a low average daily dose; his pulse rate is in the lower range; and his blood pressure is not elevated.

7. Propranolol could decrease the blood sugar level. Insulin dosage would have to be adjusted.

8. metoprolol, atenolol, acebutolol

CHAPTER 24—
Cholinergics and Anticholinergics

Questions 1–8: refer to text.

9. opposite
10. muscarinic
11. skeletal
12. stimulate bladder and gastrointestinal tone, constrict pupils, increase neuromuscular transmission, decrease heart rate and blood pressure, and increase salivation
13. urecholine
14. cholinesterase
15. constriction
16. atropine
17. glaucoma
18. decrease gastrointestinal motility, decrease saliva-tion, increase heart rate, dilate pupils of the eyes, and others

19. a
20. b
21. c
22. a
23. c
24. variable: monitor vital signs, observe for side effects, auscultate breath and bowel sounds, monitor intake and output, administer one hour before or two hours after meals, recognize effects on laboratory values
25. c
26. c
27. a
28. d
29. c
30. b
31. a
32. c
33. d
34. variable: monitor vital signs, observe for side effects, assess intake and output, report urinary retention, check for constipation, suggest hard candy for dry mouth, avoid alcohol
35. b
36. c
37. c
38. b

Critical Thinking Exercise

1. Anticholinergic. It has similar action and effects as atropine.
2. The dose (60 mg/d) is within therapeutic range (10–20 mg, tid/qid).
3. contraindicated for clients having narrow-angle glaucoma, severe ulcerative colitis, paralytic ileus
4. similar to anticholinergics; urinary retention, increase in heart rate, dry mouth, constipation
5. The dose (6 mg/d) is within therapeutic range (6–10 mg/d).
6. 15 ml of trihexyphenidyl

$$\frac{D}{H} \times V = \frac{6\,mg}{2} \times 5\,ml =$$

$$\frac{30}{2} = 15\,ml$$

7. Both drugs are anticholinergics. Trihexyphenidyl is used primarily for the early phase of parkinsonism for suppressing tremors and decreasing muscular rigidity. Dicyclomine is used to decrease gastrointestinal spasms.

CHAPTER 25—
Drugs for Neuromuscular Disorders: Parkinsonism, Myasthenia Gravis, Multiple Sclerosis, Alzheimer's Disease, and Muscle Spasms

Questions 1–5: refer to text.

6. dopamine and acetylcholine

7. dopamine

8. levodopa

9. carbidopa

10. Parsidol and Disipal

11. myasthenia gravis

12. edrophonium (Tensilon)

13. myelin sheath

14. traumatic, chronic

15. Dantrium

16. pregnancy and lactation

17. drowsiness, nausea, vomiting, anorexia, photosensitivity, and liver toxicity

18. Aricept (donepezil)

19. enhance

20. nausea, vomiting, diarrhea, dizziness, headache, rhinitis, depression, anorexia, and constipation

21. selegiline

22. liver

23. c

24. c

25. b

26. d

27. b

28. c

29. b

30. d

31. variable: monitor vital signs, assess for weakness, instruct to eat high-fiber foods, avoid alcohol, etc.

32. d

33. a

34. b

35. c

36. c

37. a

38. d

39. c

40. d

41. a

42. b

43. variable: assess for difficulty in breathing or swallowing, monitor muscle strength, observe for signs and symptoms of cholinergic crisis, etc.

44. variable: advise not to drive or operate hazardous machinery, avoid alcohol or central nervous system depressants, take medication with food, etc.

Critical Thinking Exercise

1. bradykinesia, rigidity, tremors

2. parkinsonism—lack of dopamine and too much acetylcholine at basal ganglia; myasthenia gravis—lack of acetylcholine

3. Levodopa is converted to dopamine in the brain; replaces the lack of dopamine.

4. Nausea, vomiting, orthostatic hypotension, cardiac dysrhythmias, psychosis.

5. Carbidopa inhibits the enzyme dopa decarboxylase, allowing more dopamine to reach the brain.

6. Used mostly for early cases of parkinsonism and pseudoparkinsonism (drug-induced parkinsonism). D.G. would *not* be a candidate for anticholinergic antiparkinsonism drug since he had the health problem for six years (not newly diagnosed).

7. Amantadine is an antiviral drug for influenza A. This drug may be used for early diagnosed parkinsonism and drug-induced parkinsonism. It has fewer side effects than anticholinergics.

8. All are dopamine agonists. They are for early treatment of parkinsonism. Pergolide is more potent than bromocriptine.

9. a. Don't abruptly discontinue the drug as rebound parkinsonism symptoms may occur.

   b. Take drug with food.

   c. Report side effects such as dyskinesia.

   d. Urine may be discolored and darkens when exposed to air. Others: report dizziness.

CHAPTER 26—
Antiinflammatory Drugs

Questions 1–5: refer to text.

6. injury and infection

7. should not

8. redness, heat, swelling, pain, loss of function

9. aspirin

10. delayed

11. does

12. higher or increased

13. 24

14. Ketorolac (Toradol)

15. b

16. a

17. d

18. c

19. b

20. c

21. b

22. d

23. c

24. c

25. b

26. a

27. b

28. c

29. b

30. b

31. d

32. c

33. d

34. a

35. a

36. b

37. a

38. d

39. c

40. 250 mg tablets: 2 tablets/ dose; 4 tablets/24 hrs

500 mg tablets: 1 tablet/ dose; 2 tablets/24 hrs

41. 500 mg tablet; only one tablet twice a day

42. take with food or a full glass of water

Critical Thinking Exercise

1. 325–650 mg q4h PRN; maximum = 4 g/d; >maximum dose

2. 15–30 ng/dl; >50 ng/dl

3. potassium, T_3, T_4, PT, uric acid

4. inhibition of prostaglandin synthesis

5. side effects

6. tinnitus, agranulocytosis, bronchospasm, leukopenia, anaphylaxis

7. variable: take medicine with meals, notify *all* providers of high aspirin dosing, keep out of children's reach, avoid alcohol

CHAPTER 27— *Antibacterials: Penicillins and Cephalosporins*

Questions 1–9: refer to text.

10. inhibit

11. kill

12. inhibition of bacterial cell wall synthesis, alteration in cell wall permeability, inhibition of protein synthesis, and interference with metabolism within the cell

13. greater

14. are not

15. 4th–5th

16. 7th

17. acquired

18. nosocomial

19. hypersensitivity reaction, superinfection, organ toxicity

20. resistant

21. cross resistance

22. absorption, distribution, metabolism, and excretion of the drug

23. drug toxicity

24. constant; time

25. age, white blood cell count, organ function, circulation, immunoglobulins

26. variable: ask client about allergies, culture and sensitivity (C&S) before initiating treatment, monitor for superinfection, monitor for allergic reaction, monitor body temperature, dilute for IV use

27. variable: identification bracelet if allergic, side effects, increase fluids, take all of medicine as prescribed, take medicine with food

28. *Haemophilus influenzae* and *Neisseria gonorrhoeae*, *Enterobacter spp.*, and anaerobes

29. Pseudomonas, *Serratia spp.*, *Acinetobacter spp.*

30. IM and IV

31. b

32. d

33. b

34. a

35. a

36. d

37. c

38. a

39. 5 ml; 20 ml

40. c

41. d

42. d

43. c

44. a

45. b

46. a

Critical Thinking Exercise

1. penicillinase-resistant penicillin

2. 250-500 mg q 6h IM; 500 mg-1g q4-6h IV for severe infection

3. intramuscular, intravenous

4. 2 cc or ml

5. epinephrine

6. broad-spectrum penicillins: to treat both gram-positive and gram-negative bacterias; more costly than penicillin penicillinase-resistant penicillin: for treating penicillinase-producing *Staphylococcus aureus*; not effective against gram-negative organisms, less effective than penicillin G against gram-positive organisms. (See Figure 27–2.)

7. variable: monitor for allergic reaction, monitor site of infection, monitor body temperature, dilute antibiotic for IV infusion

CHAPTER 28—
Antibacterials: Macrolides, Tetracyclines, Aminoglycosides, Fluoroquinolones

Questions 1–4: refer to text.

5. bactericidal

6. erythromycin

7. *Staphylococcus aureus*

8. protein

9. variable: monitor liver enzymes, obtain C&S before initiating treatment, monitor vital signs and intake and output; take with food if gastrointestinal upset

10. vancomycin

11. nephrotoxicity; ototoxicity

12. toxic

13. netilmicin; D

14. ototoxicity and nephrotoxicity

15. variable: C&S before initiating treatment; monitor intake and output; monitor for superinfection; monitor serum peak and trough levels

16. bactericidal

17. chloramphenicol (Chloromycetin)

18. gonorrhea

19. *N. gonorrhoeae* and *H. influenzae*

20. b

21. a

22. d

23. a

24. b

25. b

26. d

27. d

28. first dose 500 mg + 12.5 ml; daily dose X4 250 mg = 6.125 ml

29. decreases; take medication on an empty stomach

Critical Thinking Exercise

1. Yes, one indication is for treatment of lower respiratory infections.
   Vital signs; intake and output, renal function tests, drug history, etc.

2. Mild to moderate infection:

   A:PO: 250–500 mg q12h

   IV: 200 mg q12h (over 1h)

   Severe infections:

   A:PO: 500–750 mg q12h

   IV: 200–400 mg q12h (over 1h)

3. seizure disorders, elderly, <1 year, and clients taking theophylline

4. AST, ALT, BUN, serum creatinine

5. variable: monitor intake and output, vital signs, assess for superinfection; monitor BUN and creatinine.

6. variable: avoid caffeine, do not operate machinery; use sunblock and sunglasses.

CHAPTER 29—
Antibacterials: Sulfonamides

Questions 1–3: refer to text.

4. folic acid

5. penicillin

6. trimethoprim

7. are not

8. is not

9. liver; kidneys

10. bacteriostatic

11. increase

12. Sulfamylon

13. sulfacetamide sodium

14. b

15. 2; 4

16. d

17. b

18. c

19. a

Critical Thinking Exercise

1. LD: 75 mg/kg; then 150 mg/kg/d in divided doses; loading dose = 3.75 g

2. more stable in urine

3. variable: administer medicine with full glass of water; monitor intake and output and vital signs; observe for early signs of hematologic reactions including sore throat, purpura, and decreasing WBC and platelet counts; observe for signs and symptoms of superinfection including stomatitis, furry black tongue, anal or genital discharge or itching

4. variable: instruct Y.M. to drink several quarts of fluid per day; avoid antacids because they decrease absorption rate; alert client and significant others to cross-sensitivity of sulfonamide preparations; take medicine one hour before or two hours after food; to report bruising or bleeding; avoid direct sunlight and wear protective clothing to decrease photosensitivity

5. to prevent crystalluria and formation of kidney stones

```
P E N I C I L L I N T F T Q I
F O L I C A C I D K U I P C U
L K Z Q I S Y E N D I K I I H
M R I B O S S B S Z T T B N L
M I E U S S R R E O A N R C G
C R R V O A A D N T I I T R N
A P C P I P C S S Z I M S E O
F P V W O L I O X G T D P A L
X Q B A U H I T S L Q J A S Y
F W S P L R T V E S H Y Y E M
C J X G E U U E O X N W Z M A
W S X T G X A Q M N D Y W Z F
F E C K P M F L N I E U L U L
X A N H Q C C W U G R R Q Y U
B C B Q P I B E N Z O T A D S
```

CHAPTER 30—
Antitubercular Drugs, Antifungal Drugs, Peptides, and Metronidazole

Questions 1–5: refer to text.

6. streptomycin

7. is not

8. more

9. B_6 pyridoxine

10. ototoxicity

11. liver disease

12. 6–12 months

13. disseminated

14. rifabutin (Mycobutin)

15. polyenes, imidazoles, antimetabolites, topicals

16. lung or central nervous system

17. mouth, skin, intestine, vagina

18. amphotericin B; IV

19. is not

20. increases

21. fluconazole and itraconazole

22. neurotoxicity and neph- rotoxicity; BUN and serum creatinine

23. bactericidal

24. gram-negative

25. IV

26. is

27. a

28. c

29. b

30. d

31. c

32. d

33. b

34. a

35. c

36. d

37. variable: administer drug one hour before or two hours after food; admin- ister with pyridoxine;

monitor serum levels; collect sputum specimen in AM; schedule eye examinations; stress importance of adherence to drug regimen

38. d

39. d

40. a

41. b

42. a

43. d

44. c

45. a

46. d

47. amebiasis, anaerobic infections, bacterial vaginosis, perioperative prophylaxis, and rosacea

48. 1 ½ tablets/dose

Critical Thinking Exercise

1. yes

2. superinfection

3. Candida

4. "swish and swallow": put prescribed amount of drug in mouth, swish solution around mouth so it contacts the mucous membrane, and in a few

minutes, swallow the solution (or expectorate the solution after "swish- ing;" ask health care provider for recommen- dation).

5. variable: stress adherence to drug regimen to avoid relapse; follow-up with laboratory testing as scheduled; instruct on swish and swallow; report side effects; avoid operating hazardous machinery and alcohol while taking amphoteri- cin B, ketoconazole, or flucytosine because these may cause visual changes or sleepiness

6. Both drugs belong to polyene group.
    amphotericin B: ad- ministered IV in low doses; not absorbed from the GI tract; highly protein-bound; long half- life; highly toxic so urinary output, BUN, and creatinine levels require close monitoring
    nystatin: administered orally or topically; poorly absorbed from GI tract; protein-binding and half- life are unknown

CHAPTER 31—
Antiviral, Antimalarial, and Anthelmintic Drugs

Questions 1–3: refer to text.

4. replication

5. is

6. slower; toxicity

7. rimantadine HCl; renal and hepatic

8. herpes simplex I, herpes zoster, varicella zoster, and cytomegalovirus

9. didanosine (Videx)

10. a

11. erythrocytic

12. intestine

13. trichinosis; muscle biopsy

14. Yes; one-half tablet

15. b

16. c

17. c

18. d

19. c

20. d

21. a

22. c

23. a

24. d

25. a

26. d

27. d

28. c

29. c

30. b

31. d

```
S R A L L E C I R A V K R H H
D U E A U I S Z Q K W E E O E
I A R N C O Y K J A W R D T R
D Y C I A V R K B O P A S C P
A B P E V L M I L E X U E Y E
N K R Y V O T S S P V U S T S
O D C S W T L S R U J U G I Z
S L P W C I I A H I D M J C O
I P S L S M U Z G E F K L I S
N A R C P T J A Q E P A W X T
E A K L V T M O G U M A W O E
H X E C X K O S H W O O T T R
M X X I E L M J X U V K T I J
I R E P L I C A T I O N B Y C
R I M A N T I D I N E H C L C
```

Critical Thinking Exercise

1. antimetabolite

2. 30–60 minutes before meals with water

3. CBC, BUN, creatinine, liver enzymes

4. decreased urine output, dizziness, anxiety, confusion

5. soft toothbrush, several times each day; prevents gum bleeding and irritation

CHAPTER 32—
Drugs for Urinary Tract Disorders

Questions 1–6: refer to text.

7. tubule and bladder

8. before

9. nitrofurantoin

10. decreases

11. brown, teeth

12. Pyridium

13. decreased

14. micturition

15. contraindicated

16. 5.5

17. crystalluria

18. Urecholine

19. sulfamethoxazole-trimethoprim (Bactrim, Septra)

20. Monurol (fosfomycin tromethamine)

21. b

22. c

23. b

24. c

25. a

26. d

27. b

28. b

29. d

30. a

31. d

32. b

33. c

34. a

35. variable: monitor intake and output; obtain urine culture prior to initiating antiseptic therapy; observe for side effects of drugs; recognize drug-drug, drug-lab, and drug-food interactions; nitrofurantoin can stain teeth so the client needs to rinse the mouth thoroughly, and so on.

Critical Thinking Exercise

1. urinary antispasmodic

2. 2.5 mg, bid, po; inform health care provider

3. drowsiness, blurred vision, dry mouth

4. urinary or gastrointestinal obstruction, glaucoma; yes, based on limited data provided

5. none significant

6. Pro-Banthine with frequent dosing may cause urinary hesitancy or retention so advise the client to void before each dose.

CHAPTER 33—
HIV- and AIDS-Related Agents

Questions 1–5: refer to text.

6. b

7. c

8. d

9. a

10. d

11. a

12. c

13. a & b

14. c

15. c

16. a

17. b

18. a

19. d

20. c

21. d

22. a

23. b

24. d

25. c

26. d

27. c

28. a

29. d

30. b

31. c

32. a

33. c

34. a

35. d

36. b

37. variable: need for HIV testing, refer as appropriate; chemical signs of depressed immune system; use of prescription, OTC, herbal products; medical care; psychological support

38. variable: Risk for infection; Knowledge deficit; Disturbed body image; Fear; Imbalanced nutrition, less than body requirements; Social isolation; Ineffective coping

39. variable: apply standard precautions; promote adherence; monitor laboratory results; refer for preventive services, nutrition, and spiritual support

40. variable: health teaching how virus damages immune system; need for monitoring health practices; protective precautions (avoid people with URIs); drug therapy plan in writing, establish client/family partnership in plan; how to minimize and manage side effects of drugs; BRAT diet

41. d

42. a

CHAPTER 34—
Vaccines

Questions 1–5: refer to text.

6. the remainder of an individual's life

7. weakened

8. placenta

9. German measles

10. 2; 4–8

11. measles, mumps, and rubella

12. is not

13. influenza and pneumococcal

14. seroconversion

15. four weeks (28 days)

16. varicella, Td, hepatitis B, and hepatitis A

17. a

18. c

19. d

20. c

21. a

22. d

23. a

24. c

25. d

26. b

27. a

28. c

Critical Thinking Exercise

1. tetanus

2. headache, irritability, muscle spasms (jaw, neck, arms, legs, back, and abdomen)

3. Td

4. IM

5. influenza and pneumococcal

6. previous anaphylactic reaction to any of its components, or to eggs; moderate to severe acute illness

CHAPTER 35—
Anticancer Drugs

Questions 1–9: refer to text.

10. CCS (cell-cycle specific)

11. is

12. time required for a number of cancer cells to double its mass

13. multiple

14. they attack all cells; antibiotics only bacterial cells

15. do not

16. do not

17. are not

18. CCNS (cell-cycle nonspecific)

19. vesication

20. estrogen

21. antiestrogens

22. greasy; dairy

23. hemorrhagic cystitis

24. two years

25. nephrotoxicity

26. c

27. c

28. a

29. b

30. d

31. c

32. b

33. b

34. d

35. c

36. d

37. c

38. d

39. d

40. d

41. b

42. c

43. b

44. a

45. d

46. a

47. d

48. 100 mg; 2 tablets

49. store in airtight container at room temperature

50. c

51. a

52. c

53. variable: bleeding, anemia, infection, stomatitis, alopecia, fatigue, nausea, vomiting, diarrhea, low WBC and platelet counts

Critical Thinking Exercise

1. CCNS

2. alkylating

3. variable: hydrate the client before starting chemotherapy; administer an antacid before po drug, administer antiemetic 30-60 minutes before drug; seek advice about childbearing; diet low in purine to alkalize urine; avoid citric acid; good oral hygiene; promptly report signs of infection, bleeding, anemia; prepare for possible loss of hair

4. yes

5. dose of digoxin may need to be adjusted

6. 10-14 days

7. 5-FU is an antimetabolite, CCS and CCNS; is not administered by mouth

CHAPTER 36—
Biologic Response Modifiers

Questions 1–5: refer to text.

6. recombinant DNA and hybridoma technology

7. enhance host immunologic function, destroy or interfere with tumor activities, promote differentiation of stem cells

8. alpha

9. flu-like syndrome

10. should

11. 30–33%; >4 points

12. biphasic

13. bone pain

14. Leukine

15. respiratory

16. b

17. c

18. a

19. d

20. e

21. a

22. d

23. b

24. b

25. d

26. a

27. a

28. d

29. c

30. c

31. d

32. b

33. a

34. no, GCSF does not affect megakaryocyte line

35. report to health care provider, discontinue EPO, assess for signs and symptoms of clotting, prepare client for therapeutic phlebotomy

36. e

37. e

38. GMCSF stimulates macrophage production, GCSF does not; GMCSF can cause more bone pain; GCSF is indicated for postchemotherapy administration neutropenia

39. fluid retention

Critical Thinking Exercise

1. convert 150 pounds to kilograms and multiply these values by 0.037

2. Accurate fluid balance status will need to be monitored, and pulmonary, renal, and cardiac status assessed. Health care provider may opt not to use IL-2 because of potential side effects.

3. These are side effects of IL-2, but they do need to be assessed by a health care provider and treated with steroids, antihistamines, and possibly urinary catheterization.

4. Symptoms are related to IL-2. The client should be hospitalized for IV fluids and further evaluation.

CHAPTER 37—
Drugs for Common Upper Respiratory Infections

Questions 1–5: refer to text.

6. common cold, acute rhinitis, sinusitis, acute tonsillitis, and acute laryngitis

7. common cold

8. two to four

9. constricted

10. are not

11. urinary

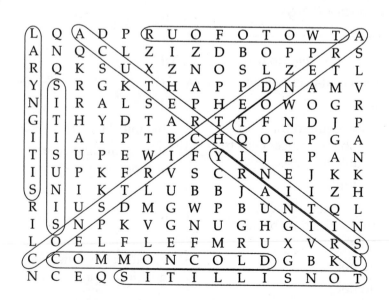

12. rebound

13. six

14. antitussives

15. water or fluids

16. are not

17. minimal

18. d

19. b

20. c

21. d

22. a

23. c

24. a

25. c

26. d

27. b

28. c

29. a

30. d

31. variable: observe color of secretions—yellow or green indicate infection; adequate fluid intake; rest; avoid cold remedies at bedtime; read OTC label *carefully*, especially if you have health problems; etc.

Critical Thinking Exercise

1. 2–3 gtts in each nostril bid

2. 3–5 days only

3. rebound congestion; decrease

4. short-term use because frequent use can result in tolerance that results in vasodilation rather than vasoconstriction; take only as prescribed, limit use

5. caffeine, which can increase restlessness and palpitations

6. check with health care provider before using; read labels

CHAPTER 38—
Drugs for Acute and Chronic Lower Respiratory Disorders

Questions 1–4: refer to text.

5. cyclic adenosine monophosphate (cAMP)

6. epinephrine

7. beta$_2$-adrenergic agonists

8. nonselective

9. aminophylline

10. increases

11. synergistic

12. shorter

13. methylxanthine/xanthine; asthma

14. glucocorticoids

15. prophylactic; histamine

16. rebound bronchospasm

17. are not

18. montelukast (Singulair)

19. evening

20. 10 mg adult; 5 mg child without food

21. mucolytic

22. antibiotics

23. b

24. c

25. b

26. c

27. d

28. c

29. b

30. a

31. d

32. c

33. c

34. a

35. d

36. b

37. a

38. c

39. d

40. b

Critical Thinking Exercise

1. No, takes 1–4 hours for full effect.

2. Take with food to avoid ulceration.

3. Hoarseness, dry mouth, coughing, throat irritation; use of spacer

4. Fluid retention, thinning of the skin, purpura, increased blood sugar, impaired immune response

5. variable: obtain medical and drug history, assess breath sounds, theophylline levels, hydration

6. variable: discuss ways to reduce anxiety, report allergic reaction (rash, urticaria) to health care provider, wear ID tag, correct use of inhaler; advise that high-protein, low-carbohydrate diet increases theophylline elimination; low-protein, high-carbohydrate diet prolongs the half-life

CHAPTER 39—
Drugs for Cardiac Disorders

1. foxglove
2. digoxin
3. have
4. decrease
5. increase; increase; decrease
6. decrease
7. it undergoes first-pass metabolism by the liver
8. 2–5 minutes; repeated every 5 minutes three times
9. headache
10. beta blockers
11. verapamil (Calan)
12. reflex tachycardia and pain
13. long-term
14. hypotension, psychiatric and neurological symptoms, nausea, vomiting, diarrhea, confusion, and heart block
15. alcohol, caffeine-containing fluids, and cigarettes
16. photosensitivity
17. stressed or exerted
18. at frequent times daily with increasing severity
19. is at rest
20. spasm
21. reduction of venous tone
22. is
23. variable: avoid heavy meals, smoking, extremes in weather changes, strenuous exercise and emotional upset
24. b
25. c
26. d
27. b
28. b
29. b
30. d
31. c
32. b
33. d
34. c
35. c
36. a
37. b
38. b
39. c
40. c
41. d
42. d
43. a
44. c
45. b
46. a
47. b
48. a
49. c
50. d
51. a
52. d
53. Apical pulse is a reliable indicator of heart beat. Do not give if the pulse rate is < 60 bpm.
54. Serum digoxin level has a narrow range (0.5-2.0 ng/ml). A serum digoxin level >2.0 ng/ml is an indicator of digitalis toxicity.
55. Nausea, vomiting, pulse rate <60 bpm, headache, and visual disturbances are indicators of digitalis toxicity.
56. A low serum potassium level enhances the action of digoxin; thus, digitalis toxicity might occur. Fruits, fruit juices, vegetables, meats (some) are rich in potassium.
57. not to touch the medication on the transdermal patch; clean area; do not

apply to hairy areas of the body

58. a

59. c

60. d

61. c

62. b

63. Hypotension is associated with most anti-anginal drugs, especially nitrates (nitroglycerin) and beta blockers.

64. Dryness in the mouth may inhibit drug absorption of sublingual tablets.

65. Nitroglycerin SL tablets are given for chest pain. May be repeated twice, five minutes apart. If chest pain persists, medical help is necessary.

66. Alcohol ingestion while taking nitro product can enhance a hypotensive state.

67. Client and nurse should avoid touching the center of the Nitro-patch; absorption could occur to the nurse. Daily rotation of patch is necessary. Avoid placing the patch on hairy areas.

68. Headaches are common when first taking a nitrate product. Acetaminophen may be used to relieve the headache.

69. Withdrawal symptoms may occur if antianginal drug is abruptly discontinued. Reflex tachycardia and pain may occur.

Critical Thinking Exercise

1. nitroglycerin 0.4 mg, sublingual tablets

2. Take at the onset of angina pain. If pain is not relieved in 5 minutes repeat dose every 5 minutes for a total of 3 doses. After 15 minutes if pain is still present, notify the health care provider immediately. Do not swallow the SL tablet. Place tablet under the tongue.

3. Beta blockers decrease pulse (heart) rate and blood pressure. At present, J.B. does not have low pulse rate and blood pressure, however, vital signs should be monitored.

4. Both drugs are beta blockers. Propranolol is a nonselective cardiac drug affecting beta$_1$ and beta$_2$, while metoprolol is a cardioselective drug, blocking only beta$_1$. A client with asthma should take metoprolol since it does not block beta$_2$, respiratory.

5. for blood pressure (anti-hypertensive effect) and for cardiac dysrhythmias

6. relaxation techniques, adequate rest, no smoking, proper nutrition, decrease use of salt, exercise as prescribed

7. Causes similar pharmacologic effects but is not as potent as nifedipine and verapamil. Blood pressure does not decrease as markedly as with other calcium blockers.

8. is within normal range, maximum dose is 360 mg per day

CHAPTER 40—
Diuretics

Figure

a. distal tubule: thiazides

b. proximal tubule: osmotics and carbonic anhydrase inhibitors

c. descending (loop)

d. loop of Henle: high-ceiling or loop diuretics

e. collecting tubule: potassium-sparing

1. increase in urine output

2. high blood sugar (glucose) level

3. serum potassium excess

4. sodium loss in the urine

5. decreased urine output

6. concentration of body fluids

7. diuretics that promote potassium excretion

8. to decrease blood pressure in those with hypertension; to decrease edema in those with congestive heart failure

9. reabsorption; tubules

10. thiazide and thiazide-like, loop or high-ceiling, carbonic anhydrase inhibitors, osmotic, and potassium-sparing

11. potassium

12. digoxin; digitalis toxicity

13. little

14. sparing

15. weaker

16. aldosterone

17. hyperkalemia

18. Dyazide, Moduretic, Aldactazide, and Maxzide

19. less

20. osmotic

21. decrease

22. hypokalemia

23. hypomagnesemia

24. hypercalcemia

25. hypochloremia

26. minimal loss

27. hyperuricemia

28. hyperglycemia

29. cholesterol, LDL, and triglycerides are elevated

30. a

31. b

32. b

33. b

34. c

35. b

36. c

37. a

38. b

39. d

40. a

41. d

42. d

43. b

44. d

45. b

46. c

47. d

48. c

49. c

Critical Thinking Exercise

1. two tablets

2. Hydrochlorothiazide can elevate the blood glucose level. A.D.'s oral antidiabetic drug dose may need to be adjusted.

3. Both act on the kidney by increasing fluid and sodium loss. Thiazides act on the distal tubules of the kidney, while loop diuretics act on the loop of Henle.

4. Both drugs have similar effects on blood chemistry; however, loop diuretics lower serum calcium level, while thiazides increase the serum calcium level.

5. A.D. should not take hydrochlorothiazide, because it increases serum calcium level.

6. a. check blood sugar levels frequently

   b. eat foods rich in potassium because diuretics excrete potassium

   c. emphasize the importance of compliance

   d. keep medical appointments; others: rise slowly because of possible blood pressure drop, use sunscreen

7. A.D.'s serum potassium level is low average. Diuretics could decrease the level further. A.D. is taking digoxin, and a decrease in serum potassium level (hypokalemia) can cause digitalis toxicity.

8. bradycardia (pulse rate less than 60 bpm) or a marked decrease in pulse rate; anorexia, nausea, vomiting, blurred vision

9. all potassium-wasting diuretics, such as thiazides, loop diuretics, and osmotic diuretic decrease serum potassium level; potassium-sparing diuretics can increase serum potassium level

10. When a client has a low average serum potassium level, such as with A.D., a combination of drugs prevents excess loss of potassium. If the client's fluid retention is severe, a potassium-wasting diuretic is usually more effective than a potassium-sparing diuretic.

CHAPTER 41—
Antihypertensive Drugs

1. block the alpha adrenergic receptors, thus causing vasodilation and decrease in blood pressure

2. block beta$_1$ receptors causing a decrease in heart rate and blood pressure

3. decrease calcium level and promote vasodilation

4. inhibit angiotensin-converting enzyme which blocks the release of aldosterone

5. block the angiotensin II receptor causing a decrease in peripheral resistance and vasodilation

6. obesity, aging, family history, hyperlipemia, and others

7. relaxation techniques, salt restriction, weight reduction, exercise, decrease alcohol use

8. sympatholytics: centrally-acting, peripherally-acting, alpha$_1$ blocker, alpha-beta blocker

9. beta blocker, calcium blocker, angiotensin antagonist (ACE inhibitors), diuretics

10. stepped-care approach

11. individualized

12. increased exercise; decreased weight, sodium intake, alcohol, smoking

13. diuretics

14. beta blockers and ACE inhibitors, also AII inhibitors

15. calcium blockers

16. stage 3

17. diminished; lowered

18. African-American

19. cardioselective

20. -olol

21. decreases very-low–density lipoprotein (VLDL), LDL, and increases high-density lipoprotein (HDL)

22. prazosin, doxazosin, terazosin

23. diazoxide and nitroprusside

24. angiotensin II receptor antagonists (A-II blockers)

25. c

26. d

27. b

28. e

29. f

30. g

31. d

32. b

33. a

34. c

35. d

36. b

37. c

38. d

39. a

40. d

41. b

42. d

43. b

44. d

45. a

46. b

47. c

48. b

49. c

50. b

51. a

52. d

53. Baseline vital signs for future comparison should first be taken. Blood pressure should be closely monitored to determine the effectiveness of the drug.

54. BUN, serum creatinine, protein, and potassium levels may be increased when taking an ACE inhibitor. If a client with diabetes mellitus is taking an oral antidiabetic agent, hypoglycemia might result. WBC should be monitored because neutropenia might occur.

55. ACE inhibitors are usually potent antihypertensive agents and may cause hypotension when the drug is first started. If dizziness persists, health care provider should be notified.

56. Rebound hypertension could result.

57. Severe adverse reaction of ACE inhibitors is petechiae or bleeding.

58. Food could decrease 1/3 of the drug absorption.

59. b

60. c

61. b

Critical Thinking Exercise

1. centrally acting sympatholytic drug; drug dose is within normal range

2. Methyldopa stimulates the alpha$_2$ receptors to decrease sympathetic activity, and to decrease serum epinephrine, norepinephrine, and renin release. Thus, peripheral vascular resistance is reduced.

3. It is a diuretic. A side effect of methyldopa is fluid retention. Diuretics given with methyldopa will cause fluid loss via kidneys and also will decrease the blood pressure.

4. Potassium, sodium, and magnesium imbalance can result. Hydrochlorothiazide is a potassium-wasting diuretic.

5. S.H.'s blood pressure should be closely monitored. His medications should not be discontinued because his blood pressure is not extremely low nor was there a large blood pressure drop. The health care provider will adjust drug dose as needed.

6. Client teaching: the importance of drug compliance and taking drugs at specified times; eating food rich in potassium and proper nutrition; checking S.H.'s blood pressure; proper rest; exercise if appropriate.

7. Methyldopa is a sympatholytic agent acting on the alpha$_2$ receptors, whereas beta blockers act on the beta-adrenergic receptors. Both drugs are antihypertensive agents.

8. Side effects: dry mouth, drowsiness, dizziness, slow heart rate

9. Serum electrolytes should be checked periodically, and also the liver enzymes

CHAPTER 42—
Drugs for Circulatory Disorders

Word Search

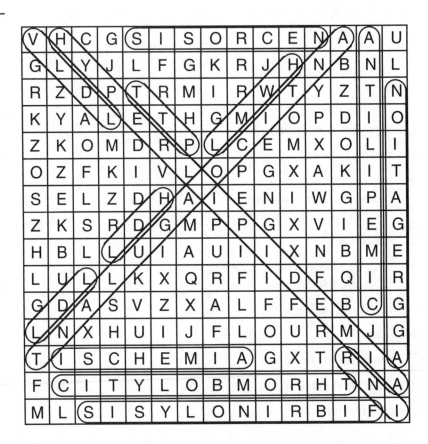

a.   HDL

b.   INR

c.   LDL

d.   LMWH

e.   PTT

f.   VLDL

g.   aggregation

h.   anticoagulant

i.   antilipemic

j.   fibrinolysis

k.   hyperlipidemia

l.   ischemia

m.   necrosis

n.   thrombolytic

1.   artery and vein

2.   clot formation

3.   do not have

4.   venous thrombus that may lead to pulmonary embolism

5.   subcutaneously, intravenously

6.   standard heparin; lower the risk of bleeding

7.   warfarin

8.   decrease

9.   4 to 6

10.   plasminogen to plasmin

11.   hemorrhage

12.   HDL

13.   12 hours

14.   gastrointestinal discomfort

15.   weeks

16.   <200 mg/dl

17.   clofibrate

18.   vessel occlusion

19.   microcirculation

20.   b

21.   c

22.   b

23.   d

24.   a

25.   e

26.   f

27.   b

28.   e

29.   f

30.   c

31.   c

32.   b

33.   a

34.   c

35.   d

36.   a

37.   b

38.   b

39.   d

40.   a

41.   c

42.   b

43.   d

44.   variable: monitor vital signs; check lab test results; check for bleeding from mouth, gums, injection sites, etc.; keep antagonist vitamin K or protamine available; etc.

45.   c

46.   a

47.   a

48.   c

49.   d

50.   a

51.   c

52.   variable: take medications with meals; avoid alcohol, smoking, and aspirin; explain possible side effects of drug, such as flushing, headache, and dizziness

53.   < 200 mg/dl

54.   < 130 mg/dl

55.   > 60 mg/dl

56.   b

57.   c

58.   b

59.   Serum lipid levels (cholesterol, LDL, HDL, and triglycerides) need to be closely monitored, every 3 to 6 months, to determine if drug dose is adequate or needs to be increased or decreased.

60.   The ALT, ALP, and GGT should be checked every 6 months. If liver disorder is present, drug dose should be decreased. Antilipemics are metabolized by the liver.

61.   Antilipemics can cause GI discomfort. Taking antilipemics with sufficient water and at mealtime decreases the possibility of GI distress.

62.   Cataracts have been reported when taking

some of the antilipemics. Annual eye test is advised.

63. Antilipemics are not a substitute for diet and decreasing the blood lipid levels. Low-fat diet is suggested.

64. When first taking antilipemics, it takes several weeks before the blood lipid levels decline.

Critical Thinking Exercise

1. 0.5 ml of heparin

2. Heparin cannot be given orally because it is poorly absorbed through the gastrointestinal mucosa.

3. For heparin, the PTT (partial thromboplastin time) and the aPTT (activated partial thromboplastin time) monitor heparin dosage and effect. PTT: 60–70 seconds with 1.5–2 × control in seconds; aPTT: 40 seconds with anticoagulant effect is in 60–80 seconds.

4. two tablets

5. INR—international normalized ratio, used to monitor the oral anticoagulant warfarin.
   PT (prothrombin time) values can differ from laboratory to laboratory. INR is the result of reagents used in the PT test and compared to international standard reference.

6. Side effects of warfarin (Coumadin) include bleeding (skin, gums, nose, gastric, rectal),

anorexia, nausea, vomiting, diarrhea, abdominal cramps, fever.

7. Warfarin: protein-binding—99%; half-life—0.5–3 days. Highly protein-bound and long half-life.

8. < 200 mg/dl. B.C.'s serum cholesterol level is elevated. He is at high risk for a heart attack.

9. Atorvastatin is an antilipemic drug that inhibits the synthesis of cholesterol. This drug would lower B.C.'s serum cholesterol level. To have therapeutic effect, it may take several weeks.

10. Atorvastatin —protein-binding–98%; highly protein-bound. Two highly protein-bound drugs, warfarin and lovastatin, will compete for protein-binding sites. With insufficient protein sites, a percentage of warfarin will be free drug. Drug dose should be adjusted; bleeding could result due to excess free circulating warfarin.

11. The INR should be monitored for warfarin, and serum liver enzymes should be checked periodically.

12. Client teaching: report adverse effects such as bruising marks (ecchymosis), have laboratory tests checked periodically, eat foods low in cholesterol and fat (check food labels)

CHAPTER 43—
Drugs for Gastrointestinal Tract Disorders

Questions 1–7: refer to text.

8. a. oral cavity; b. trachea; c. diaphragm; d. liver; e. gallbladder; f. duodenum; g. ileocecal valve; h. salivary glands; i. superior esophageal sphincter; j. esophagus; k. esophagus; l. stomach; m. pancreas; n. large intestine (colon); o. small intestine; p. rectum; q. anus

9. chemoreceptor trigger zone (CTZ) and vomiting center

10. antihistamines, anticholinergics, phenothiazines, cannabinoids, and miscellaneous

11. antagonists

12. antiemetics

13. gelatin, Gatorade®, weak tea, carbonated beverages (flattened), and Pedialyte® for children

14. 30

15. are not

16. antihistamines

17. marijuana

18. Menière's

19. increases

20. to promote adsorption of poison/toxic substance(s)

21. opiates, opiate-related, adsorbents, and combination

22. decrease gastric motility

23. constipation

24. abuse and misuse

25. soft; soft watery

26. osmotics, contact, bulk-forming, and emollients

27. irritation; diagnostic tests and surgery

28. water accumulation

29. congestive heart failure

30. do not

31. fat soluble; A, D, E, K

32. c

33. d

34. b

35. c

36. b

37. c

38. c

39. c

40. a

41. d

42. b

43. c

44. c

45. b

46. c

47. d

48. b

49. b

50. a

51. variable: increase water intake and foods rich in fiber; avoid cathartic-type drugs that may cause electrolyte imbalances and laxative dependence; suggest exercise to increase peristalsis; inform clients that laxa-

tives may cause urine discoloration; and so on.

Critical Thinking Exercise

1. insufficient water, poor dietary habits, fecal impaction, bowel obstruction, chronic laxative use, neurologic disorders, ignoring urge for defecation, lack of exercise, and certain drugs

2. yes; 10–15 mg po; max = 30 mg; probably morning to decrease sleep interruption

3. increase peristalsis by direct effect on smooth muscle of intestine.

4. draws water into the intestine

5. hypersensitivity, intestinal/biliary obstruction, appendicitis, abdominal pain, nausea, vomiting, rectal fissure

6. decreased effect with antacids, histamine$_2$ blockers, and milk

7. swallow tablets whole; take only with water to promote absorption; not to take within one hour of any other drug; take to avoid interfering with sleep or other activities

8. increase fluid intake (if not contraindicated); not for long-term use; increase fiber-rich foods; exercise; keep records of intake; report rectal bleeding, nausea, vomiting, or cramping to health care provider immediately

CHAPTER 44—
Antiulcer Drugs

Questions 1–3: refer to text.

4. 2–5

5. corrosive

6. mechanical disturbances, genetic influence, environmental influence, and drugs

7. gnawing aching

8. antacids, tranquilizers, anticholinergic, histamine$_2$ blocker, pepsin inhibitor, proton pump inhibitors, and suppression of gastric acid secretion

9. do not

10. are not

11. constipation, diarrhea

12. protective

13. can

14. h

15. i

16. f

17. c

18. g

19. d

20. j

21. b

22. a

23. e

24. c

25. a

26. a

27. d

28. b

29. a

30. b

31. c

32. c

33. b

34. b

35. a

36. d

37. a

38. d

39.–47. Refer to nursing process in text.

Critical Thinking Exercise

1. No; 600 mg 1h p.c. and hs; chewed with water or milk

2. neutralization of gastric acidity; ranitidine: inhibiting histamine at hista- mine receptors in parietal cells; sucralfate: with gastric acid, forms a protective covering on the ulcer surface

3. increase effect of benzodi- azepines; decrease effects with tetracycline, iso- niazid, phenothiazine, phenytoin, digitalis, quinidine, and amphet- amines. Lab: increase urine pH, calcium and phosphate levels, and electrolytes may be affected.

4. constipation

5. hypophosphatemia; caution in the elderly

6. variable: avoid foods and liquids that cause gastric irritation such as caffeine- containing beverages, alcohol, and spices

7. variable: encourage to drink one ounce of water after antacid to ensure that drug reaches the stomach; do not take antacids at mealtime because they slow the gastric emptying time; report pain, coughing, vomiting blood, diarrhea, constipation to the health care provider; unlimited amount is contraindi- cated; read labels if on sodium-restricted diet; contact health care pro- vider after taking self- prescribed antacids for more than two weeks; instruct on use of relax- ation techniques; advise that stools may become white or speckled

CHAPTER 45—
Drugs for Disorders of the Eye and the Ear

1. foreign body

2. tears

3. intraocular

4. diuretic; open-angle glaucoma

5. decrease

6. anuria or dehydration

7. blood sugar

8. cycloplegics

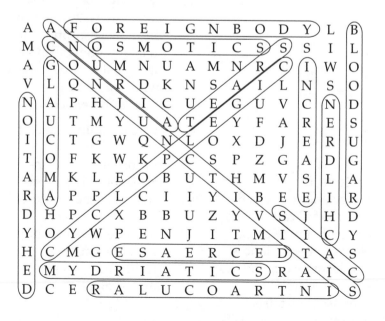

9. children

10. increase

11. conjunctivitis

12. carbonic anhydrase inhibitors

13. increase

14. carbonic anhydrase inhibitors

15. osmotics

16. mydriatics

17. take your time, be patient, include return demonstration in all teaching plans; caution with confused clients to prevent overdose; instruct client/significant others in proper administration of eyedrops/ointment; maintain sterile technique and prevent dropper contamination; instruct to report change in vision, blurring, loss of vision, difficulty breathing, or flushing to the health care provider; store drug in light-resistant container away from heat; not to abruptly stop the medication; check labels on all OTC preparations; encourage medical follow-up, and carry ID medical alert

18. overgrowth

19. are not

20. carbonic anhydrase inhibitors

21. tympanic membrane

22. Burow's solution, hydrogen peroxide 3%; hypertonic HCl solution 3% and acetic acid

23. ceruminolytics

24. are not

25. are

26. b

27. c

28. c

29. a

30. c

31. a

32. b

Critical Thinking Exercise

1. stimulation of pupillary and ciliary sphincter muscles; to decrease intraocular pressure

2. no; therapeutic range is 1–2 gtts tid/qid; report immediately to health care provider; consider dosage adjustment

3. side effect of pilocarpine

4. coronary artery disease, obstruction of GI/GU tract, epilepsy, asthma

5. blurred vision, eye pain, headache, eye irritation, brow ache, stinging and burning, nausea, vomiting, diarrhea, increased salivation and sweating, muscle tremors, contact allergy

6. avoid driving or operating machinery while vision is impaired; check all labels on OTC preparations; need for regular medical follow-up; not to suddenly stop the medication; use of relaxation techniques

7. Ocusert system an important consideration for

D.Z. Advantages: accurate dose, sustained over time, disk changed every week

Disadvantages: potential for corneal abrasion

CHAPTER 46—
Drugs for Dermatologic Disorders

1. c

2. d

3. b

4. a

5. benzoyl peroxide 10%, topical antibiotics such as tetracycline

6. antibiotics; glucocorticoids

7. is not

8. lower

9. 1 to 2%; 30

10. keratolytics

11. coal tar products and anthralin

12. Stevens-Johnson

13. sensitizing lymphocytes

14. chemical or plant

15. first

16. Sulfamylon, Silvadene, silver nitrate solution, Furacin

17. podophyllum

18. mild acne

19. a. epidermis; b. dermis; c. subcutaneous tissue; d. sebaceous gland; e. blood vessel; f. hair shaft; g. sweat gland; h. fatty tissue

20. a

21. b

22. c

23. c

24. d

25. c

26. a

27. b

28. d

29. d

30. a

Critical Thinking Exercise

1. second degree: epidermis, lower dermis; mottled, blistering, intense pain. Third degree: epidermis, dermis, nerve ending involvement, subcutaneous tissue; pearly white, charred, no pain

2. yes

3. inhibits bacterial cell wall synthesis; silver sulfadiazine

4. assess for infection, culture wounds, assess vital signs, fluid and pain status

5. administer prescribed analgesia before applying medication as needed; use aseptic technique; monitor fluid and renal function; assess for side effects, vital signs, and acid-base balance. Store drug in dry place at room temperature.

6. rash, urticaria, burning sensation, pruritus, swelling

7. be alert to changes in respiratory status; instruct family, including return demonstration, on care to the wound using aseptic technique; application of topical medications and dressings, as needed; home safety tips; importance of hand exercises

CHAPTER 47—
Endocrine Pharmacology: Pituitary, Thyroid, Parathyroids, and Adrenals

```
T F M L E I B G H M X Y I B P N L D E T S A X
B T R I I O D O T H Y R O N I N E N M E C Q L
S H Y P O P H Y S I S B E A C L S S L G D O A
V Y R U I M T S D L A N G J E L I F L I P M P
H R T A C T H I K N I G R B T T A F O T Y R U
F O I D B S A U O X X A A C N D E C J L K D I
I T Z H G F U L O H J L L A M O I P L I B A K
R O O B E X S R S U T B G I D T E T O N E B Y
J X I B N S Y E Y A M I N P R A V J H Q O D G
Y I P M E H T O B J G I D O O L K M O L A S N
A C R E T I N I S M S W C M V D I U Q E R Y M
W O G N A T M J K T Y O O T A L U G E R U H I
B S P D L I Y R E G L U C O C O R T I C O I D
P I Y O V R I A K A C R O M E G A L Y E M N F
A S O C Y L P U R A E B H T E S S C P O L Q C
L K K R E I E E R S O N A L T E L N E F S O
R E J I U G N E U R O H Y P O P H Y S I S V L
J H I N N I C E Y A M K N P E A V J H Q O D E
S T C E M Y X E D E M A T A C L S F L G T O R
P A D E N O H Y P O P H Y S I S S L F E M N W
```

a. acromegaly
b. adenohypophysis
c. ACTH
d. ADH
e. cretinism

f. endocrine
g. gigantism
h. glucocorticoid
i. hypophysis
j. mineralocorticoid

k. myxedema
l. neurohypophysis
m. thyrotoxicosis
n. thyroxine
o. triiodothyronine

1. anterior and posterior
2. bones and skeletal muscles
3. dwarfism; gigantism
4. diabetes mellitus
5. adrenocorticotropic hormone (ACTH)
6. primary and secondary
7. vasopressin
8. variable: check for edema; monitor weight; monitor vital signs, urine output; adhere to medical regimen; check laboratory results, especially electrolytes, and glucose
9. thyroxine (T_4), and triiodothyronine (T_3)
10. hypotension and vascular collapse
11. agranulocytosis
12. calcium
13. hypoparathyroidism; hyperparathyroidism
14. twitching of the mouth, tingling and numbness of fingers, carpopedal spasm, spasmodic contractions, and laryngeal spasm
15. b
16. b
17. a
18. b

19. a
20. b
21. b
22. a
23. b
24. b
25. subcutaneous
26. glucocorticoids
27. dexamethasone (Decadron)
28. tapered over several days. Rationale: to allow adrenal cortex to produce steroids (cortisol and others)
29. sodium and water retention
30. protein
31. b
32. c
33. b
34. d
35. d
36. a
37. c
38. b
39. b
40. d
41. b
42. c
43. d

44. d
45. c
46. Cortisone drugs cause increase in sodium and water, thus, an increase in blood pressure.
47. Weight increase can occur due to water retention. A weight increase of 2 ½ to 5 pounds may occur in several days.
48. Glucocorticoid drugs promote sodium retention and potassium loss. These agents also increase blood sugar.
49. Glucocorticoid drugs can irritate the gastric mucosa and may cause a peptic ulcer.
50. This group of drugs promotes potassium loss. Foods rich in potassium, i.e., fruits, fruit juices, vegetables, meats, and nuts, should be eaten.
51. An adrenal crisis could result if the cortisone drug is abruptly stopped. Tapering drug dose permits the adrenal glands to adjust their function of secreting adrenal cortex hormones.
52. High doses of glucocorticoids promote loss of muscle tone and loss of calcium from the bone.

53. High doses of glucocorticoids may cause moon face, puffy eyelids, edema in the feet, increased bruising, dizziness, and menstrual irregularity. Any of these symptoms should be reported.

54. c

55. b

56. a

Critical Thinking Exercise

1. Yes, safe dosing is between 5–60 mg daily in divided doses.

2. Digoxin is a cardiac glycoside and hydrochlorothiazide is a potassium-wasting diuretic.

3. Prednisone, a glucocorticoid, and hydrochlorothiazide, a potassium-wasting diuretic, promote the loss of potassium via urine excretion.

4. M.N. is taking two drugs that promote potassium loss; therefore, she should be eating foods rich in potassium, such as fruits and vegetables, and should be taking potassium supplements.

5. M.N.'s serum potassium level is low, most likely due to prednisone and hydrochlorothiazide. Hypokalemia enhances the action of digoxin and can cause digitalis toxicity. Potassium replacement is necessary to correct deficit and to

prevent reoccurrence of hypokalemia.

6. Muscle weakness and wasting; thinning of the skin; fat accumulation in the face and trunk (moon face and buffalo hump); elevated cholesterol and glucose levels; hypokalemia.

7. Prednisone, prednisolone, and dexamethasone are all glucocorticoids. Prednisone is the mildest of the three drugs. Prednisolone and dexamethasone are potent glucocorticoids. Prednisolone may be taken to alleviate severe asthma and may be injected into the joints to alleviate acute inflammation. Dexamethasone can be taken orally or given parenterally for severe allergy or to reduce edema from a head injury.

8. When discontinuing glucocorticoids, the drug dose should be tapered to allow for the adrenal cortex to resume function in secreting cortisol (adrenal cortical hormone). Glucocorticoids such as prednisone suppress adrenal gland function.

9. Teaching points for M.N.: take prednisone with food; eat foods rich in potassium; avoid persons with respiratory infections; report side effects such as edema, bleeding.

CHAPTER 48—
Antidiabetic Drugs

1. chronic disease resulting from deficiency in glucose metabolism

2. a protein secreted by the beta cells in the pancreas that is needed for carbohydrate metabolism

3. insulin reaction because of excessive circulating insulin. Client becomes nervous, trembling, uncoordinated, cold and clammy skin, decreased blood pressure, increased pulse rate

4. insulin-dependent diabetes mellitus, requires insulin

5. noninsulin-dependent diabetes mellitus, usually requires oral antidiabetic drug

6. presence of ketone bodies (fatty acids) in the body as a result of fat catabolism due to inadequate amount af insulin

7. tissue atrophy or hypertrophy

8. increased thirst

9. increased hunger

10. increased urine output.

11. polyuria, polydipsia, and polyphagia

12. glucocorticoids, thiazide diuretics, and epinephrine

13. 0.2 to 0.5 Units/kg/d; clients with type 1 need 0.2 to 1.0 units/kg/d

14. insulin and oral hypoglycemic or oral antidiabetic drugs

15. lipodystrophy

16. regular

17. less; more

18. would

19. pork

20. headache, nervousness, tremor, excess perspiration, tachycardia, slurred speech, memory lapse, and blood sugar < 60 mg/dl

21. thirst, polyuria, fruity breath odor, Kussmaul's sign, tachycardia, dry mucous membranes, and blood sugar > 250 mg/dl

22. sulfonylureas; are not

23. c

24. e

25. a

26. b

27. f

28. b

29. a

30. b

31. c

32. b

33. d

34. c

35. b

36. c

37. a

38. c

39. a

40. c

41. b

42. The reference values for blood glucose are 60-100 mg/dl; for serum glucose 70-110 mg/dl. A blood sugar < 60 mg/dl, hypoglycemia results and > 110 mg/dl, hyperglycemia is present. It should be monitored periodically.

43. Signs and symptoms of a hypoglycemic reaction include nervousness, tremors, cold and clammy skin, excessive perspiration, slurred speech, tachycardia, and others.

44. Orange juice or sweetened beverage adds sugar to the body for insulin utilization. They are a quick source of sugar.

45. Blood sugar test should be checked daily to determine if the blood sugar is within normal range. More or less insulin may be needed.

46. Prescribed diet is calculated according to the amount of insulin given per day. Exchange list of foods should be available to the client.

47. During a severe hypoglycemic reaction, the client may be unable to swallow orange juice. Glucagon would be needed to reverse the hypoglycemic state.

48. Client should have either a medical alert card or tag in case of a severe hypoglycemic reaction in which the client is semi- or unconsciousness.

49. a

50. b

51. d

52. b

53. c

54. d

55. d

56. variable; recognize signs of hypoglycemic reaction; maintain prescribed diet; take insulin at prescribed dose and time; monitor blood sugar; keep appointments with health care provider; be aware of effect of exercise, infection and fever

57. variable; monitor blood sugar; take oral hypoglycemic drug(s) at prescribed dose and time; maintain prescribed diet; monitor weight; participate in regular exercise

58. a

59. d

60. a. diminishes serum glucose following a meal

    b. decreases absorption of glucose from the small intestine

    c. does not produce hypoglycemic or hyperglycemic reactions

    d. answer is correct

61. b

62. c

63. b

64. d

65. b

Critical Thinking Exercise

1. Humulin insulins have the same amino acids as the client. These insulins have a very low incidence of allergic effects and insulin resistance. Pork insulin has one different amino acid than human insulin, and beef insulin has four different amino acids.

2.

3. Clients taking sulfonylureas usually would need 40 units or less of insulin daily.

   N.V. has type 1 diabetes or insulin-dependent diabetes mellitus. He is taking a total of 50 units of insulin daily.

4. Instruct N.V. to follow insulin injection site rotation recommended by the American Diabetic Association. This group suggests that insulin should be injected daily at a chosen site for one week. The injections should be 1 ½ inches apart at a site area each day.

5. The average insulin dosage according to weight is:

   0.2 unit × 72 kg = 14 units/d;

   1.0 unit × 72 kg = 72 units/d

   N.V.'s daily insulin is 50 units/d (Average: 14–72 units/d)

6. Regular insulin peaks in 2–4 h, whereas NPH insulin peaks in 6–12 h. If N.V. receives insulin at 0700, hypoglycemic reaction might occur between 1300 to 1900 (1600 to 1700 is the likely time that hypoglycemia could occur).

7. Most common symptoms include nervousness, tremors, cold or clammy skin, slurred speech, confusion, and later, seizures.

8. client teaching for N.V.: injection sites, rotation of injections, angle for injections, hypoglycemic reactions, not to withhold insulin during stress and infection, diet, use of a med-alert bracelet or tag, card stating that the client is a diabetic

9. When mixing insulins, there may be a loss of regular insulin. NPH does not cause as great a loss of regular insulin as does Lente.

10. a. Client should recognize (if possible) the onset of a hypoglycemic reaction.

    b. Have available orange juice, soda with sugar, or candy. Take immediately at the onset of an hypoglycemic reaction. Have glucagon available in case N.V. cannot drink sugar-containing fluid.

CHAPTER 49/50—
Drugs Associated with the Female Reproductive Cycle I and II

Questions 1–6: refer to text.

7. are not

8. influence of circulating steroid hormones on liver metabolism of drugs; more rapid excretion of drugs through kidneys due to increased glomerular filtration rate and increased renal perfusion; dilution of drugs within the expanded maternal circulatory system; and change in clearance of drugs in late pregnancy

9. do not

10. does not

11. slower

12. breast

13. timing; dose; duration

14. sphingomyelin and lecithin

15. fetal lung maturity

16. betamethasone suspension; 48–72 hours; 7 days; 33rd week; the client will not deliver for at least 24 hours after receiving the drug

17. prevention or rescue

18. convulsions; vasospasm

19. nausea; heartburn (pyrosis)

20. 18 mg; 60 mg; 120 mg; 6 weeks; 2 weeks; hemoglobin

21. will not

22. Mexico

23. 4 weeks; spontaneous abortion

24. 1 hour; 3–4 hours; greater chance of a depressed fetus or neonate

25. beginning; to allow a smaller quantity of drug to cross the placenta due to blood vessels becoming a bit more constricted and remaining so temporarily, which prevents the fetus from receiving an immediate large drug bolus

26. a, c, d

27. d, e

28. c

29. c

30. g

31. b

32. d

33. h

34. f

35. b

36. d

37. a

38. b

39. a

40. variable: eat crackers before arising, avoid fatty or highly seasoned foods, eat small frequent meals, eat high-protein bedtime snack, stop or decrease smoking, etc.

41. variable: avoid highly seasoned, fatty, or gas forming foods, decrease fluids with meals, avoid reclining immediately after meal, avoid citrus juices, etc.

42. b

43. b

44. d

45. b

46. d

47. c

48. a

49. b

50. d

51. b

52. a

53. c

54. variable: nutritional counseling, signs and symptoms to report to health care provider, weigh daily, specifics of magnesium sulfate or hydralazine

55. a

56. c

57. b

58. b

59. c

60. d

61. a

62. d

63. c

64. a

65. d

66. b

67. a

68. d

69. a

70. d

71. drug causes sustained uterine contractions, thus, may cause decreased FHR with fetal hypoxia; tetanic contraction of an enlarged uterus poses risk of uterine rupture (life-threatening to mother and fetus; may also trap uterine contents inside uterus (fetus and/or placenta if given too soon)

Critical Thinking Exercise

1. Review definition of PTL; consider factors such as gestational time period, contraction interval and rhythmic pattern, pelvic sensation, length of time since episode began

2. Consider fetal factors (weight, response on monitor strip to contractions); cervical factors (consistency, effacement/dilatation: >80%/>2cm)); membrane status; bloody show/vaginal discharge

3. Consider client age; previous history; socioeconomics; resources; job stressors; personal stressors

4. Consider the relationship among the four factors with impact on S.B. her children, and her employer in terms of biopsychosocial issues. Consider the time of day that the incident has occurred; distance to home/doctor/triage unit; job responsibility; employer reaction; time period to be temporarily off her feet and resources in store for reclining, drinking fluids, and

voiding; availability of child caretaker (if necessary), etc.

5. Review absolute and relative contraindications to tocolytic therapy (e.g., bulging membranes or PROM; gestational age <20 weeks; severe fetal compromise-decelerations; cervical dilatation >5 cm; severe IUGR; maternal hemorrhage; cardiovascular disease; severe PIH; etc.)

6. Decrease; uterine; inhibit; additional; fetal; uterine

7. (1) Consider factors such as time and amount of fluid started (including prehydration); amount and time of each increase in infusion rate until contractions >15 m apart; time of each decrease; time, type and level of side effects (especially chest pressure, palpitations, dyspnea) (and any change in dosage to accommodate side effects); time and findings of each cervical exam

   (2) Consider contraction pattern, FHR during and 1 hour after discontinued

   (3) Consider difficulty breathing, chest pain, changes in diastolic and systolic BP, signs of imminent delivery

(PROM, sudden rectal pressure), major GI distress; FHR > 180

8. >15 minutes apart; does not progress

9. Suppress recurrent episodes of PTL

10. (a) Consider ideas such as conference with employer, solicitation of assistance from coworkers through employer; alteration in nature of job to more sedentary position temporarily, attractive fanny pack to carry medication; scheduled breaks; approval for plastic water bottle under counter.

    (b) Take the medication, since less than 1 hour has elapsed

CHAPTER 51—
Drugs Associated with the Postpartum and the Newborn

Questions 1–6: refer to text.

7. benzocaine and witch hazel

8. Anusol, proctofoam, Dibucaine ointment

9. prolactin

10. state that will provide for bowel movement without straining and greater comfort

11. question the order; because enteric coating

may dissolve and result in abdominal cramping and vomiting

12. no; to do so may cause tissue burns

13. express ointment on 2 x 2 gauze square and place against swollen anorectal tissue (approx. 5 x/d) and place inside peripad
    select approach to avoid additional trauma to an area swollen from childbirth and tender—especially if there is also an extension of an episiotomy as well; also avoids risk of introducing organisms
    may get burning sensation in some clients if anoderm not intact secondary to childbirth; also if episiotomy or laceration with sutures present in rectal area (3rd or 4th degree episiotomy), prefer to decrease pressure on sutures that can increase discomfort.

14. mineral oil

15. conjunctivitis; blindness

16. a. evaluate pain level for tolerable level using pain scale following product use

    b. evaluate content of client communications for need for additional pain relief

    c. reevaluate characteristics of perineal/anal tissues for integrity and healing progress within accepted standard

and lack of side effects

Select "B" because pain is what the client says it is and nurse cannot fully perceive another's pain; therefore, give top priority to client communications about status

17. Grasp 4 x 4s by corner tip when placed in the solution and alternate position of each one so will be easy to retrieve from solution, pick up by corner and let briefly drain; fold in half using only tips of corners; gently squeeze from the back side leaving the rounded front edge very damp; holding by the back edge, reach down and place against perineal tissue without touching self; then place peripad over the top.

18. bowel; to all 4 quadrants; simethicone, chewed; 8 oz water; suppository

19. d

20. a

21. d

22. b

23. b

24. c

25. b

26. a

27. d

28. b

29. a

30. c

31. d

32. c

Critical Thinking Exercise

1. Written lab reports (confirmation of blood types and actual Rh status for mother; blood type and Rh of this baby; potentially blood type and Rh of baby's father; results of indirect and direct Coombs tests); history of pregnancy events that may have increased opportunity for mixing of fetal and maternal blood (blood loss beyond expected/placental expulsion difficulties; any data related to prenatal testing or procedures or untoward events which occurred during pregnancy (chorionic villus sampling, amniocentesis, fetal blood sampling or surgery on the fetus, blows or trauma to the pregnant abdomen); previous pregnancies and their duration and outcome (abortions/ectopics/abruptions) (also whether client received Rh immune globulin D after these pregnancies); history of blood replacement with known Rh+ blood, prenatal Rh immune globulin D at 28 weeks; religious beliefs about blood products that might suggest she could decline Rh immune globulin D; allergic history to immune globulin products.

2. Knowledge deficit related to meaning of Rh incompatibility and sensitization; knowledge deficit related to use of Rh immune globulin D and when and why needed.

3. antibodies

   antigen

   antibody

   nonsensitized

   prevent

   sensitized

   antibody

   antigen

4. b

5. a

6. b

7. a

8. b

9. a

10. a

11. b

12. positive

    antibodies

    antibody

    absent

    negative

    72 hours

13. Rh immune globulin D is created from blood plasma. As with any blood product, the client could experience an allergic reaction. Risk is minimized through careful verification that the specific product, individualized for a particular client, is what is actually received.

14. Check the lab slip directly for a titer of greater than 1:10 or a positive ELISA antibody report

and make certain the addressograph data on the report is really Mary; contact the health care provider's office for verification through office prenatal records in case her status is recorded differently there.

15. If the client receives Rh immune globulin D and rubella vaccine at the same time, the outcome may be suppression of rubella antibodies with a need to recheck the rubella titer in approximately 3 months.

16. Do not become pregnant for at least three months (birth control implications); have rubella titer rechecked in three months.

CHAPTER 52—
Drugs Related to Women's Health and Disorders

Questions 1–4: refer to text.

5. estrogen progestin; progestin-only

6. A= abdominal pain (severe)

   C= chest pain or shortness of breath

   H= headache, dizziness, weakness, numbness, speech difficulties

   E= eye disorders including blurring or loss of vision

   S= severe leg pain or swelling of calf or thigh

7. triphasics

8. altering the cervical mucus

9. suppressing ovulation; changing pH of vaginal mucosa; sperm

10. Disagree; Nurse did not calculate re-injection dates correctly because she did not use a wheel that takes variable numbers of days in month into account; thus, client will progressively be late in getting re-injected and level of protection could be compromised; also, nurse did not document site of injection (important with re-injections that need rotation)

11. b

12.1 b, d, e

12.2 a, c

13. c

14. b

15. weight gain, increased appetite, migraine, breast soreness, sleep disorder, backache, joint pain, constipation, emotional lability, depression, difficulty concentrating on tasks.

16. exercise—aerobic; increase water
    diet—limit salty foods, alcohol, caffeine, chocolate; eat 4–6 small high CHO meals (low fat); pack portable snacks (rice cakes, vegetables, bagels, fresh fruit, pasta, soups, cereals); increase dietary magnesium
    use of NSAIDs from symptoms to beginning

of menses in conjunction with vitamins (Mg/Ca/pyridoxine/vitamin E, and zinc)
    acknowledge reality base of Sx
    convey research to client, family, community
    start and keep a feeling log
    discuss issues of drug dependency/withdrawal if alprazolam is used

17. Irregular menses, vasodilation, vaginal alterations, decreased bone mass

18. Hormone replacement therapy

19. true

20. is not

21. c

22. d

23. b

24. c

25. c

26. d

27. c

28. d

29. a

30. a

31. b

32. c

33. d

34. b

35. b

36. *Advantages:* decreased ovarian cysts, decreased menstrual migraine headache, easy to use, low failure rate. minimal risks; not linked to sex

act, decreased dysmenorrhea, decreased chance of endometrial cancer. *Disadvantages:* risky for fetus if pregnancy occurs, may perceive side effects as bothersome, if nonmonogamous there is increased risk of STDs.

37. variable: teach ACHES, moderate caffeine intake, advise use of barrier method for first month of use and for three months after discontinuing use, instruct about missed pills, take pill with food, report breakthrough bleeding, perform monthly breast self-exam.

38. c

39. b

40. a

41. a

42. d

43. b

44. c

45. a

46. variable; monthly breast self-exam, notify health care provider immediately of headache, visual disturbances, chest pain, or signs of thrombophlebitis; take medication with meals to avoid nausea and vomiting

Critical Thinking Exercise

1. Reduced estrogen support for the vaginal tissue; has

2. vascular changes she may be experiencing: hot flashes, tachycardia, sleep disturbances changes in height; backache

3. fractures due to decreased bone mass associated with osteoporosis; C.W. has been menopausal for over a year and it is known that the most rapid decrease in bone mass occurs in the first 3–5 years postmenopause (thus, time is of the essence).

4. fear of breast cancer and resumption of withdrawal bleeding.

5. reduction in incidence of coronary artery disease; retardation of osteoporosis; reduction in vasodilation symptoms; thicker vagina with increased moisture and lubrication with decreased discomfort; placed in this order because (A) coronary artery disease is the major health problem for older women, as it is for men, and research studies show significant decreases in heart attacks and possibly strokes; total cholesterol is lowered and HDL is increased; (B) acceleration in loss of bone density due to estrogen loss results in pain, suffering, lost productivity, and diminished life quality for hundreds of thousands of women each year with high personal and health-care costs for women often aged 75–85 with diminished resources. Therefore, need to start early to have an impact on the problem.

(C) Sleep deprivation and somatic discomforts from vasodilation manageable and not life-threatening or as costly; same with vaginal discomforts.

6. added to minimize the risk of endometrial hyperplasia, endometrial cancer, and breast cancer from use of unopposed estrogen alone; goal is to use the lowest effective dose of the least metabolically active progestin to oppose the stimulation of the endometrium.

7. plan for at least 10 years postmenopause and probably longer for cardiovascular benefits; explain that it is true that the goal for initiating HRT has a bearing upon the dosage form. Explain that the best bone protection will be through prolonged systemic therapy which will also aid vaginally; tell her that she could use just local estrogen cream for the vaginal problem but that this won't help with the other aspects; you could also use systemic HRT and a product such as K-Y jelly.

8. breast cancer (known or suspected), thrombophlebitis, liver disease (acute), undiagnosed genital bleeding; pregnancy

9. the progestin component; communicate with the health care provider regarding individualizing the dose; also may consider use of cyclic versus

combined continuous approach with health care provider

10. normal finding to bleed day 25–30, last 2–3 days, be lighter and have less premenstrual symptoms; normal to have an occasional hot flash while going through withdrawal bleeding (she should report any headache, visual changes, thrombophlebitis signs or chest pain)

CHAPTER 53—
Drugs Related to Reproductive Health I: Male Reproductive Health

Questions 1–5: refer to text.

6. testosterone

7. plateau, orgasm, resolution

8. negative feedback loop

9. longer

10. ⅓ to ⅕

11. monitoring of endocrine status

12. decreased muscle tone, polyuria, and increased urine and serum calcium

13. antiandrogens

14. menotropins, immediately

15. GnR, LH, FSH

16. adulthood; surgical excision, radiation therapy and chemotherapy

17. L-dopa

18. nitrates; cardiovascular disease

19. d

20. b

21. a

22. b

23. a

24. c

25. a

26. d

27. d

Critical Thinking Exercise

1. The motivation for treatment and M.T.'s self esteem should be assessed.

2. There is no evidence that treatment results in greater growth.

3. A drug is selected on the basis of the desired balance of growth and sexual maturation.

4. At minimum, endocrine, renal, gastrointestinal effects should be monitored.

5. Treatment can be expected to last 3–6 months.

CHAPTER 54—
Drugs Related to Reproductive Health II: Infertility and Sexually Transmitted Diseases

Questions 1–6: refer to text.

7. infertility, life-threatening illness, and neonatal illness, and death.

8. vertical

9. syphilis

10. predominately sexual, sexual and nonsexual

11. gonococcal conjunctivitis neonatorum

12. hepatitis B

13. syphilis, penicillin

14. abstinence, one faithful partner

15. diabetes, HIV/AIDS

16. acyclovir

17. one year

18. hormone replacement therapy

19. 15

20. danazol, suppress gonadotropin output

21. progesterone

22. emotionally, financially

23. thins cervical mucus

24. a

25. c

26. a

27. b

28. c

29. c

30. b

31. a

32. a

33. a

34. a

35. c

36. d

37. b

Critical Thinking Exercise

1. Tess might have incurred fallopian tube scarring if

the infection ascended her reproductive tract.

2. HIV more readily enters the body through lesions such as those associated with other STDs; the fact that a partner passed on gonorrhea indicates that he could have passed on another STD, including HIV.

3. Side effects include breast discomfort, fatigue, dizziness, depression, nausea, vomiting, increased appetite, weight gain, urticaria, dermatitis, anxiety, restlessness, weakness, heavier menses, vasomotor flushing, abdominal bloating, pain, and gas. Adverse effects that may require interruption of therapy include visual impairment, ovarian hyperstimulation resulting in ovarian enlargement, midcycle ovarian pain, and cysts.

4. Ovulation is predicted by a 0.5° F drop in basal body temperature followed by a 1° F rise. The couple should engage in coitus every other day from four days before ovulation to three days after. Sex on schedule might become a chore and feel dehumanizing to one or both partners.

5. One or both partners may feel inadequate as a man or woman and self esteem may be damaged; they and their families may engage in blaming of the other partner.

Alternatives might include adoption, becoming a foster parent, becoming involved with family members' children, and volunteering in youth organizations or services.

CHAPTER 55—
Adult and Pediatric Emergency Drugs

Questions 1–6: refer to text.

7. b

8. c

9. b

10. a

11. a

12. PSVT (paroxysmal supraventricular tachy-cardia)

13. confusion, drowsiness, hearing impairment, muscle twitching, and/or seizures

14. c

15. c

16. c

17. b

18. d

19. d

20. opiate; morphine, meperidine, codeine, Darvon, heroin

21. b

22. milk or milk products

23. a

24. b

25. c

26. b

27. d

28. d

29. a

30. c

31. c

32. a

33. d

34. c

35. a

36. b

37. d

38. c

39. c

40. a

41. a

42. bronchodilator; asthma and anaphylaxis/allergic reactions

Critical Thinking Exercise—Case Study #1

1. The initial CVP reading was low, indicating the patient was "dry" or volume depleted; a component of his shock state was hypovolemic in origin. The fluids corrected the hypovolemia as evidenced by the CVP increasing to 9 cm H_2O. Administering dopamine when hypovolemia is present worsens the low perfusion state by causing further vasoconstriction that is detrimental.

2. Enhanced cardiac output by increased myocardial contractility (beta$_1$ effect) and elevation of blood pressure through vaso-

constriction (alpha-adrenergic effect).

3. By IV infusion through an electronic infusion pump for accuracy.

4. Continuous heart and blood pressure monitoring are essential. Carefully document vital signs and intake/output as ordered (usually at least q1–2 hours in the acute period). Assess for significant adverse effects: tachycardia, dysrhythmias, myocardial ischemia, nausea, and vomiting. Assess IV site for signs/symptoms of drug infiltration. Do not abruptly discontinue dopamine; severe hypotension can result.

5. Notify primary health care provider immediately; restart infusion in another site as soon as possible to prevent hypotension from abrupt discontinuation of the drug (central access sites are preferred). The site

must be infiltrated with phentolamine (Regitine), 5–10 mg diluted in 10–15 ml of normal saline to prevent or reduce tissue damage. Surgical debridement and skin grafting may be required if tissue necrosis occurs.

6. No. The high rate was most likely related to fever and hypovolemia; it was best treated with methods to reduce fever and correct the client's fluid status. Verapamil and adenosine are indicated for paroxysmal supraventricular tachycardia (PSVT). As an aside, the rate of PSVT is usually > 150 beats per minute.

Critical Thinking Exercise—Case Study #2

1. Yes. C.S.'s chest pain should be considered to be cardiac in origin.

2. Heart rate and blood pressure. A full description of the chest pain and

any associated signs/symptoms (i.e., nausea, vomiting, dyspnea, diaphoresis) will also be useful.

3. Naloxone (Narcan)

4. Continuous cardiac and blood pressure monitoring; use of a volumetric infusion pump for accuracy of drug delivery

5. Decrease the NTG infusion until BP is > 100 mm Hg

6. Turn off the NTG infusion. Place the patient's head down and elevate his legs until his BP increases. (The half-life of NTG is short; if the BP drop is due to the NTG alone, it should be of short duration once these actions are taken.)

7. Atropine: minimum adult dose = 0.5 mg IV; maximum adult dose = 3 mg IV

8. It blocks the effects of the vagus nerve (vagolytic action).

Appendix A
Basic Math Review

OBJECTIVES

- Convert Roman numerals to Arabic numbers
- Convert Arabic numbers to Roman numerals
- Solve problems with fractions
- Solve ratio and proportion problems
- Convert percentage to decimals, fractions, ratios and proportions
- Complete the math review test with a grade of 80% or higher

TERMS

Roman numerals   divisor
Arabic numbers   dividend
ratio   least common denominator
proportion

INTRODUCTION

Principles of basic mathematics surround us each day; they are part of life. Knowledge of arithmetic and how to do basic mathematical calculations are needed in everyday living and throughout one's nursing career.

Keep in mind that your goal is to prepare and administer medications in a safe and correct manner. The following recommendations are offered:

- **Think.** Focus on each step of the problem. This applies to simple as well as difficult problems.
- **Read accurately.** Pay particular attention to the location of the decimal point; and the operation to be done, i.e. addition, subtraction, multiplication, and/or division.
- **Picture the problem.**
- **Identity an expected range** for the answer.
- **Seek to understand the problem;** not merely the mechanics of how to do it.

The basic math review describes arithmetical operations that form the foundation that nurses use to calculate ordered dosages of medications. Specific information includes converting Roman and Arabic numerals; addition, subtraction, multiplication, and division of fractions and decimals; and solving percentage, ratio, and proportion problems.

The basic math review is followed by a test on the material (in the Instructor's Manual). You may want to review this section first or go directly to take the test. It is strongly recommended that you attain a test score of at least 80% before going ahead. In reality, aim to score 100% on the test because it is essential material for understanding future chapters and calculating medication dosages.

NUMBER SYSTEMS

Arabic and Roman are the two systems of numbers associated with drug administration.

The *Arabic System* is expressed in numbers 0, 1, 2, 3, 4, 5, 6, 7, 8, 9. Each has a place value reading from right to left. For example the number 123, has 3 in the one's place; 2 in the ten's place; and 1 in the hundred's place. Each successive numeral indicates a value ten times more than the preceding one.

The *Roman System* is expressed by selected capital or lower case letters; i.e. I, V, X, i, v, x. The Roman letters may be changed to equivalent Arabic numbers:

The equivalents are:

Roman Numerals		Arabic Number
I	i	1
V	v	5
X	x	10
L	l	50
C	c	100
D	d	500
M	m	1000

Roman numerals are commonly used when writing drug dosages in the Apothecary System. The Roman numerals are written in lower case letters, i.e., i, v, ix. The lower case letters may be written with a line above the letters, i.e. $\bar{i}$, $\bar{v}$, and $\bar{ix}$ and a dot above each ī, īī, īīī.

Roman numerals may appear in combination, such as xi and ix. Addition and subtraction are used to read multiple Roman numerals.

Expressing Roman numerals:
#1. When the first Roman numeral is greater than (>) the following numeral(s), then ADD

Examples
xiii = 10 + 3 = 13
vi = 5 + 1 = 6

#2. When the first Roman numeral is less than (<) the following numeral(s), then SUBTRACT the first number from the second.

Examples
ix = 10 − 1 = 9
XL = 50 − 10 = 40

#3. Numerals are never repeated more than three times in a sequence.

Examples
iii = 3
xxx = 30

#4. When a smaller numeral is between two numerals of greater value, the smaller numeral is subtracted from the numeral following it.

Examples
xix = 10 + (10 − 1) = 19
mcmxci = 1000 + (1000 − 100) + (100 − 10) + 1=
                1000 + (900) + (90) + 1 = 1991

Practice Problems I:
Express the following as Arabic numbers:

1.	XVI _____		4.	XXII _____	
2.	XC _____		5.	L _____	
3.	XIV _____		6.	MXL _____	

Express the following as Roman numbers:

7.	100 _____		10.	259 _____	
8.	36 _____		11.	85 _____	
9.	30 _____		12.	60 _____	

FRACTIONS

A fraction is one or more of the equal parts of a unit. In the fraction ½, the 2 is the denominator and indicates into how many parts the whole is divided. The 1 is the numerator and indicates how many of the equal parts is taken.

The value of a fraction depends mainly on the denominator and when it increases, the value of the fraction decreases because it takes more parts to make a whole. For example: with the fractions $\frac{1}{3}$ and $\frac{1}{12}$, the larger value is $\frac{1}{3}$ because three parts make the whole; whereas for $\frac{1}{12}$ it takes 12 parts to make a whole.

Proper, Improper, and Mixed Fractions

A **proper faction** has a numerator less than the denominator.

Examples: ¾, ⅞, ⅓

An **improper fraction** has a numerator equal to, or greater than, the denominator.

Examples: ⁸⁄₆, ¹¹⁄₁₁, ⁶⁄₃

These may be changed to a whole or mixed number by dividing the numerator by the denominator.

Examples: ⁸⁄₆ = 1 ²⁄₆ or 1 ⅓
                  ¹¹⁄₁₁ = 1
                  ⁶⁄₃ = 2

A **mixed number** is a whole number and a fraction, i.e., 2 ⅛, 3 ⅓, 6 ½. Mixed numbers can be changed to improper fractions by multiplying the denominator by the whole number, then adding the numerator.

Examples: 2 ½ = 1 ¹⁷⁄₈; 3 ⅓ = ¹⁰⁄₃; 6 ½ = ¹³⁄₂.

Addition/Subtraction of Fractions

To ADD fractions with the same denominator, add the numerators, keep the same denominator, and reduce to lowest terms.

Examples: ½ + ½ = ²⁄₂ = 1
              ⅜ + ⅞ = ¹⁰⁄₈ = 1 ²⁄₈ = 1 ¼
              ⅚ + ⁴⁄₆ = ⁹⁄₆ = 1 ³⁄₆ = 1 ½

To ADD fractions with different denominators, change to fractions having the least common denominator (LCD) which is the smallest whole number that contains the denominator of each of the fractions. Divide the LCD by the denominator of each fraction and multiply both terms of the fraction by the quotient.

Example: ⅙ + ⅜ + ¾ + ⁵⁄₁₂

Twenty-four is the smallest number that yields a whole number when divided by denominators in example 6, 8, 4, and 12. Then multiply both numerator and denominator by the same number. Then add as you would with fractions of the same denominator and reduce to lowest terms.

⅙	=	⁴⁄₂₄
⅜	=	⁹⁄₂₄
¾	=	¹⁸⁄₂₄
½	=	¹⁰⁄₂₄
	⁴⁴⁄₂₄	= 1 ¹⁷⁄₂₄

To SUBTRACT fractions with the same denominator; subtract the smaller numerator from the larger, keep the denominator, and reduce to lowest terms.

Example: ⁹⁄₁₀ − ¹⁄₁₀ = ⁸⁄₁₀ = ⅘

To SUBTRACT fractions with different denominators, change fractions to LCD; subtract the numerator and keep the denominator.

Examples: ⅚ − ⅓ = ⅚ − ²⁄₆ = ³⁄₆ = ½ (LCD=6)
              ⅝ − ¼ = ⅝ − ²⁄₈ = ⅜ (LCD = 8)

Multiplying Fractions

To MULTIPLY fractions:
   a)   multiply the numerator
   b)   multiply the denominator
   c)   reduce fraction to lowest terms

Example 1: ⅓ × ⅜ = ³⁄₂₄ = ⅛

Answer is ³⁄₂₄ reduced to ⅛. To reduce to lowest terms; 3 goes into both numbers evenly; i.e., 3 ÷ 3 = 1 and 24 ÷ 3 = 8

Example 2: ⅛ × 4 = ⅛ × ⁴⁄₁ = ⁴⁄₈ = ½

A whole number is considered the numerator over one (⁴⁄₁). Four divided by eight (4 ÷ 8) = ½. (0.5 = ⁵⁄₁₀ = ½)

Dividing Fractions

To DIVIDE fractions, invert the *second* fraction (or divisor) and then multiply.

Example 1: $\frac{1}{2} \div \frac{1}{4} = \frac{1}{2} \times \frac{4}{1} = \frac{4}{2} = 2$

Example 2: $\frac{9}{10} \div \frac{1}{3} = \frac{9}{10} \times \frac{3}{1} = \frac{27}{10} = 2\frac{7}{10}$

Decimal fractions: To change fractions to decimals, divide the numerator by the denominator, i.e., $\frac{1}{2} = 1{:}2 = 0.5$; $\frac{1}{8} = 0.125$.

Practice Problems II

1. Which has the greatest value, $\frac{1}{6}$ or $\frac{1}{8}$?

2. Reduce improper fractions to whole or mixed numbers:

    a. $\frac{16}{4} =$ c. $\frac{7}{3} =$

    b. $\frac{36}{6} =$ d. $\frac{21}{8} =$

3. Add fractions:

    a. $\frac{1}{10} + \frac{3}{10} =$ c. $\frac{1}{16} + \frac{5}{8} =$

    b. $\frac{1}{8} + \frac{3}{24} =$

4. Subtract fractions:

    a. $\frac{7}{9} - \frac{1}{9} =$ c. $2\frac{1}{4} - 1\frac{3}{8} =$

    b. $\frac{3}{8} - \frac{1}{16} =$

5. Multiply fractions:

    a. $\frac{3}{8} \times \frac{1}{6} =$

    b. $6\frac{1}{4} \times 2\frac{1}{3} =$

6. Divide fractions:

    a. $\frac{1}{3} \div 2 =$ c. $4\frac{1}{2} \div 4 =$

    b. $\frac{7}{8} \div \frac{1}{3} =$ d. $6\frac{3}{5} \div 3 =$

7. Change fraction to a decimal:

    a. $\frac{1}{3} =$ c. $\frac{3}{10} =$

    b. $\frac{3}{5} =$

DECIMALS

Decimals are referred to as (1) whole numbers and (2) decimal fractions. The following number, 1234.8765, is an example of the division of units for a whole number with a decimal fraction.

Decimal fractions are written in tenths, hundredths, thousandths, and ten thousandths. Decimal fractions are rounded off to tenths after solving problems using decimals. To round off in tenths, when the hundredth column is five or greater, the number in the tenth column is increased by one, i.e., 0.47 = 0.5; 0.12 = 0.1

Decimal fractions are an integral part of the metric system. Tenths refers to the first decimal place 0.1 or $\frac{1}{10}$; hundredths the second decimal place 0.01 or $\frac{1}{100}$; and thousandths the third decimal place 0.001 or $\frac{1}{1000}$. When a decimal fraction is changed to a fraction, the denominator is based on the number of digits to the right of the decimal point (first = 10; second = 100; third = 1000).

Examples:

1.   0.9 = $\frac{9}{10}$ or 9 tenths

2.   0.33 = $\frac{33}{100}$ or 33 hundredths

3.   0.444 = $\frac{444}{1000}$ or 444 thousandths

Multiplying Decimals

To multiply decimal numbers, multiply the multiplicand by the multiplier as you would two numbers. Identify how many numerals are to the right of the decimals in both numbers. Counting from right to left, mark off the same number of spaces in the answer. Round off to tenths.

Example:

```
    1.65        Multiplicand
    4.4         multiplier
   660
   660
   7.260
```

Answer: 7.3 Since 6 is greater than 5, the "tenth" number is increased by 1.

Dividing Decimals

The decimal point in the divisor is moved to the right to make a whole number. The decimal point in the dividend is then moved to the right an equal number of decimal spaces. Carry number to two places beyond the decimal point.

Example: 3.69 ÷ 1.2 or $\frac{369}{1.2}$ (dividend)
(divisor)

```
                  3.075        = 3.1
divisor     1.2 ) 3.6900         dividend
                  36
                   90
                   84
                   60
```

Practice Problems III

1.   Multiply   a)   4.7 × 0.284

           b)   6.1 × 1.052

2.   Divide: a) $74 \div 3.6$

b) $18.7 \div 0.41$

3.   Change the decimals to fractions:
    a. $0.21 =$
    b. $0.02 =$
    c. $0.068 =$

RATIO AND PROPORTION

A **ratio** is the relationship between two numbers and is expressed with a colon separating the numbers, i.e., $3 : 4$ (3 is to 4). A ratio is another way of expressing a fraction, i.e., $3 : 4 = \frac{3}{4}$.

    Proportion is the relationship between two ratios and is expressed with a double colon or equal sign separating the ratios, i.e., $3 : 4$ (:: or =) $6 : 8$

    The middle numbers of the proportion example are called *means* and the end numbers are called *extremes*. The product of the means equals the product of the extremes.

Example 1:

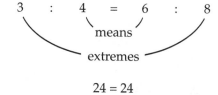

$$24 = 24$$

    When the value of one number of the proportion is not known, it is represented by an "X". To solve for "X", the means are multiplied and the extremes are multiplied. The number with the X is always the divisor.

Examples:

1.

$$X \quad : \quad 4 \quad :: \quad 6 \quad : \quad 3$$

$$3\ X = 24$$
$$X = 24 \text{ divided by } 3$$
$$X = 8$$

Check: substitute the answer for "X"

$$8 \quad : \quad 4 \quad = \quad 6 \quad : \quad 3$$
$$8 \quad \times \quad 3 \quad = \quad 4 \quad \times \quad 6$$
$$24 \quad = \quad 24$$

2.

$$X \quad : \quad 12 \quad = \quad 3 \quad : \quad 24$$

$$24\ X = 36$$
$$X = 36 \text{ divided by } 24$$
$$X = 1.5$$

Check:

$$1.5 \quad : \quad 12 \quad = \quad 3 \quad : \quad 24$$
$$1.5 \quad \times \quad 24 \quad = \quad 12 \quad \times \quad 3$$
$$36 \quad = \quad 36$$

The ratio and proportion problem may be set up as a fraction. Cross multiply to solve for X or to prove the computation.

Example: ratio and proportion

$$X \quad : \quad 4 \quad = \quad 3 \quad : \quad 1$$
$$X \quad = \quad 12$$

fraction

$$\frac{X}{4} \quad = \quad \frac{3}{1}$$
$$X \quad = \quad 12$$

Check

$$\frac{12}{4} \quad = \quad \frac{3}{1}$$
$$12 \quad = \quad 12$$

Practice Problems IV

Solve for "X":

1. $\qquad 2 \quad : \quad 20 \quad :: \quad 5 \quad : \quad X$

2. $\qquad 0.8 \quad : \quad 100 \quad :: \quad X \quad : \quad 1000$

3. Change ratio and proportion to fraction:

$$1 \quad : \quad 3 \quad :: \quad X \quad : \quad 18$$

4. It is 1500 miles from New York City to Miami, Florida. Your car uses one gallon of gasoline per 32 miles on average. How many gallons of gasoline are required for the trip?

PERCENTAGE

Percent means parts of 100; thus 4% means four parts of 100 and 0.4% means 0.4 parts (less than 1) of 100. A percent may be expressed as a fraction, a decimal, or a ratio. Example:

Percent	Fraction	Decimal	Ratio
20	$\frac{20}{100}$	0.20	20 : 100
0.5	$\frac{0.5}{100}$	0.005	0.5 : 100

To change percent to decimal, move the decimal point two places to the LEFT. Unless noted otherwise, the decimal point is assumed to be after the number, i.e., 20% = 20.%

Practice Problems V

Change percent to fraction, decimal, and ratio

Percent	Fraction	Decimal	Ratio
1			
$\frac{3}{4}$			
300			

ANSWERS

Practice Problems I

1. $10 + 5 + 1 = 16$

2. $100 - 10 = 90$

3. $10 + 4 = 14$

4. $10 + 10 + 2 = 22$

5. 50

6. $1000 + (50 - 10) = 1040$

7.   C

8.   XXXVI

9.   XXX

10.   CCLIX

11.   LXXXV

12.   LX

Practice Problems II

1. $\frac{1}{6}$ has the greater value; there are 6 parts in a whole and not eight.

2.   a. 4   b. 6   c. $2\frac{1}{3}$ d. $2\frac{5}{8}$

3.   a. $\frac{1}{10} + \frac{3}{10} = \frac{4}{10} = \frac{2}{5}$

   b. $\frac{1}{8} + \frac{3}{24} = \frac{3}{24} + \frac{3}{24} = \frac{6}{24} = \frac{1}{4}$

   c. $\frac{1}{16} + \frac{5}{8} = \frac{1}{16} + \frac{10}{16} = \frac{11}{16}$

4.   a. $\frac{7}{9} - \frac{1}{9} = \frac{6}{9} = \frac{2}{3}$

   b. $\frac{3}{8} - \frac{1}{16} = \frac{6}{16} - \frac{1}{16} = \frac{5}{16}$

   c. $2\frac{1}{4} - 1\frac{3}{8} = \frac{9}{4} - \frac{11}{8} = \frac{18}{8} - \frac{11}{8} = \frac{7}{8}$

5.   a. $\frac{3}{48} = \frac{1}{16}$

   b. $\frac{25}{4} \times \frac{7}{3} = \frac{175}{12} = 14\frac{7}{12}$

6.   a. $\frac{1}{3} \times \frac{1}{2} = \frac{1}{6}$

   b. $\frac{7}{8} \times \frac{3}{1} = \frac{21}{8} = 2\frac{5}{8}$

   c. $\frac{9}{2} \times \frac{1}{4} = \frac{9}{8} = 1\frac{1}{8}$

   d. $\frac{33}{5} \times \frac{1}{3} = \frac{33}{15} = 2\frac{3}{15} = 2\frac{1}{5}$

7.   a. 0.33   b. 0.60   c. 0.30

Practice Problems III

1.   a. $1.3348 = 1.33$

   b. $6.4172 = 6.42$

2.   a. 20.5

   b. 45.6

3.   a. $\frac{21}{100}$

   b. $\frac{2}{100}$

   c. $\frac{68}{1000}$

Practice Problems IV

1. $2X = 100$
   $X = 50$

2. $100\,X = 800$
   $X = 8$

3. $\frac{1}{3} = \frac{X}{18}$
   $3\ X = 18$
   $X = 6$

4.   1 gal : 32 mi :: X gal : 1500 mi
   $32\,X = 1500$
   $X = 46.875$ gal
   $X = 47$ gallons

Practice Problems V

Percent	Fraction	Decimal	Ratio
1. 1	$\frac{1}{100}$	0.01	1 : 100
2. 3/4	$\frac{0.75}{100}$	0.0075	0.75 : 100
3. 300	$\frac{300}{100}$	3.00	300 : 100

Appendix B
Prototype Drug Chart

Prototype Drug **Chart**	Generic name: _____

Drug Class:	Dosage:

Trade Name:

Pregnancy Category:

Contraindications:	Drug-Lab-Food Interactions:

Caution:

Pharmacokinetics:	Pharmacodynamics:
Absorption:	*Onset:*
Distribution:	*Peak:*
Metabolism:	*Duration:*
Excretion:	

Therapeutic Effects/Uses:

Mode of Action:	Adverse Reactions:

Side Effects:	Life-Threatening: